D0311003

A Guide to the

Selection, Combination and Cooking of Foods

VOLUME 1

Selection and Combination of Foods

A Guide to the Selection, Combination, and Cooking of Foods

VOLUME 1

Selection and Combination of Foods

by CARL A. RIETZ

Mechanical Engineer in the food and chemical process industries
President, Rietz Manufacturing Company,
Santa Rosa, California
Former Lecturer in Food Technology,
Mills College, Oakland, California
Director of Food Technology Foundation

WESTPORT, CONNECTICUT
THE AVI PUBLISHING COMPANY, INC.
1961

LONDON:
FOOD TRADE REVIEW LTD.
7 GARRICK STREET, LONDON, W.C.2.

REGISTERED AT STATIONERS' HALL
LONDON, ENGLAND, 1961

Library of Congress Catalog Card No. 61-12137

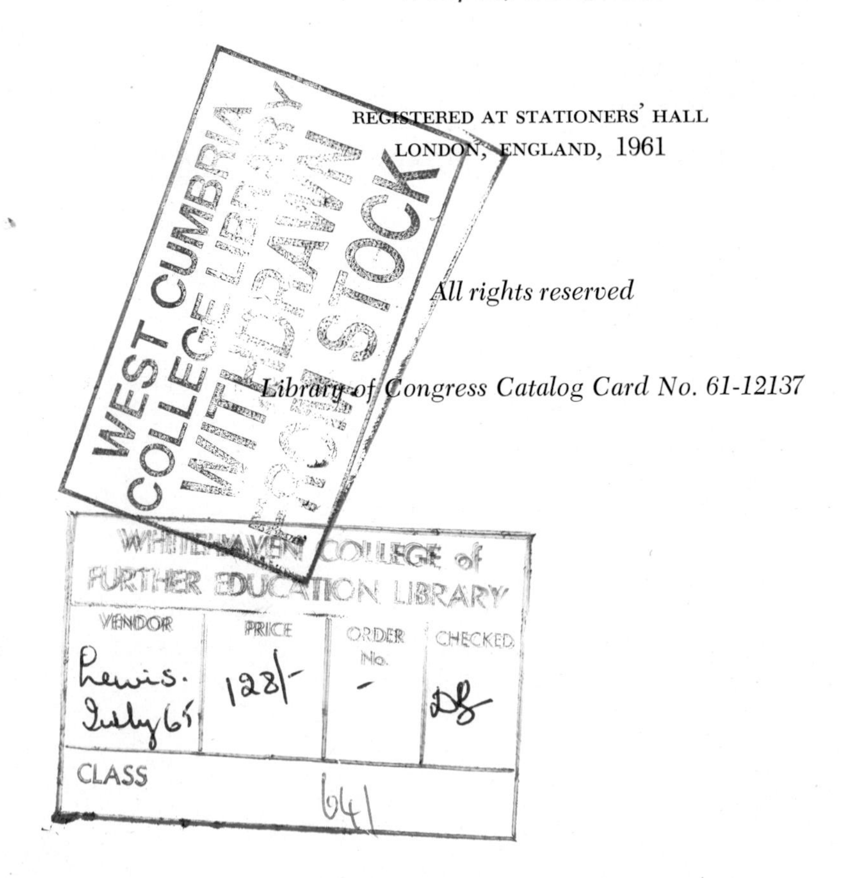

Printed in the United States of America
BY MACK PRINTING COMPANY, EASTON, PENNSYLVANIA

Preface

In this country of lavish, almost shameful abundance, the great majority of Americans go through life without experiencing, a single, technically evaluated, good, representative dinner.

We are a people accustomed to quantitative rather than qualitative judgments; a city, a building, a person's income is judged according to size. We have been quick to embrace the *new*, to belittle traditions. Yet, paradoxically, most of the cooking in our homes is based on folklore, on memories of what Mother or Grandmother or Aunt Matilda used to cook, and how they did things. We become overweight, and rush to consult a calorie chart—and then deliberately starve ourselves in the midst of plenty. In a country whose soil, forests, and streams can produce a tremendous variety of foods, we persist in eating the same few unimaginative "traditional" foods our grandparents used.

Those who call themselves "gourmets" are apt to judge a meal for its elaborateness, rather than by the quality of its food. Although we long ago outgrew the belief that a house is to be judged by its towers, stained glass, and "gingerbread," we cling to the "gingerbread" concept of "good" food.

One of the purposes of this book is to prove that good cooking is, like good work in other crafts, *simple*.

The pure, clean lines of a good building, the true, precise notes of a symphony are more difficult to obtain than false elaborateness, but they are the sign of the artist. And there are artists with food as well.

There should be more of them.

In general this book deals with the food behavior of man. One of the difficulties in dealing with this subject at once becomes apparent. It is a trait of human nature that each individual considers himself an "expert" in any field that constitutes a part of his every-day experience, and the consumption of food is certainly a universal experience. With extremely few exceptions, all human beings can be said to like food and the process of eating.

The vast majority of people *feed. They do not eat.* Now, animals also *feed.* Food is necessary to maintain life, and the animal feeds because it has an instinct to preserve life. But man is more than an animal; he is equipped with intelligence and potential powers of selection, discrimination, and appreciation. Yet it is an almost universal fallacy of man that, if he knows how to *feed*, he thinks he is judge of eating and tasting.

Anyone can *enjoy* a sensory experience (such as feeding), but in order to *appreciate*, he must be educated. In order to discriminate, he must first have a wide range of experience to provide him with a broad standard of comparison. In order to select, he must know a great deal about what materials are available, as well as the constituents of those materials.

There can be no such thing as a "compleat epicure" unless the epicure can cook. Literature contains numerous accounts of feasts, meals, food experiences written of or by gourmands, gourmets, and epicures. But the authors were people who enjoyed food, and who spoke of the enjoyment of the food experience. Very few of those accounts were written by master cooks—men who had a thorough knowledge of the preparation of the food the epicureans enjoyed.

The purchase of a cook book is not the first step toward becoming a good cook. Someone has said that it takes 20 years to train a chef. That is probably a conservative understatement. Before he ever enters a kitchen, a good cook must first have a basic knowledge of many sciences. Cooking, though not an art, is a craft in which the arts have application. It involves discipline in the use of knowledge which has been furnished by many sciences. The more complete the scientific basis of a craft, the more perfect the craft; this generalization applies as well to cookery.

The epicurean cook must know, for example, the fundamentals of anthropology, psychology, and the scientific bases of the visual arts.

A recipe is a blueprint. A master cook must know the fundamental principles upon which the recipe is based, and he must know how to draft one of his own. Otherwise he has no means of understanding the failures which may result from his attempt to follow a blueprint.

One of the cardinal premises of this book is that it is not possible for a person to qualify as a judge of food who does not know how to prepare it. Only one who has had a *formal education in what is involved in cookery*, including the selection, preparation and service of food can begin to qualify as a food judge. It is important here to stress that training in cookery does not necessarily qualify one for judging taste or flavor. That must be comparative.

Adequate skills in selection, preparation and appreciation of food, then, are dependent upon a scientific training. Starting with basic school curricula and ending with internship, professional education and training require a minimum of twelve years. A specialist can approach the top of the ladder with another eight years of externship, but even then, eight years does not allow enough time in the majority of cases to provide well-rounded experience in general practice.

For example, one may search in vain to find a chef under the age of forty who could be considered highly proficient. Yet there are a fair number of good cooks who are under thirty years old, and surprisingly, there are a great many youngsters in their early twenties who are fairly good cooks. They have a higher-than-average set of qualifications in taste judgment and food skills.

Part I of this volume indicates a number of sciences which are directly connected with the science of food preparation. Before one ever approaches a kitchen he should be familiar with the rudiments of such subjects as biology, botany, chemistry, nutrition, pharmacology, physics, physiology, neurology and psychology.

To go into each of the sciences named, in the detail necessary for such training, would be impossible here. A good working knowledge of these subjects must be acquired outside this book. A bibliography is given as a starting point. Our purpose here is to tell the would-be educated eater and cook where to begin.

Part II of the book deals with the *Gustametric Master Chart,* its method, and its use in food *selection.* This main section is concerned with the development and training of *taste perception* and its important corollary, comparative flavor appraisal. Only if it is understood that all of our ideas about taste are based upon *sensory perception* can an orderly investigation of the mechanics be made.

It is impossible to be exact about measuring taste and to provide for exact and predetermined taste experiences. On the other hand, a world-wide observation has demonstrated that although not all peoples have precisely similar taste perceptions yet there is sufficient similarity of taste under similar conditions to warrant the following proposition:

All foods can be rated according to their flavor intensity, registered on a common logarithmic scaling system.

The use of this Gustametric Master Chart makes it possible to determine quickly and exactly *which combinations of foods make for agreeable* meals. It covers all types of foods and more than 600 individual foods.

The concept of the Gustametric Master Chart is based upon the thesis that all of man's aesthetics are developed on the basis of his organoleptic perception. (By this, we mean the response of any sensory organ to outside stimulus.) *Man's aesthetic appreciation is in direct proportion to his anatomical and physiological aptitudes.*

As a natural corollary to this thesis it follows that *individual aesthetic capacity* is approximately the same for each of the aesthetic facilities of an individual. This proposition is discussed in Chapter 3, *Organoleptic Reception and Perception.*

The reader is warned to approach this study with the realization that the over-all subject matter is one of the most complex expressions of man's behavior. Accordingly his grasp of what is involved will vary with the amount of work he is willing to devote to the subject.

The part of Volume II dealing with *Preparation* is not meant to be a cookbook, although it is an introduction to the kitchen. It analyzes most traditional recipes and subjects them to formulation. It discusses efficient and effective methods of food processing. It includes a discussion—not always favorable—of new kitchen equipment and new "supermarket" techniques. Here again there will be emphasis on the aesthetics involved in the serving of food.

Volume II contains a brief exposition of the subject of *Food Aesthetics,* its elements and its function in the life of man.

The entire book is directed toward the reader who is concerned with the aesthetics of food habits, who cares for *the art of eating,* as opposed to *the biologic necessity of feeding.*

It is a study long overdue if we are to enjoy our lives with the grace of civilized people.

Note on the Organization of the Book

It is considered illogical to attempt anything approaching complete coverage of all the factors involved in any single food or a single classification of food in the discussion of either an individual food or a single classification. No single book has been produced, nor is it considered likely that one ever will be written, that provides a complete exposition of a single food. This work can at the most be considered merely an introduction to an encyclopedic coverage of the foods of man. Individual and class coverages are limited to skeletal discussions and outlines, more or less syllabic references, to the different factors involved in individual foods, their classification, and particularly to the almost infinite variations of food processing, service and participation.

Different phases of a single subject that is generally applicable to all foods are variously discussed under different foods. Thus, visual and tactile considerations apply to all foods, but are expanded in different ways as they apply to different foods. Thus kinesthetics *per se* is discussed under physiology; again under food processing; occasionally within the scope of food selection; and finally with reference to its part in food aesthetics. The subject of kinesthetics is cited as a single example of the impossibility of applying its coverage as a template to each classification of food, and it would be wildly absurd to discuss it in relationship to each individual food.

The influence of kinesthetics in the selection of a food is perhaps more specifically discussable as a subdivision of quality control wherein textures are graded by a scoresheet evaluation. A given food is there rated according to its intrinsic physical composition, the yield, penetration and shear-test rating.

To all my family, friends and associates who have by reason of such relationships been forced to accompany me through the tangled path toward a nascent science of gustometry, I am the happy debtor. My gratitude, though indivisible, is yet shared among too many to allow naming in the short space available. Among them I owe special thanks to these: Stanley S. Kline, M.D., Sherman Oaks, for an average of 20 hours a week for two years on medical aspects of the book; Robert P. Baylor, Food Technologist in Scientific Research of California Packing Corporation, for 20 years of advice on fruits and vegetables; Carl Schreffler, Enologist and former General Superintendent of Roma Wine Company, now of Rietz Manufacturing Company, for more probing and flavor determination work with me than any other person—more than 25 years; Lucien Heyraud, Chef des cuisines, emeritus, of the Sheraton-Palace Hotel, for critical work on cookery and food aesthetics for about ten years; J. W. Wong, Director of the Winner House and Winner Palace, Hong Kong, and Wong So, Director of Hong Kong hotels and restaurants, for a professional initiation into the crafts of Chinese cookery; Fenner Fuller, restaurant operator of Berkeley, and part time good cook, with whom I have spent a good many kitchen hours learning about the ups and downs of an exacting operator of a small but good restaurant; Roderick David Jones, Pharm.D., Assistant Professor of Pharmacy, University of California Medical Center, for seven or eight years' work on chemistry and Pharmacology; Nathan Podhurst, Botanist, of Nature's Herb Company, San Francisco, for more than two years of much patient research and experimentation; Julia P. Hindley, home economist and author, for seven or eight years on food flavors and comparative international cookery; Philip Harben, British Broadcasting Corporation, chef and author, for more than five years on food of the British Isles and the Commonwealth; Richard Wistar, Ph.D., Professor of Chemistry at Mills College, for more than five years on chemistry and food flavor determinations; Hazel S. Kraemer, Ph.D., now Professor of Child Development at Mills College, for five years' laboratory work with me on individual and group food behavior; Salvatore Lucia, M.D. Professor and Chairman of the Department of Preventive Medicine at University of California Medical Center, Burton W. Adams, M.D. (psychiatry), J. Randolph Sharpsteen, M.D. (ophthalmology), and Howard A. Cogswell, Assistant Professor of Biological Sciences at Mills College, each for years of patient listening and critical reading form the standpoint of his specialty; for specialized knowledge in their respective fields, freely shared as was their time, to Frank Allhands, U. S. Dept. of Fisheries, San Francisco (on aquatic foods); John A. Kneeland, Chief Chemist of Pacific Vegetable Oil Company, San Francisco (on oils and fats); Emil Weiler, Flavor Chemist of Eng-Skell Company, San Francisco (on beverage flavors); G. F. Steward, Ph.D. Chairman of the Department of Food Science and Technology of the University of California (on animal meats and poultry); Sherman Leonard, Associate Food Technologist in the Department of Food Sciences and Technology of the University of California (on coffee), Fred Johnson, President of Spice Islands Company, San Francisco (on spices); Maynard A. Amerine, Ph.D., Professor of Viticulture and Enology of University of California (on wines); to W. V. Cruess, Ph.D., Professor Emeritus of Food Technology, University of California, Maynard A. Joslyn, Ph. D., Professor of Food Science and Technology, University of California, and Emil Mrak, Ph.D., Professor of Food Science and Technology, University of California, for reading and suggestions about most of the manuscript; to Elly Hinreiner Platou, Ph.D., Food Technologist, Julia Hindley, and Margaret M. Lippman for revision and criticism of large parts of the manuscript; to the several assistants who have transcribed uncounted gross and minute revisions, and for their years of rewriting; for the direct communication given to many ideas that one of my background can best or only express in graphic form—to Don Lindquist of Mill Valley, who did the superior art work on the drawings; to Donald K. Tressler, Ph.D. and his Avi Publishing Company staff for indispensable encouragement and guidance in accepting and overseeing the preparation of the manuscript for publication, and to Mack Printing Company staff for art in production and patience up to and including page proofs.

C. A. RIETZ

June 1, 1961

Foreword

Most books contain few if any new ideas. Ordinarily they review, criticise, summarize, or "digest" data and information already available in technical, technological, and scientific journals and books. About the most that one can expect is that the author has given his own interpretations to that which he has "digested" and presented in his book.

The *Guide to the Selection, Combination and Cooking of Foods* is a new type of book, for it is the first attempt ever made to determine what foods "go together" and to indicate a simple method of selecting combinations which are sure to please the average palate. The Gustametric Charts summarize a lifetime of study of the flavor ratings of all common, and many uncommon foods, and present the data in nomograph form. With a little study, anyone, even a person who does not understand the rating system used, can use these charts to intelligently improve recipes and select pleasing combinations of flavors.

Because of the novelty of the flavor rating system proposed, and the boldness of proposing to use it as a nomographic system of food selection and combination, this book is bound to be the subject of much discussion both favorable and unfavorable. Researches by others may indicate modifications in the Rietz flavor ratings. Other workers may extend the nomographic system and determine the effect of the method of cooking employed on the intensity and nature of the various flavors. But, in the end, the system will be perfected and become a very useful tool used by all who are engaged in food development. The modifications of the system will not detract from Mr. Rietz' accomplishments but will only serve to emphasize their value.

Because it is novel and thought-provoking, the "Guide" should be read and studied carefully by all those who desire to place the selection and combination of foods on a scientific basis.

Donald K. Tressler

Contents

List of Illustrations

PART I

Understanding and Appreciating Foods

CHAPTER 1

Educational Requirements

Aptitudes

What are the important fundamental physical and mental qualifications prerequisite for culinary skills?

There are anatomical and physiological as well as mental requirements. The demands of the food judge and cook probably call for the same abilities and qualities that would be required of a good mechanic. This is not to say that the good mechanic will be a good food judge or cook; many other qualities are demanded as well.

There should be a clear understanding of gradations in abilities. Relative superiority of different individuals varies by degrees of performance and aptitude. Questions of relative importance of inherited tendencies versus environmental development, education, are academic subjects on a par with common expressions like "born mechanic," a gardener "born with a green thumb," and similar ideas suggesting inborn abilities. While psychological research tends to the opinion that most abilities are developed, the result of educational processes, it must be considered that a very large percentage of human beings are mechanically inept; they are deficient in what we may consider as the *tool sense*—for which the physiological explanation is centered about the functioning of most of the mathematical-associational senses.

Manual dexterity is the commonly accepted evidence of possession of a tool sense. But these other things, it must be realized, are also part and parcel of the tool sense. The ability to cut or draw a straight line, to cut a straight slice, accurately and quickly; in hearing, to judge by hearing and by feeling in a mathematically related way; *the ability to make things come out even.*

We all have hands, we all have them connected to the same brain centers. That is, anatomically we are similar, but we do not all have the same physiology. The hands function better or worse, with different individuals. The apes have practically identical anatomy with man—same kind of brain, arms, hands, but in spite of all that has been done up to the present, an ape cannot be trained to talk. Talking is one of the *facultative senses.* The facultative senses are very definitely those that man is born with—e.g. using the hands in a certain way. The tool sense is a facultative sense. It cannot be taught. In aptitude examinations, the simplest of manual dexterity trials will reveal the presence or absence of the tool sense. It cannot be too strongly emphasized that there are many, many people who just should not be in a kitchen, because they are deficient in the tool sense. They are the people who continually cut themselves and burn themselves. They are the "cooks that spoil the broth."

Whether the required abilities are inborn or developed, it is incontrovertible that abilities of individuals vary radically in their usage of kitchen tools and appliances, and certainly in their application of culinary physics.

It is probable that the majority of cooks may be considered the equivalent of *common labor* in the kitchen. They lack the qualifications that by any normal process of training would develop them as technicians. Assuming 70 per cent of mankind having the equivalent of common labor abilities, it is within the remaining 30 per cent that we must look for the technicians; within that 30 per cent perhaps 10 per cent possess the aptitudes required for development into technologists.

The man who is handy around the house and the woman who is deft in the performance of her housework may both develop into good cooks. But only a small percentage of good cooks have the qualifications that lead to culinary mastery qualifying for all that the term *chef* implies.

Stoves and appliances "act up." Gadgets jam in the drawer; buttered bread "always drops to the floor face down," and many comparable phenomena are what the engineer amusedly considers as occasional manifestations of the *innate perversity* of *inanimate objects.* Explanation of the specific experience is usually simple. Temperamental outbursts—the cook "blowing her top," demonstrate personal inability to cope equably with simple mechanical problems.

Comparative Ability

Knowledge, ability, and performance should be considered relative to norms (codes of standards). Qualifications of the individual are the first consideration in the forming of a food judge: first, his inherent aptitudes and abilities; next, his education; finally, his training and experience.

Within the different classifications (i.e., levels of qualification) there are established and accepted standards for each. These standards include the ratings or norms within the standards. The classifications are "reduced to practice" within the fields of trades, crafts, and professions. Within the trades and crafts, individuals are rated as *journeymen,* persons having qualified themselves for their vocations by a period of apprenticeship. The rating requires certain prerequisites of knowledge, followed by some years of *different kinds of experience* within the specific fields. Within the professions, after meeting basic requirements of mental and physical aptitudes—and surviving the educational grind, each person must pass through a fair number of years of intern-and-externship before meeting the *norm* requirements of *senior* professional ratings.

Until recent years carpenters, electricians, and mechanics were among the trades that required *journeyman* experience and ability to rate at the top. Trade literacy and background were required. While the oldtimers were carpenters and builders they knew they weren't architects. The electricians and mechanics knew they weren't engineers. Journeymen cooks didn't presume to be master cooks—*chefs*. Incidentally (since *food* is our subject) the profession of *chef* never has had an established norm of educational and training standards!

A handyman around the house develops his abilities hit-or-miss through a process of meeting the requirements of any given situation according to the limits of his knowledge and experience. He doesn't necessarily have to learn carpentering in order to drive a nail, or learn to be an electrician for simple wiring. To make a shelf installation he doesn't have to be able to read blueprints—to say nothing of being able to do mechanical drawing.

The evolution of the average domestic cook can be fairly compared with her more-or-less handyman husband. Consider the tuition (if any) and training or experience factors in cookery of the average housewife. Compare them with journeymanship in the trade of cookery, with the lores and crafts and arts of chefs!

Perhaps the housewife-cook, like her handyman husband, is in reality a product of the do-it-herself-as-best-she-can school—a vestigial process of education, considered by any normal standards.

Discrimination and Selection

Discrimination is easy to define but difficult to analyze. The basic definition comes from *discriminatus*—"Divided, discerned." Primarily, to discriminate is to distinguish between different things, qualities, and degrees.

One of the most baffling phases of this enterprise is the study of *sensory discrimination.* We may use deductive reasoning to analyze statistical laboratory records; we can measure that which is measurable. But any attempt to apply inductive reasoning to man's sensory behavior within or beyond laboratory panel conditions must be considered more as a philosophy of man's idiosyncrasies. Most laboratory projects are concerned with investigation or production of averages, and with what may be reproduced. The scientist is more concerned with mass effects than with small quantities, and very little with the rare. Marketing research caters to mass desires. Minorities are neglected or even ignored.

The vast majority of people live with the least effort. Each approaches his own sensory perception at best subconsciously and at worst unconsciously.

Discrimination takes effort—energy and determination—which few individuals can or will use to a maximum.

Marketing analyses show: substantially more than half the people, in some fields more than 75 per cent, follow average preference patterns. The volume of consumption within many categories by what the different trades call "repeat business" leads to one incontrovertible conclusion—*majority trends are toward static tastes.* People like what is habitual.

Within the minority there are those who can be termed the "discriminating few." The connoisseurs fall within the very low percentage of this minority, and the epicures are calculable as minute integers buried in the recessed tip of the statistical social cone.

In accounting for tastes, one of our most difficult problems is to decide why a minority likes what the majority dislikes. Why will some human beings accept what all but starving animals will reject? The obvious answer is *educated taste,* but to fathom what underlies the process of the individual's education involves unraveling the skein not only of individual, but of group lives; only rarely are there isolated unconnected or disconnected growths of tastes. Most tastes are the result of group influences. Is it conceivable that any untutored youngster would eat a raw oyster? Can you conceive anyone voluntarily selecting limburger cheese as food unless led to it—or unless under conditions of desperate starvation? And what about reaching for "well hung" game, the decomposing odor of which you can smell before you see it—someone has to indoctrinate you with the idea that "it is good to eat" against your better judgement.

Going back to that word "discernment" as part of the definition of discrimination, we realize that the senses of sight, smell, and feeling are involved. Discernment denotes *seeing,* not just *looking.* Smelling and feeling imply *perception* for their senses. But some of the queerest of our psychosomatic idiosyncrasies enter in here. We must consider the exceptions—what we will accept as digressions from whatever we have of common or average sensory patterns. In our food behavior as well as all of the other phases of our lives, we occasionally, more or less consciously, select aberrations from our normal food paths. Just as in music we learn to accept some kinds of dissonance; as in painting we learn to accept asymmetric composition and broken color, so in food we learn to eat things that don't look good, don't smell good, don't feel good and—let's admit it—they don't taste good. We learn to process them before, during, or after eating. Some of them differ greatly from over-all standards within almost every classification of food.

Discrimination by Vision

If mold is *seen* on or in food, the food is almost invariably rejected, because mold is assumed to be a sign of decomposition. But what we reject in other foods we welcome in cheese; we have been educated to accept surface and deep molds as *natural* in the "blue" cheeses and most of the ripened cheeses such as brie, camembert, and most of the brick and solid *natural* cheeses. At most the surface molds are scraped or trimmed away.

We insist on smooth looking surfaces of some foods and various degrees and kinds of roughness on others.

Color or lack of color is the deciding factor in the selection of many foods; but the bases for visual discrimination vary from deeply rooted customs to scientifically developed standards. What we accept as an agreeable color in one food is rejected if it appears in another. We accept grayishness in raw oysters, but we would recoil from grayishness in poultry. Blue, almost universally disliked in food, is accepted, in various shades, in cheese and fruit. In one of our subdivisions of seasonings, *flowers as food*, some of the colors rarely found and accepted in what we will eat are present in sugared violets and sugared rose petals.

Discrimination by Smell

What we will accept and what we will reject in the classification of smells from the lightest of aromas to the heaviest of odors are graphically shown in Figs. 14, 15 and 16.

Discrimination by Feeling—Touch

As will be seen from several of the charts, our standards of texture and consistency range from the lightest of *body* in liquids and beverages to an almost infinite range from soft to hard for solids; and our discrimination in the range of temperature varies from hard-frozen to hot.

Man's idiosyncrasies in the application of his sensory perceptions are outlined in the first section of this book; but the scoresheet approach in Volume II provides an appraisal method with which to judge and to account for some of man's tastes in different kinds of foods and food experiences.

Educational Requirements

The terms *cook* and *cookery* are among the most loosely used, defined, and interpreted in the English language. By common educational processes *cooks,* both domestic and institutional, are trained by *first learning the operating techniques.* The implications of this fact are more far-reaching than is generally realized. To put it another way: everywhere, cookery is taught without formal educational processes. It is taught as a *craft*. The bases of instruction are almost entirely restricted to operating techniques.

A *food technologist* is one who has studied, and has been trained in, the sciences on which food processing is based. His approach is through primary studies of the underlying sciences followed by a long training period in the practical application of basic principles by classroom and laboratory coverage. Knowing the underlying sciences thoroughly and having a working knowledge of his field, he is a professional, applying that knowledge to the practice and development of food processing.

A *food technician* is one who has been formally trained to carry out in a responsible manner approved techniques which are either of common knowledge or specially prescribed by technologists. He is expert in the technical details of the processes with which he is concerned; at his best he knows enough of the pure sciences to understand the underlying principles of those processes, and to cope effectively with anything that may go wrong. Essentially the technician is a practical person.

In the light of these definitions and interpretations where does the average cook fit in? Because of the tremendous complexity of modern food processing the technically unqualified cook (unqualified by any formal training in the underlying sciences concerned with food) is actually called upon to be a *food processor*. By far the great majority of restaurant cooks know less about cookery than, say, the average of domestic cooks—housewives—in the upper educational bracket. The simple explanation is that most professional cooks ply their trade within restricted applications of cookery. Fry-cooks tend to remain fry-cooks, etc. The housewife who is at all interested in cookery and the welfare of her family does a little of everything. It must be considered that her performance, by any fair comparison, is better than that of most restaurant cooks.

Most *professional cooks* have their practice and knowledge limited to a small area of the country that produces them. Very, very few intra-national cooks are sufficiently familiar, to say nothing of being sufficiently competent, to reproduce regional dishes of a specific country. They know nothing of the cookery of other parts of their country, let alone other parts of the world. Many chefs supervise international kitchens which are properly more nearly ratable as continental kitchens—but nationals of particular countries tell us that the different dishes submitted are at best "in the style of" France, Germany, Italy, or any other country.

We are considering the educational requirements of a person to be a qualified *judge of food*. Chefs, as can be seen from the preceding remarks, although superlative cooks, are not necessarily good judges of food

The ability to produce a single dish or number of dishes, some of them very elaborate, does not qualify the individual as a cook; much less does it qualify him as a food judge. It is true that to be a food judge in the complete sense, he must be a trained cook, but that is not all he must be.

A food technician is not *per se* a good judge of food. As a general rule, his training has been limited to objective studies, and his work is almost exclusively concerned with material examinations and processing. As should be apparent from perusal of the forepart of this book, qualifying as a judge of food probably takes far more training, education, and experience than what is necessary to qualify a technician or a technologist, to say nothing of a cook or a chef. In general, the technician need only be concerned with objective factors within his own limited field. The judge must qualify himself objectively and subjectively. He must be able to pass judgment in perspective. He is an *appraiser.* He must be able to stand off. In other words, a *food judge* is required to savor food, in the process of which he must take into consideration all of the factors concerned (the technician need only be concerned with the food itself) including selection, processing, service, and conditions of participation. The condition of the food itself would rate only a maximum of 50 per cent on any scoresheet he maintains.

The education of the *food judge,* therefore, must include the education of the food technician, the food technologist, the chef, plus the arts and sciences necessary to an understanding of the individual's physical qualifications, and of the factors of aesthetic discrimination.

It is probably one of the most absurd of all contemporary assumptions that gourmets and epicures are necessarily good judges of food. To be specific, I insist that a judge of food must know all of the elements of food selection, food preparation, food service, and food participation. That is where the gourmet and the epicure come in. They *enjoy* but do not necessarily *understand* what has gone into the performance. They are experts in the art of enjoying but not one in a thousand of them thoroughly understands and is qualified to judge the composition of the food he is enjoying. They do understand the elements of *ambient atmosphere* —up to a certain point, but if you put a scoresheet in front of them, they would probably go around in circles.

Cookery Training

Teaching cookery in the home as well as courses in cookery in Home Economics in the schools can be described as *manual training* with a thin and fragmentary veneer of nutrition, and to a lesser extent some of the food arts. With rare exceptions cookery is poorly taught. Further, it is probable that there is no single course of instruction in the food arts anywhere in the world today that is taught comprehensively. There is no single instance of a formal educational course in cookery and the food arts.

One of the anomalies of contemporary "cooking school" curricula is that in the majority of cases there are no prerequisites of education in physics and chemistry. With few exceptions there is no teaching within those sciences to provide a foundation for a substantial comprehension of

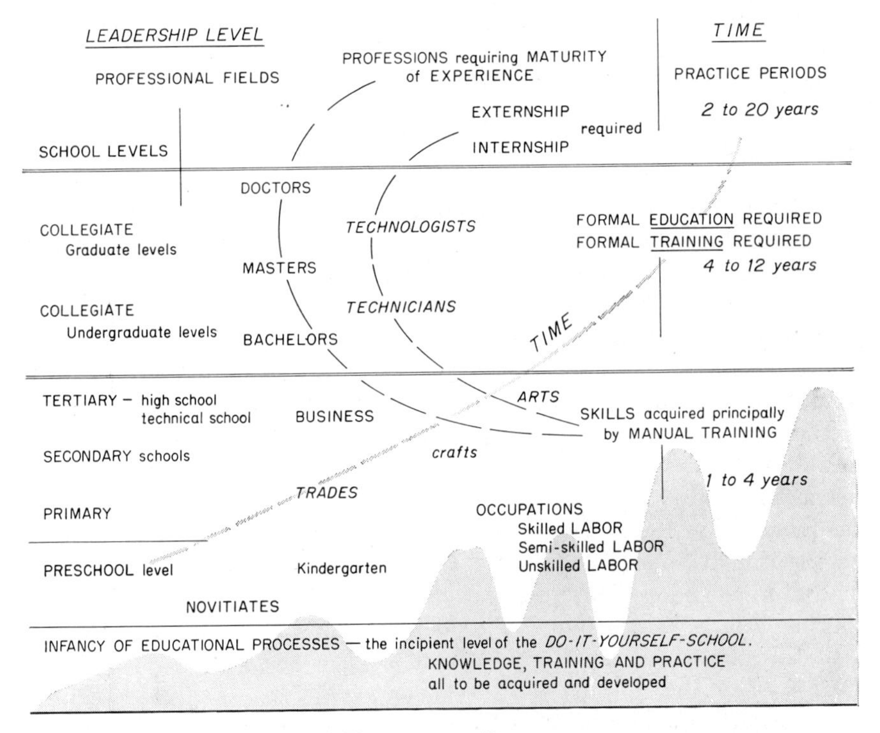

Fig. 1. Educational Requirements

The learning, training and experience needed to become a skilled judge of food.

what is involved in cookery. Furthermore, the average cooking school approach is based on domestic precepts and practices instead of what they should be based on, namely: professional—preferably technological—precepts and practices. This book presents a series of abstractions submitted as a starting point, and possibly as a guide for the serious student.

Neither this nor any other book can cover all the factors involved in cookery; all we can hope to do is to stimulate the reader's interest, so that he will continue with literary exploration and concurrently practice as he reads—and thinks. Beyond choice of material, equipment, and facilities, the important element is *time* in which to convert your knowledge to practice. You will realize a chef attains his position only after years of training and practice—usually starting with apprenticeship and then following with what amounts to internship in many different kinds of kitchens. As an amateur you can never hope to attain the skills of such professionals, if for no other reason than your inability to match their experience factors. But you can hope, if you seriously follow the course outlined in this book, to select and cook well, to eat and live better than you have in the past.

The beginning cook enters the kitchen with only the vaguest idea of what it is all about. Of our high school graduates something like one-third have had no chemistry and about one-quarter have had no physics. It may be safe to assume that the majority of girls have had neither home nor school training in cookery. Obviously, then, it must be a very small percentage of girls who enter marriage with anything approaching substantial training in simple cookery, and it is probable that the number who acquire what can be fairly called an academic education in cookery is negligible—a very small number.

We are first to lament the dropping of laboratory sciences at the high school level and to scoff at much of the teaching of cookery under "Home Economics" at the collegiate level. We are of the many who "view with alarm" and warn against the dangers inherent in the lowering of our high school curricula, to the point where too many high schools can be classified as coddling institutions of adolescent baby-sitters. Why not call them high-picnics instead of high schools, and shall we dance? If this approach sounds too facetious, study the average high school outline of courses and the average requirements for graduation. Educators have been screaming about this for years.

Cookery is included in the curricula of collegiate Home Economics in what amounts to a lick-and-a-promise. For one thing, the term "Home Economics" is not a good one. It is probably technically correct, but the phrase is one that is without any doubt "viewed with suspicion" or at least incomprehension by the majority of candidates. The term *home studies* may be much better. The criticism of Home Economics teaching of cookery is that no American college teaches cookery as every other subject is taught, i.e., in academic alignment. All other subjects are taught on the basis of complete exposition from beginning to end, from the historical beginning to the contemporary. The bulk of Home Economics teaching of cookery is top-heavy in chemistry and—strange as it seems—almost completely lacking in physics; and Mills College is the only school in the world today with a course on the history of cooking. It isn't called that—the title of the course is "International Cuisine," but it starts with an historical outline of the food behavior of man and then spreads into comparative studies of the customs of different peoples.

The fragmentary kind of cookery teaching at the collegiate level is no doubt dictated by the spirits within the great ivory towers being appalled by what is involved in teaching cookery in the same way that they teach all other subjects—in teaching what amounts to "the food behavior of man." Just making an exposition of the history of the subject is appalling, since that requires studies of virtually everything that concerns man in his everyday life—man himself, the conditions within which he lives, and the things with which he lives. For what amounts to a conventionally complete course in cookery all of the fundamentals of this subject must be progressively exposed in terms of the past and the present. Food as a word with its meaning limited to nutrition is only one facet of a many-sided subject. For any comprehension of *food aesthetics* there must be coverage of man himself, his anatomy, his physiology, his psychology, his comparative history—ethnology—and his historical social development. Concurrently there should be understanding of the history of food habits and food production of man from the prehistoric hunters and the historic gatherers and producers to the present processors. Physics and chemistry likewise require historical development for a clear understanding of usages, for contemporary applications of food matter and equipment.

The teaching of cookery should follow the elements of procedure of all other applied sciences; and right here and now let us debunk cookery as an "art" and call it by a fair term: a science, because most of it can be quite exactly defined, while in the same breath we say that much of food preparation and food service can be artistic. Let us also be fair in considering most cookery procedures today to be based on folklore and customs, habits, and styles.

Eating and Diet

Most people know practically nothing about *eating*. They do not know how to taste, have very limited ideas of selection, know practically nothing about cookery, and have never stopped to analyze their own food behavior either before, during, or after a meal. The majority of diners-out have never entered the kitchen of their favorite restaurant. Moreover, they have no idea of how the food was selected or prepared.

Technically, their selections are *foods found on the menu* and are influenced by *chance*.

One fundamental idea of this book is that the diets of prescription and health, in disease and for malaise, as well as our normal food behavior, should be based on knowledge, training, and experience far beyond what the large majority of people possess. The indisputable fact is that comparatively few people have a broad knowledge of food, and even fewer have substantial experience coupled with such knowledge.

The use of "reducing pills" reflects one of the most pathetic of the many foibles of the unthinking person. Reliance on cure-alls, like Br'er Rabbit's faith in smartenin' pills, brands the gullible as mentally immature, with that blindness to reality and worldliness characteristic of *younger* children.

The fact that health can no more be given by pills than intelligence by injection is overlooked by people who should know better. Yet they approach the subject of *food behavior* with the idea that they can remedy their ills by following some short and easy path.

To the serious student of what is involved in a diet, our counsel is to take up the subject of food behavior as an avocational project and to go through an educational process that will familiarize him with the fundamentals of *anatomy, physiology,* and *psychosomatics.* These he will have to know to understand metabolic processes. Then he must learn about *selection* of foods according to kinds and varieties, on a qualitative basis. Third, he should acquire a working knowledge of *cookery.* Fourth, he should know and practice the mechanics and crafts involved in food *service.* Fifth, he must develop sensitivity to food *aesthetics.*

The meaning of all this educational planning is that the individual is to learn *how to eat* instead of going on a regimen merely to *feed himself.*

Use of this Book

Within the limits within which this book can be produced, it is necessary to resort to a syllabic approach hereafter; abstracting the main subjects of each section to suggest a course of study.

Notice that the plan of education just given follows in essentials the plan of this book. In Part I we have just enough material on *anatomy, physiology,* and *psychosomatics* to introduce the student to those subjects from the standpoint of food study; he takes his cues from there, and must study those fields on his own. The matters of *selection, combination, cookery,* and some *service,* and *aesthetics* are treated more comprehensively, though in syllabic form, in Part II of this volume. Cookery *per se,* Service and Food Aesthetics are treated in Volume II.

Charts

Some of the charts are based on Eddington's *principle in the philosophy of science,* which may be stated thus: "All the quantitative propositions of physics, that is, the exact values of the pure numbers that are constants of science, may be deduced by logical reasoning from qualitative assertions, without making any use of quantitative data derived from observation."

The author can anticipate moans of anguish that will come from within ivory towers and disdainful comments that these charts are "arbitrary" and "unproven by years of laboratory determinations." But in defense—if a defense is necessary—his retort is that he has a sound background of authority for advancing theories which he apprehends as demonstrable by performance. He is entirely content to advance the theories he is outlining as structure of order and similarity. The numerical order of much of the charting is subject to statistical analysis and subsequent correction, but like the artist with a blank piece of paper before him, he begins by making a mark.

Likewise he is making at least a beginning in some of the fields of food behavior that to his knowledge have not been statistically reported. Classically, the charting represents studies of the projective properties of numerical values with arbitrary notions of distance and with only limited definitions of cross-ratios; the analyses are in the direction of qualitative concepts of order, in an effort to lead other students to greater degrees of power and generality than is possible with limited quantitative concepts of measurement, or which are encompassed within the limited range of one person's thinking and laboratory determinations.

An example of such properties—i.e., implied possibilities, that which is potentially inherent—in the numerical values shown, is cabbage. Cabbage has an agreeable characteristic when steamed, but becomes repugnant with the liberation of the sulfur compounds as soon as it becomes overcooked or anything like scorched. There are some animal matters that—for example in the mutton family—become capric or "goaty." Some animal meats contain minute glands which should be cut out because of this tendency to become repugnant. That is why knowledge of butchery should be a requirement in cookery procedure, so that the student becomes acquainted with some of the glands. For instance, in the stern assembly of a chicken there are two glands which in maturity become musky and distinctly unpleasant.

THE ART OF ENJOYING FOOD

Enjoyment of food can be developed into an art. Or to put it more correctly: some of the principles of the other arts can be applied to enjoyment of food. When developed to a sufficiently high degree, the enjoyer becomes the appreciator.

Part IV in Volume II of this book is an exposition of this art and of its practitioner, the food appreciator. Beside the application of the liberal arts to the presentation and service of food, virtually all of the factors of *aesthetics* can be developed and applied to the contemplation and participation in food experiences. The principles of art appreciation similarly may be applied with reference to food and food behavior. The approach might be to consider the art of appreciating as food behavior, as apart from consideration of food itself. Food *per se* is objective; food behavior is subjective—first person singular.

The considerations of matter used, of form, flavor, and color, kinesthetic variations, presentation and planning, and *ambience*—i.e. atmosphere and company—will be taken up in the discussion of *aesthetics* in Part IV. There also is treated the *disturbing influence*, the outstanding fault of American food behavior.

CHAPTER 2

Anatomical and Physiological Limitations of Man

Man is a monogastric animal. That is, he has one stomach. Other animals, including cows, sheep, goats, poultry, have two or more stomachs, and are therefore called polygastric. A cow has four stomachs.

This difference between man and those other animals parallels another difference: man is an omnivore—"eater of everything." That means that he eats food of either animal or vegetable origin.

The polygastric animals are herbivores—"eaters of vegetable matter."

Man is not a grass and hay eater. Man can eat "anything," but he is by nature primarily interested in eating meat. However, he has been in late years educating himself to go into competition with the herbivores, with which he is equipped to compete in only a limited way. These are the facts. You may judge for yourself:

A cow must chew its cud. If the cud is only partially digested, the cow brings it up and goes to work over it. But once you have swallowed anything, Mister, you have had it. And if it is hay, you will know you have had it, for the next twelve to twenty-four hours. And you may have to go to your doctor as a consequence.

The doctor won't tell you, but he may be thinking, "You darn fool—putting hay into your one and only stomach." The doctor may be one of those in the medical profession who believe you must have a diet balanced between animal and vegetable fibers.

To those, some of us say: Stefansson had a long argument on the subject, testifying that many Eskimos lived on an exclusive meat diet. They never ate vegetables. They didn't have any vegetables to eat. And to end that argument, Stefansson set himself up as a guinea pig, living six months on a straight meat diet. He made an important qualification, however: he insisted on the right to choose his meat, so that he would have a more or less balanced diet of organ meats as well as prime meat from young animals, and not from animals starving or deficient in one thing or another.

This belief that man needs a diet "balanced" with vegetable fiber should be gravely doubted.

And continuing: If there are any other disputants who do not believe Stefansson, there are not a few, but tens of millions of people in the world today who live on meat only. Many of them live to a ripe old age, and most of them live free from many of the deficiency diseases that modern medical science seems to be anxious about.

So when you reach for vegetables, it is very largely because of educational processes. You have been taught that vegetable matter is essential. There is a preponderance of fact in its favor. But there should be a reduction of vegetable fiber in the vegetable matter that is consumed. Man's digestive tract is not equipped to handle much fibrous bulk.

We should not eliminate vegetables from our diet. Certain kinds of vegetables and vegetable matter can be easily digested. But vegetable matter which provides heavy bulk should be avoided; not only the kind of vegetable should be considered but the time when it is eaten. For example: do not take a green leaved salad ahead of the entrée. The Europeans eat salads after the entrées—the end of the meal, and if they are satisfied beforehand, they will not take much salad, if any.

A good many of our vegetable troubles come from overcooked vegetables. The Orientals, particularly, just about heat the vegetables through, and take them off. Much of our metabolic distress from vegetables is attributable to three things: (1) over-cookery, (2) the kind of vegetables, and (3) the amount of fibrous matter in the vegetables we take. For instance, before celery is braised, the outer fiber should be stripped from the stalk.

Vegetables should be distinguished from vegetable matter. Vegetables were not developed by man until very late in his historical development. Cereals were used by man from his earliest historical period, from perhaps 4000 B.C., but vegetables were comparatively few up to the beginning of the Christian era.

In prehistoric times, undoubtedly man ate grass when he was starving. No one questions that there is a clear line of demarcation, in prehistoric times, between hunter and gatherer.

Egypt had very few crops. There were turnips, onions, garlic. White potatoes were unknown before Columbus in Europe or the Orient. But some of the yam-like ones were there. A fairly large number of the world's people, both primitive and the isolated peoples, particularly the men, reserve the prime meats for themselves and the women may have what is left, the "innards." In many civilizations the men—particularly the fighters—by a tradition that was practically a religious commandment, were restricted to animal meat diet. Egyptian kings were restricted, by custom, to a diet of veal and goose. Here the reader should refer to the Gustametric Chart.

Somatic Limitations—the Mouth

The dental equipment of man is very slight in comparison with that of the herbivores. The latter are equipped to chew and to reduce vegetable fiber far beyond the ability of man.

Fowls ingest shells and even sand with food, because, not having teeth in the mouth, they utilize these materials as teeth in the stomach. Man, on the other hand, does not have teeth in his stomach. He cannot with impunity ingest rocks, gravel, or sand. He gets into trouble. When you are about to ingest vegetable food which you saw an herbivorous animal eat, stop and consider what kind of an animal it is and what his equipment is to digest it, or to handle it in his intestinal tract.

Man is limited in comparison to some other animals in his oral equipment for tasting. He also grows much more limited as he grows older. We don't have nearly as many taste buds at maturity as we had in infancy. A baby less than one year old has many more taste receptors—called taste buds—than the child. The child has many more than the adolescent, and the adolescent more than the adult.

The baby has taste buds around the walls of the mouth. These apparently disappear in childhood. The adult has taste buds only on the tongue, with a very few elsewhere in the mouth close to the tongue.

There is no such thing as a "discriminating palate." That is a misconception embedded in the language of taste. There are no taste buds in the palate.

Somatic Limitations—the Nose

A dog has approximately 160 times the smelling area in the nasal mechanism compared with man. The olfactory receptors of a dog cover approximately 40 square inches, as against man's 1/4 of a square inch!

Animals test many foods by smell before they eat. We don't. Some persons would be alive if they had smelled their food. Many who died could have smelled that something was wrong, but they didn't.

CHAPTER 3

Organoleptic Perception — Interrelation of Taste to Other Senses

The Meaning of Organoleptic Perception

This chapter is concerned mainly with organoleptic perception. One of the limited definitions of "organoleptic" is "making an impression on the whole organism." "Lepsis" means "seizing upon," "laying hold of," so that the word has a basic meaning which describes an event involving a *mechanical registration* upon a *physical receptor*.

Now, we call this process "organoleptic perception." But the word "perception" involves a subjective process which is described by another word, "appreciation." Strictly speaking, the proper phrase is "organoleptic *reception*" or merely "organolepsis."

In a given individual the average of *reception* may be the same for all senses, but the average of *perception* differs by virtue of environment and training. In a group of individuals *reception* varies according to biological differences; *perception* varies according to educational differences.

Look at a painting. Every eye will receive exactly the same impression. What you receive is the visual image. But what you see in the painting—that is perception. You perceive what you are educated to see.

Now, appreciation is a matter of education; ergo, appreciation is the same as perception, which is relative.

It is not only important but necessary for the serious student to know both the underlying physical and mental factors which influence his food behavior. In a word, he must understand his own processes of sensory reception, his own mechanical processes of organolepsis, and the psychological process of transforming these into sensory impressions.

Having acquired some understanding of his psychosomatic relationship to the problem of food, he then begins to understand what is involved in food selection—i.e., first must come a knowledge of how he selects his food, then what he selects. He can then approach the problem of how to prepare, serve, and eat the food.

The relation of reception to perception and appreciation can then be summed up by stating that the reaction to stimulation is sensory or organoleptic reception. Qualitative sensory perception is equivalent to appreciation.

With reference to food it is important to emphasize the necessity of directing organoleptic reception. Remembering that "organoleptic" means "seizing upon" a sensory organ or receptor, this directing means that we will place before the receptor a stimulus which will take hold of,

1. Sight 2. Hearing 3. Smell 4. Touch 5. Taste 6. Heat 7. Cold	Conspicuously related to ectoderm (external stimuli)
8. Appetite 9. Hunger 10. Thirst 11. Satiety 12. Peristalsis—(Vagus Nerve)	Visceral—Senses related to digestion (principally internal stimuli)

13. Sex
14. Pressure
15. Muscular
16. Motor
17. Pain

18. Static—Balance, Rotation
19. Direction

20. Expression (physical)
21. Speech

22. Cryptesthetic—Perception other than through the motor senses. The impressionistic sense
    Experience—Suggestion
    Hyperesthesia—Clairvoyance
23. Some of the factors of intelligence—Fundamentals of "Reasoning"
    "Instinct"—What is it?
    "Intuition"—Prejudices
24. Facultative senses..........requiring comparison and judgment.

Musical harmony Color harmony Order harmony—arithmetic—mathematics	Mathematical associational group
Food (taste) harmony Expression, physical, rhythm Speed	Sense of Agreement/Disagreement

Play—a. pleasure—(games), humor
    b. sport

Fig. 2. The General Senses

This is not a complete list, and uses a sequence of convenience.

or impress, the receptor in a way which we have determined beforehand. In food, this is done by the educated selection of foods for certain factors—including flavor, texture, and many others—which make that food impress the eater's receptors in a way which he has predetermined.

To know what to select, he must have a good working knowledge of what can be described as the mechanics of psychosomatics—what is involved in his own processes of sensory reception and perception, and how he applies sensory impressions. Therein lies the field probably most neglected in man's approach to his own food behavior.

Closely related, actually intertwined with his sensory behavior, will be the knowledge and the application of the processes of preparation to substantiate the last part, food service and the way he eats. In other words, first must come a knowledge of how he selects, then what he selects, followed by how the food is prepared, served, and eaten. It is absurd to contemplate "going on a diet" without seriously studying all of the elements involved in his food behavior.

There is a range of flavor intensity which is common to humans with average sensory reception. The quality of sensory perception, on the other hand, is subjective.

The Primary Senses

The so-called "primary" senses are sight, hearing, touch, smell, and taste. Refer to Fig. 2 listing these and other senses.

For the moment we are going to pass over *sight* and *touch,* with the remark that they are both—as are all sensory receptors—dependent upon contact or impact of a thing outside—a mechanical registration upon a physical receptor.

Each sense consists of an organ which is connected to a seat in the brain by a nerve or a set of nerves. All sensory perceptions must come through bodily receptors before they can be transmitted as stimuli to the brain. In the case of touch, this is obvious. With sight it is less so; nevertheless there is a physical light wave which "hits the eye."

The functions of the original five senses are self-explanatory. Equally obvious, I believe, are their collective importance to the phenomenon of taste.

Hearing.—Hearing plays a very important part in the mechanics of eating. How do audile sensibilities affect flavor registration?

Possibly the most common misconception about hearing is that we and other animals hear only through our ears. The simple fact is that what is commonly thought of as the ear is the external appendage of the organ of hearing—most of which is internal.

Expressed in radio phraseology, the ear lobes may be thought of as part of the ear's antenna, much of which is wrapped around the eardrum condenser; which in turn transceives sound impulses from internal stimuli—principally the mouth.

The inner ear is our center of reception and transmission of what is commonly understood as hearing. It receives most (but not all) external impulses via sound waves, while from the bony structure of the head it gets both sound and tactile stimuli.

Sound is the sensation due to stimulation of the auditory nerve centers of the brain, usually by vibrations transmitted in a material medium (commonly thought of as only "via air") affecting the organ of hearing through the tympanic membrane. Internal sensory stimuli transmit their signals to the inner ear as assonant impulses.

Audible stimuli may be considered as all sensory impulses transmitted to and through the organ of hearing and interpreted as *sound. It isn't sound unless you hear it as such.*

There are people who are ear-minded, the audile type. They are perhaps hypersensitive to audible stimuli.

Auditory Factors with Relation to Kinesthetic Experience.—The influence of auditory perception in the process of eating should be studied, particularly in the direction of the extreme range where crunching and crackling sounds are so high as to dominate the weaker or lower sensibilities of taste and smell.

Example: Steamed smoked finnan haddie with its high flavor rating may be at the top of flavor tolerance for some people. Add coarsely-cut blanched almonds in the proportion of—say—one to four. In the process of munching fish and nuts together, it will be discovered that the fish seems to taste less fishy. This is attributed to an illusion caused by the dominance of the auditory sense over that of taste and smell generated by the kinesthesis of munching. The crackling sounds telegraphed within the skull are stronger than the weaker waves of other sensory perception.

Experiment: Take a sip of sherry, and then munch some peanuts concurrently; the flavor of the sherry seems to lose itself. Like a mirage it is there one moment and gone the next.

Oral kinesthetic experience is primarily perceptible through the sensory process of hearing conjoined with feeling. Tactile senses in oral mechanics are intertwined with hearing. They may be thought of as being intermeshed, perhaps interlocked.

A conjuncture of two kinesthetic senses occurs in the process of chewing and crunching food—two dominant perceptors over and above the perceptors of taste and smell. You can probably hear and feel celery more than you can taste it. That is a simple example of comparative quantitative sensory perception.

Feeling

All sensory perception is felt, including sight, smell, and sound. The moment you say "hearing" you realize there are sound waves, just as in sight there are light waves. Actually, these waves are felt. We have, therefore, a kind of feeling, received by an electrochemical process in the body.

All of the physiological phenomena of taste and smell are indisputably electronic. The degree of recordance and transmission may vary from extremely minute arithmetic quantities usually expressed as wave lengths (frequencies) to recordance and transmission of flavor impulses at or above the threshold of perception, which would then be comprehensible to any normal person in terms of quantitative common arithmetic denominators.

Consider your tasting experiences in terms of physical feeling. Then consider the general assertion that all directly subjective flavor appraisal is physical—not mental. Common flavor judgments are psychosomatic reactions based on both subjective, psychological, and objective, physiological, reactions. Thus, if in your studies of food behavior you sometimes limit your consideration to what you know are phenomena of feeling, it will materially simplify your approach to the elementary factors of taste and smell.

Reducing this to loose idiom, *you actually feel what you taste.* If you think of it this simply, you will get along very well in the great majority of taste experiences. If you can draw a curtain between what you think and what you *actually feel* when you make a flavor appraisal, you will be predisposing yourself toward accuracy.

On the other hand, for the niceties of discrimination within the factors upon which food aesthetics are developed, you must then go on to considerations involving the associational or *facultative senses.*

The idea to be grasped by the reader here, then, is this: flavor experiences are most simply evaluated in terms of physiological recordance and transmission, and so far as possible freed from psychological influences. Bear in mind that some of the most careful and consequently most accurate panel determinations of flavor values are made in darkened sound-proof cubicles. Try to visualize yourself in a somewhat similar situation when you make a flavor judgment. It will vastly simplify your tasting procedure.

The sense of feeling is involved in processes of palpation and percussion. Palpation is the act of touching or feeling, stroking or manipulation with the hand, for the purpose of tactually ascertaining a surface or subjacent condition. A muskmelon is pressed to determine yield under the surface.

Percussion is the act of firmly tapping the surface of a body to elicit sounds or vibratory sensations of diagnostic value. Auditory percussion, palpatory percussion, and threshold percussion are all used together. Auditory percussion is that in which attention is concentrated upon the character of the sounds produced. A melon is thus examined. Palpatory percussion is direct percussion, which concentrates attention upon the sensation of resistance detected by fingers or hands used as hammers—a probe-tapping procedure. Threshold percussion is the determination of the border or area of internal solid characteristics. Here the expert uses the three processes as a diagnostic process, all senses alert for reactions. Example: The difference between the textures of salt and of sugar is extremely important to a cook working in the dark.

The lightest pressure on the surface of the skin allows one to feel texture. If heavier pressure of the same object is used, the texture of the object's surface is no longer felt. The sensation of texture disappears and that of pressure replaces it. If very heavy pressure is used, the sensations of texture and of pressure may disappear altogether, to be replaced by the sensation of pain.

FOUR PHASES OF THE SENSE OF FEELING

(1) **Tactile**

  (a) **Sharpness** as distinguished from dullness.
  (b) **Roughness** as distinguished from smoothness.

(2) **Pressure**

  (a) **Atmospheric Pressure** is perceived without conscious contact. Here is a perfect example of the intangible tangible—sensory perception without conscious reception. (Here is a fair place to point out that extra-sensory perception may be to some degree compared with our consciousness of atmospheric conditions.)
  (b) **Sense of Weight.** Aptitudes of individuals vary from ability to judge weight within fractions of an ounce, to inability to distinguish between $1/_2$ lb. and 2 lbs.

Interrelation of the Senses; Relation of the Senses to Organoleptic Perception

The ultimate object of this section of our work is to provide bases and frameworks for the plotting of *flavor profiles.* Then it becomes possible to make a fairly accurate system of flavor prediction and consistent flavor formulation. Something has already been said of the importance of some of the sciences to an appreciation of the complex matter of flavor perception; it is time now to consider more specifically the different senses of the human organism.

The term *sense* has been commonly interpreted to mean one of the five faculties for determining external stimuli. Nowadays, the consensus of authoritative opinion is that there are many other faculties, capacities, drives, urges—call them what you will—of which the human organism is capable, which are as deserving of being called senses as the original five. There will follow a list of these "senses" together with some comments, when the author considers them relevant, as to their bearing on taste perception.

Heat and Cold

There are two distinctly different senses of heat and cold. Both heat and cold can be apprehended without the intervention of any of the other external senses; a person, for example, is aware of the presence of ice a few inches from his skin, although he may never touch it. Taste is radically affected by heat and cold as any cook who has varied the seasonings of soup to match its temperature well knows. Taste perception is impossible beyond certain limits of heat and cold (as we will show graphically later) and the good cook also knows that very hot and very cold foods are not agreeable when served together.

Visceral Senses

These are the senses numbered 8 through 12 in the list of senses.

These are a group of five senses related to internal or digestive stimuli. They are also vitally concerned in the mechanics of taste.

The first three of these, *appetite, hunger,* and *thirst,* may well be discussed together. At first glance it would seem that appetite is indistinguishable from hunger and thirst; consider, however, the man whose physical thirst might be satisfied with a few ounces of liquid, but whose appetite for alcoholic beverages is infinitely greater! Hunger and thirst, then, are matters of biological necessity; appetite may well be an aesthetic, a cultivated thing, the satisfaction of particular desires. Appetite, exclusive of hunger and thirst, is the province of the epicure, and of those who read this book.

Satiety, next in our list of visceral senses, is also more than the mere "over-satisfaction" of hunger and thirst. To cite an example: a person may be really hungry and may enter into a conversation about some food which he heartily dislikes—eels, or frogs' legs or spinach. Immediately he feels sated although he has not eaten a bite. Or the conversation may come around to a consideration of the potency of garlic; this same hungry person, motivated by curiosity, may bite into a garlic clove—the lightest possible bite may give him this same feeling of satiety although he is still without his meal. A consideration of this particular sense is of especial importance to us. It concerns particular food likes and dislikes, all of which can be comprehended, explained away, even overcome, if we find their origins in a person's individual past, or in his religious or cultural background.

One final sense remains in this group: *peristalsis* (i.e., the subconscious, usually involuntary action of the vagus nerve which, by means of contractions and relaxations moves digested food downward from the stomach). We have called it an "involuntary action" and yet we have a measure of concern with it. In times of emotional stress this action can be affected—

by either a speeding-up or a slowing-down process. It is, of course, a matter of aesthetic concern that emotional stress should be avoided at meal-time. It is also a matter of physiological concern.

"General" Senses

There is a third group of human reactions or drives which are designated as "general" senses. There may be some argument at their being so designated. It is impossible to defend them separately in as short a space as we have here. Rather we say, "If you can think of a more definite term for them, you name them." For the purpose of examining the various human functions which affect taste perception, we call them "senses."

This group include *sex* (which has already been discussed elsewhere in all of its manifestations *ad infinitum*); *pressure,* by which we mean atmospheric or altitude pressure, which has a decided emotional effect on an individual; *muscular sense,* articular, tendonous and circulatory, which is associated with acts of eating and drinking in our culture. *Examples:* such marks of good manners as eating with our mouths closed and taking care not to belch. Some other cultures have sharply diverging ideas about some of these factors, including what we call "good manners."

Other "general" senses include our *motor sense,* which has to do with our awareness of being alive, our feeling of potential; our sense of *pain;* our *static sense,* which has to do with balance; our *sense* of *direction;* and finally our *sense* of *expression* (concerning our ability to move to rhythm or to convey meaning by motion; and our *sense* of *speech.*)

Each of these abilities or faculties represents a separate capacity; all are concerned with and affected by our eating habits—or affect them.

Cryptesthetic Senses

Beyond the group of senses directly connected with the mechanism of the human body, there are senses or faculties which are not so easily explained. They might be termed the "cryptesthetic" senses; they have to do with perception which does not come directly from the motor senses. Such a sense—to use a general term—is *experience,* which is an accumulation, not only of things actually felt but of things which we, in retrospect, *believe* that we have felt.

Consider, for example, the varying testimonies which witnesses to the same event will give about what they saw. They may all have 20/20 vision and good hearing, and yet what they think they see will be reported in terms of their past experience, their prejudices, their mood at the moment. It is prejudice which has so long delayed the examination of man's taste perception; a kind of prejudice closely related to the racial and religious prejudice which plagues the modern world. "I don't like a certain food," a person will say, "because—why, simply because it just doesn't taste good!" What he really means is that it reminds him of a kind of person, or a place, or an emotional experience which he found unpleasant. Or that he was taught to dislike it by parents who transferred their own various prejudices to him or compelled him to eat it against his will.

Prejudices, whether we are speaking of food or religion, are signs of intellectual *daziness* or laziness, of unwillingness to explore or to investigate new ideas. A man who discovers that he likes birdnest soup may be well on the way to a better understanding of the Chinese. Much of what we dismiss as "instinct" or "intuition" is simply experience, howbeit early experience, and one's experiences should be re-examined and re-evaluated frequently.

There is one other sense or kind of perception known as hyperesthesis or extra sensory perception (ESP), thus clairvoyance and hypnotism have qualifiedly been made respectable through recent investigations. Future research may evaluate their relevance in connection with food behavior.

FACULTATIVE SENSES—SENSORY CAPACITY

Finally, there are the facultative senses, those faculties which man uses to make comparisons and to pass judgment. These senses are subject to educative processes; they have to do with capacities to appreciate music, color, and food "tastes"; with mathematical, athletic, and rhythmic abilities. It appears that there is a direct relationship between exceptional ability in one of these fields, and a capacity to excel in, or at least to appreciate, the others. A superior person is too frequently educated in one or a few particular senses to the exclusion of the others. But it can be no mere coincidence that epicures almost always excel in the arts or in one of the professions which require high development of some of the facultative senses. Our thesis, then, is that there is a direct relationship between what we call "sensitivity" in one area to sensitivity in another, just as we have already stated there is a very close connection among the various motor senses.

In our opinion, a person is born with an average level of sensory perception *capacity*. For the average person a particular sense may be developed by training and experience factors far beyond his other senses. But we emphasize our belief that his *ability* as expressed in the training of one of the senses will not exceed the capacity of the others. Education, of course, will enable this capacity to develop or be refined, but no amount of education can create sensory capacity. Under normal conditions, one's grasp may not exceed one's reach. It is usually the other way around.

We can touch or reach something, but we don't grasp it! Some professional cooks have, no doubt, died of old age without having reached the point where they could make a blindfold discrimination between bouillon and consommé. A musician's child may have music pounded into it for years and still be incapable of writing a good piece of music. That there are exceptions, individuals with outstanding ability as evidenced by one or just a few sensory manifestations, goes almost without saying. But, like overdeveloped or underdeveloped glands, as your family doctor will tell you, such exceptions are surprisingly rare. In the author's experience with taste panelling he is always surprised when exceptional deficiencies show up, exceptionally low "threshold of sensory approach" or exceptionally high tolerances. The outstanding fact is that the averages tend to even out, and the great majority of individuals tend to display equal mean averages of flavor perception. And that includes the evident functioning of all of the senses herein discussed!

We believe that just as it is possible within limits nowadays to predict aptitudes in the arts, so would it be possible to measure and to predict aptitudes in taste perception. A series of tests to measure this aptitude would be of great benefit to food technicians in the future. Such tests would also bear out, we believe, our theory just stated, that there are definite connections among the various facultative senses and average sensory capacities.

Toxicity.—The value of organoleptic analysis as an aid in the detection of poisons should neither be underestimated nor overestimated. Gross contamination is readily detectable; that which meets the eye and is clear to casual sensory perception. But distinguish between that which meets the eye and what may be invisible or not perceptible under anything but laboratory conditions.

KINESTHETIC FACTORS

Introduction

The sense of touch is a complex sense, much more so than most of us realize. There are several kinds of receptors located in the skin and mucous membranes, or muscles that help to make up this complex sense. For example, pain receptors located on the finger tip; the feel of warmth or coldness, or the observation of roughness or smoothness. It is to be seen then, that the sense of touch is really many senses in one. Kinesthesia is a type of touch sensation. This special branch of touch has been defined by Webster as "the sense whose end organs lie in the muscles, tendons, and joints and are stimulated by bodily tensions; the muscle sense." Another definition is "the sense by which muscular motion, weight, position, etc. are perceived." It is this special branch of touch with which we are now concerned, and its relationship to the food behavior of man.

When a particular food is considered, factors such as weight, particle size, physical state are all recorded by the kinesthetic sense; this sensation is then integrated in the brain with other sensations such as sight, taste, hearing. The result is a total evaluation of the particular food. It is then evident that texture may play an important role in the over-all evaluation of food.

It is not until the subject of kinesthetics is taken in perspective and examined in detail, that one becomes aware of the extent to which kinesthetics influences our food behavior. It is not until we start taking the subject apart, examining it in detail, that we are made to realize that it is one of the critical every meal factors upon which we base our likes and dislikes, acceptances, and rejections.

Texture—Relation to Kinesthetics

The influence of texture in the total evaluation of food is far greater than most persons realize. Texture is known as "the disposition or manner of union of the particles of a bodv or substance." Texture, when applied to food is a term that deals with such factors as the physical states and morphological characteristics of food. Thus, this term may be classified or subdivided as *Physical* or *Morphological.*

Physical and Morphological States.—Certain foods may have a wide range of physical states, i.e., may range from complete solid to complete liquid, or complete gas. There are, then, numerous intermediate steps. This change of physical state is graphically shown in Volume II. The straight line indicates, for example, the per cent water and the corresponding per cent of solid matter at any given temperature. The curves express the relative amount of suspended particles in any concentration.

An interesting example of the important role of the gaseous state is that champagne and beer without the gas effervescence are flat and uninteresting. They are rejected by the majority of their most avid enthusiasts. In our gustametric scale the champagnes are rated at around 125, but note that the chablis rates 40, which means that the kinesthetic factor of the carbon dioxide is to a considerable extent responsible for their difference of ratings. An interesting experiment can be carried out by charging a good chablis with carbon dioxide if the experimenter has a readily available re-chargeable soda syphon.

Another example of the importance of the gaseous state to our kinesthetic sense is that lemonade supercharged with CO_2 will be enthusiastically preferred over that made with plain water.

Morphological Characteristics.—Texture has been termed the forgotten factor in good cooking, and it has been stated that the most fully-developed national cuisines in the world have rated *texture interest* as high as good flavor. Small differences in texture may be analyzed by our kinesthetic sense; this process may be regarded as kinesthetic variation or *selection.*

The morphological characteristics of food are an important part of the consideration of the texture of foods. Morphology is known as the science of forms and structure of organized beings. This may be applied to foods as the study of their sizes, shapes, form, density, hardness, etc. The many physical and morphological differences in food are differentiated by the kinesthetic sense and are recorded in the brain as a particular texture contrast; this may be demonstrated by the chart of texture contrasts. A particular food may be either rough or smooth—or perhaps, somewhere in between. The same food may also be intermediate between soft and hard. Thus any particular food *may* show a wide spectrum of texture contrasts as demonstrated by the chart.

The other chart that accompanies this discussion in Volume II cannot be said to be self-explanatory, but it does provide a graphic exposition of what is involved in food textures. The footnote to that chart, as well as to this whole discussion, is that in a number of the charts and illustrations there are allusions which are part of the subject of kinesthetics—all refer to solids in solution and suspension, variations from soft to hard, from small to large, from liquid to solid, etc. All of these allusions are part of the very potent factor of kinesthetics.

It will be shown that the size of the food particle is very important to kinesthetic sensation. Particle size may be termed as submicroscopic, microscopic, and macroscopic. These different particles may be in solution, or suspension in different kinds of liquids—by themselves, and in combination.

Particle size is also related to flavor value; it is interesting to distinguish between juice that is coarsely strained and that which is finely filtered. According to the chart in Volume II the amount of and condition of the solids in solution and suspension cause variations in flavor. Many of these solids are not visible—like sugar and salt in solution. Some submicroscopic and microscopic solids appear simply as clouds in liquids, but according to their nature, we may or may not be able to appraise them in relation to other food values. The nature of some of these solids is such that we are only aware of them in what we think of as contributing to the density of the liquid, e.g., as we say some wines "have more body" than others.

With our awareness of macroscopic particles, we encounter the field of solids that are large enough to be individually visible and more or less individually detectable by sight or feel, or otherwise susceptible to organoleptic perception. We know that they are there through our kinesthetic sense without having to comprehend the physics and chemistry of the dispersion.

An excellent example of the important role of large solid material is celery; the reader will realize this when he notes the flatness and the insipidity of filtered celery juice, sampled alongside of part of the raw stalk which has just been crunched with relish. As a rule, panelists vote filtered raw celery juice as unacceptable. The same sort of trials may be made on other vegetables such as tomatoes, carrots, peas, etc. Without exception it will be concluded that the expressed juice in each case is unacceptable. Fruits will show the same phenomena, but to a less radical degree than the vegetables, for the reason that the majority of the fruits are rather high in sugar and organic acids; the acceptability will hinge very largely on the proportion of the sugar and acid in the juice.

The kinesthetic factors of each food are critical as regards the evaluation of such food. The citations we have made refer to vegetable matter; however, the principle applies to all foods, whether liquid, solid, or gaseous.

The universally well liked watermelon will serve as another example; when pressed through a colander so the solids retain some of their identity, may be on the edge of acceptability by some, but by most people it will be rated as undesirable. However, if the watermelon pulp is pressed to produce a cloudy liquid, the majority of people will reject it. If it is filtered, nobody wants it. Part of the answer is that the sweetest watermelons have a sugar content too low to be interesting, and the other intrinsic flavor factors are not enough to compensate for the texture inherent in the whole fruit.

Muskmelon, when subjected to the same trial, will yield almost the same results. While the sweetness and acidity may be somewhat higher, it still is not enough to make the filtered juice acceptable.

The Kinesthetic Complex (Hand to mouth)

Kinesthetic discrimination may start with the feeling of food by the fingers. A good example of this is corn on the cob; most people will prefer it prepared in this manner rather than cut and placed in a dish to be eaten with a fork or spoon. Thus, there is a certain amount of satisfaction derived from touching the corn on the cob. It is important to note that vision also plays a role here; almost everyone will enjoy seeing corn on the cob. Thus, kinesthetic sensations may be modified by such factors as sight and hearing. For example in the case of celery, auditory sensation may dominate over taste or kinesthetic sense.

Oral kinesthetic experience is primarily perceptible through the sensory process of hearing co-joined with feeling, i.e., celery may be heard and felt, before it is tasted.

To use the same example, it may be pointed out that there is also kinesthetic satisfaction derived in tearing the corn from the cob with the incisor teeth; therefore, we may say that the teeth and lips show capacity for kinesthetic satisfaction.

Kinesthetic Variation

Food Selection and Flavor evaluation.—The influence of texture in evaluating the flavor of food in general is profound. Certainly, the technologist is acutely aware of the gradations which he measures in terms of penetration or shear, applied to vegetable solids and animal meats.

A good example of kinesthetic variation is that many cooks will use raisins in a pudding, not just for the flavor, but for the difference in textures. For the same reason pine nuts are added to poultry stuffing, or diced apples to chicken salad. A texture difference, then, appeals to our kinesthetic sense.

It is quite important to realize that much of our food selection is done for the kinesthetic value of the food. In this selection, the texture of the food is critical. A few examples will help to describe this concept. Raw celery, mentioned previously, provides components most easily identifiable for their registration of most food perception factors. From the standpoint of intensity of sensory perception, prime raw celery is one of the foods that we can hear and feel more than taste. In this case, the senses concerned with feeling rate higher than those concerned with smell or taste. Chopped chives in cool sour cream inserted in a split hot baked potato provide kinesthetic variations of temperature and textures.

TASTE AND SMELL—THE PREDOMINANT "FOOD SENSES"

Taste and smell are the two most important senses related to the process of savoring food. In the discussion to follow, it will be necessary to differentiate clearly between these two senses.

The taste receptors are located in the tongue and soft palate. None are found in the hard palate. For our purpose, the term "taste" will refer only to those impressions received by the receptors in the tongue.

The smell receptors are located in the olfactory cleft. We shall use the terms "odor" or "smell" only in connection with olfaction.

It is extremely important to note that the term "flavor" refers to that quality of a given substance *which may affect either taste or smell, but which more commonly involves a combination of the two senses.*

Anatomy and Physiology of Taste

There are about 9000 taste-buds in man. Each consists of a number of elongated cells ending in a hair-like process which extends through the opening of the taste-bud to the surface of the tongue. These cells are the end-organs for the sense of taste. Disregarding the sensations of touch and temperature, and the chemical sense—all of which are received by other organs as well as the tongue—the taste-buds give rise to four distinct cardinal tastes: sweet, sour, saline, and bitter. While it seems apparent from experiments that some taste-buds respond to only one sensation, others to another, morphologically they are the same. Certain areas of the tongue are far more sensitive to specific tastes than others; thus saltiness is best perceived on the tip and front edges of the tongue, sweetness near the tip, sourness along the sides, and bitterness at the back.

The chemical nature and the amounts of the substances which elicit each of these four taste responses are fairly well known. However while the compounds giving salty or sour tastes, respectively, are closely related and well-defined, there is much more structural variation among the groups of compounds that evoke sweet or bitter tastes.

Sugars, of course, are by far the most common stimuli for the sweet taste, but even among them there is considerable variation in the degree of sweetness. The monosaccharide, fructose, is sweeter (on an equal weight basis) than the disaccharide, sucrose, but it in turn is sweeter than most of the other common mono- and di-saccharides such as glucose, maltose, galactose, and lactose. Determination of the relative sweetness of sugars and other sweet substances has been the subject of a great many investigations. However, the quantitative relationships vary somewhat with the concentrations employed. For example, Cameron (1947) has found that a 3.8 per cent solution of glucose is equivalent to a 2.0 per cent solution of sucrose, but the glucose concentration necessary to match 10 per cent sucrose is 14.6 per cent, not 19.0 per cent.

The chemical moiety common to the sugars and to a number of other sweet substances (ethylene glycol, glycerin) is the chain of adjacent aliphatic hydroxyl groups. Other types of structures which commonly give a sweet taste are the following:

(1) Alpha-amino acids; example, glycine, alanine.
(2) Heavily chlorinated aliphatic compounds; example, chloroform, tetrachloroethane.
(3) Aliphatic nitrates; example, ethyl nitrate.
(4) Certain synthetic aromatic organic compounds; example, dulcin (*p*-ethoxyphenylcarbamide), saccharin (*o*-sulfobenzoic imide), 4-nitro-2-aminophenyl propyl ether. The latter is 3300 times as

sweet as a 1 per cent sucrose solution and is the sweetest substance known.

(5) Certain organic salts of lead (lead acetate "*sugar* of lead"), and the beryllium ion.

The threshold, or minimum detectable concentration, of sucrose for most people is around 0.5 per cent. However, the sweet taste is second to the bitter in sensitivity, if one considers the thresholds of the synthetic sweet compounds such as saccharin.

Soluble inorganic salts are the principal stimuli for a salty response. Both the anion and the cation seem to influence the degree of saltiness and the nature of any secondary taste reaction. The lower molecular weight salts tend to be most salty while the higher molecular weight salts tend to be predominantly bitter. Sodium, potassium, lithium, ammonium, caseium, and rubidium ions are the cations and chlorine, bromine, iodine, sulfate, and nitrate ions the anions most commonly involved in salty substances. A few organic salts which are closely related to ammonium chloride, such as methylamine hydrochloride, are also salty.

The average threshold concentration for sodium chloride is around 0.5 per cent. It should be realized that all of the thresholds given here for the basic tastes are *recognition* thresholds, not *absolute* thresholds; that is, they are the minimum concentrations at which the substances can be recognized as sweet or salty or sour or bitter, not the much lower concentrations at which the solutions can be distinguished from distilled water. It has been observed that the salt threshold of adrenalectomized rats is lowered about twenty-fold and that they will show a preference (over distilled water) for solutions far more dilute than can have any therapeutic effect. Thus it appears that the taste mechanism can be altered by changes and abnormalities elsewhere in the body.

All of the substances which give a sour reaction are acids; that is, they ionize in water to give hydrogen ions (actually hydronium ions). The degree of sourness is closely dependent on the actual concentration of hydrogen ions, being greater for a solution of a strong, completely ionized acid such as hydrochloric than for the same molar concentration of a weak, relatively undissociated acid, such as ascetic. However the apparent sourness of solutions of identical pH, or hydrogen ion concentration, is not the same for all acids, the organic acids usually giving a greater apparent sensation. This may be due to factors such as surface tension, vapor pressure, or fat-solubility of the acid. Furthermore the anion of most organic acids contributes taste, usually sweetness or bitterness, in addition to the sourness. The threshold pH for the sour taste is about 3.5 for inorganic acids and around 3.8 for organic acids. For hydrochloric acid the threshold value corresponds to a 0.0045 per cent solution.

A number of different types of compounds are associated with the bitter taste, and most of them are of relatively high molecular weight. Thus it is interesting to observe that as the molecular weight increases in going from sodium bromide to potassium bromide to caseium bromide, the compounds become less salty and more bitter. Similarly, many organic compounds that are sweet have higher homologues that are decidedly bitter.

1. Agitation, disturbance or tumultuous movement, whether physical or social.
2. Strong feeling
   Impulse to overt action and internal bodily changes in respiration, circulation, glandular action, etc.
   Any one of the states designated as:
   Fear
   Anger
   Disgust
   Grief
   Joy, mirth, humor
   Surprise
   Yearning, etc.

   Dramatic Expression
   Acting
   Pantomime
   Dance
3. Agitation of the feelings or "sensibilities"
   Reaction to sensory stimuli—
   Agreeable or disagreeable—
   i.e. sounds—music
   Noise–percussion instruments

Emotional faculties may be inversely motivated:
fear—courage
sorrow—joy
dramatics: comedy / tragedy

taste—distaste
like—dislike
tolerate
hate love

FIG. 3. THE EMOTIONAL FACULTIES

The most decidedly bitter compounds are the alkaloids, including such substances as strychnine, quinine, brucine, theobromine. Perhaps it is significant that the bitter taste sense is so much more sensitive than the others! Poisons tend to be avoided. Many glycosides, certain organic nitro compounds (particularly poly-nitro aromatic compounds such as picric acid), and a large number of miscellaneous compounds are also bitter. In the inorganic group many magnesium, calcium, and ammonium salts and many heavy iodides and bromides are bitter. The reported threshold values for bitter substances do not agree too well, but values around 0.00005 per cent are reported for strychnine and quinine, and 0.0001 per cent for brucine.

The compound phenyl thiocarbamide as well as some of its derivatives is interesting in regard to sensitivity to its bitterness. To some this compound is extremely bitter, but to many others it is tasteless. Among members of the Caucasian race about two-thirds are "tasters" and one-third "non-tasters," while in other races the proportion of non-tasters is much lower. The taste deficiency has been shown to be a recessive trait inherited according to Mendelian laws. There is no apparent connection with an individual's ability to taste other substances, and the mechanism or significance of the taste deficiency is not understood.

Sodium benzoate is another compound which is tasteless to some people and either salty, sweet, or bitter to the rest. On the basis of their reaction to these compounds Fox (1932) divided people into eight different classifications and correlated these groups with their tendency to like or dislike certain types of food.

If taste were purely a chemical phenomenon it would be expected that threshold sensitivities would increase steadily with temperature. Hahn has made a thorough study of this question using solutions at temperatures ranging from 65° to 108°F., and taking the precaution of maintaining the area of the tongue used in the tests at the test temperature by means of an ingenious tubular device through which the solutions were passed. He found that while for most sweet substances the threshold decreased as the temperature rose from 63° to 98.6°F. and increased thereafter (maximum sensitivity at normal body temperature), that for acids remained constant over the entire temperature range for most people. In some, the sour taste varied as the sweet taste with minimum threshold at 98.6°F. Sensitivity to saltiness and bitterness increased with increasing temperature throughout the range.

When a stimulus acts for some time on a receptor it usually becomes "fatigued" or insensitive to that stimulus. The degree and duration of the fatigue is dependent on the intensity of the stimulus. The interactions of the four tastes are quite interesting in this connection. A quinine solution fatigues (reduces the sensitivity) of not only the bitter receptors, but also the salt, sour, and sweet receptors. Acetic acid solutions and salt solutions both fatigue the sour, salt and bitter receptors, but actually enhance the sensitivity to sweetness. The behavior of sugar solutions is most surprising; a 5 per cent sugar solution was found to fatigue the sweet taste markedly and to a lesser degree the salt and sour, but a 20 per cent solution actually enhanced all four receptor systems. These phenomena of fatigue and enhancement find their application in such culinary "tricks" as the addition of a little salt to increase the apparent sweetness of a melon, a dish of applesauce, or a cake, and the use of sugar to reduce the bitterness of coffee.

Bitterness and Astringency.—Puckeriness or astringency, usually closely allied to bitterness, may be classified as one of the secondary tastes. It is more closely related to pain than it is to the four cardinal tastes. The extreme puckeriness of unripe persimmons is in the field of discomfiture on the verge of pain. Very few people have tasted bitter aloes, but those who have tried it never forget it.

Such an extreme combination of bitterness and astringency as in fruits like aloes seems to have the effect of cementing the inner surfaces of the cheek to the gums. One of the odd phenomena that we experience with gall-bitter foods is what seems to be concurrent arrest of mucous flow in the mouth. The mouth seems to "dry up." It feels dry without being parched. The explanation is simple: The bitter substances stimulate nerves that react by constricting the nerves that control mucous flow. This is a good example of organoleptic response—cause and effect.

There are relatively few bitter substances. Tannin is one of them. Some of the vegetables that are bitter have an astringent effect which may be caused by some affiliate of the bitter element, whatever it is. While the impression of tannin is slight puckeriness, the bitterness in milkweed and in the milk of lettuce is more astringent.

THE ANATOMY AND PHYSIOLOGY OF OLFACTION

The anatomy and physiology of olfaction are far less completely understood than for taste. No doubt this is at least partly due to the vastly greater number of distinctly different odors and the difficulty of classifying them. It is hard to imagine a system which will respond to each of several hundred thousand different volatile compounds in a characteristic way. The sense of smell, like the sense of hearing, appears to be analytical, rather than synthetic as color vision is. Thus the trained nose can pick out the separate components of a blend of odors, just as a trained ear can pick out the separate notes of a chord or the separate instruments of an ensemble by their pitch and quality. Without *a priori* knowledge or experiment, however, the eye could not disclose that the color green is a blend of yellow and blue. Green is perceived as a separate color, not as a mixture partaking of some of the characteristics of each of its components. This analytical nature of odor coupled with the phenomenon of fatigue makes it possible for some trained odor analysts to identify fairly complex mixtures from their smell alone. The first sniffs serve to identify the one or two most prominent ingredients, then as the nose becomes fatigued to these more dominant odors, the more subtle flavor notes can be perceived and identified.

The sense of smell is far more delicate than the sense of taste, and indeed concentrations of some substances can be detected by the nose that would be impossible to identify by the most delicate of chemical tests. The minimum stimulus concentration varies widely, depending on the strength of the odorous material; relatively weak odorants such as ethanol are detectable in concentrations around one part per million by weight, while more strongly odorous chemicals, such as vanillin or skatole, are perceivable in about one ten-thousandth as high a concentration—one part in 10,000,000,000! And it should be remembered that there are animals whose sense of smell is far more acute than man's.

Although the nose is generally regarded as the organ of smell, few people realize that the site of olfactory nerve endings is actually localized in two small areas about the size of a postage stamp inside each of the nasal chambers. In the process of ordinary breathing, relatively few of the air molecules reach this sensitive site; most of the air passes through the lower nasal chambers only. This is why it is necessary to take a sharp, deep breath—a conscious sniff—when we wish to perceive a relatively faint or delicate odor. While most of the lining of the nasal passages is reddish in color, the olfactory region is yellow due to a pigment which appears to be connected with the olfactory mechanisms. The pigmented olfactory cells themselves are elongated structures packed perpendicular to the surface of the olfactory region. They bear 5 to 8 fine protoplasmic "hairs" at one end which project into the nasal cavity, and the opposite end connects to the olfactory nerve carrying the sensory impulses to the olfactory bulb of the brain.

Many attempts have been made to group and classify types of odors, and a number of schemes have been proposed. All of them are completely empirical, and are either incomplete, inconsistent or ambiguous. A few of the better known systems are as follows:

Zwaardemaker's Classification

Zwaardemaker in 1895 grouped odors into 9 classes with 24 subdivisions.

Classes	Subdivisions		
1. Ethereal	a. Fruits	b. Beeswax	c. Ethers
2. Aromatic	a. Camphor	b. Cloves	c. Lavender
	d. Lemon	e. Bitter almonds	
3. Balsamic or fragrant	a. Flowers	b. Violet	c. Vanilla and coumarin
4. Ambrosial	a. Amber	b. Musk	
5. Alliaceous	a. Hydrogen sulfide	b. Arsine	c. Chlorine
6. Empyreumatic	a. Roast coffee	b. Benzene	
7. Caprilic	a. Cheese	b. Rancid fat	
8. Repulsive	a. Deadly nightshade	b. Bed-bug	
9. Nauseating or foetid	a. Carrion	b. Feces	

While many substances can be reasonably fitted into one of these nine classes, there remain a number which cannot. Furthermore, "repulsive" and "nauseating" are subjective terms; substances repulsive to one person are not necessarily so to others. In connection with this system it was proposed that there are nine types of olfactory cells responding to the nine different classes of odorous substances. Some supporting evidence actually exists that when the nose is fatigued to a particular odor it is fatigued to other odors in the same class, but not to odors of other classes.

Henning's Classification

Henning (1916) suggested six odor groups: spicy, flowery, fruity, resinous or balsamic, burnt, and foul. A given odor, however, might be intermediate between two or more of these absolute types, and to symbolize this relationship, Henning devised the olfactory prism with the six basic odors at the six apices of the prism (Fig. 4).

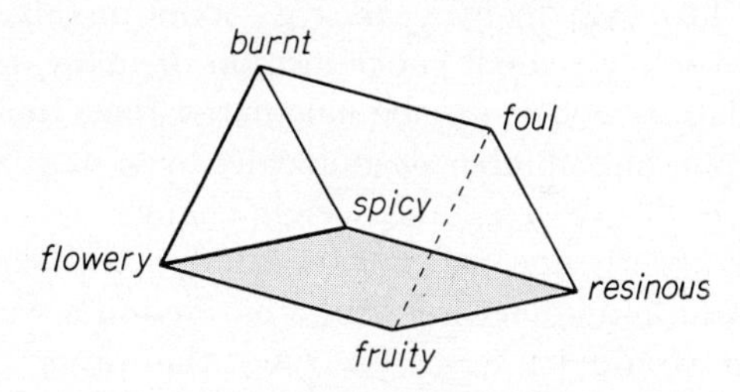

FIG. 4. HENNING'S OLFACTORY PRISM

Intermediate odors would then be along an edge of the prism if they had two components and on a plane surface if they had three or four components. The superficiality of the prism is at once apparent if we consider how many combinations are apparently barred. For example, it would appear impossible for an odor to be flowery and resinous without being fruity and spicy as well. However, this is a fault of the symbolism and not necessarily of the theory; Henning's hypothesis that an odor may be a blend of several components in varying degrees is certainly a plausible one.

Henning further associated certain spatial configurations of the molecule with each of the six groups; for example, *para*-substituted benzene derivatives were spicy, *ortho* were flowery, etc. Unfortunately there are many, many exceptions to these rules, and the few structural arrangements presented do not begin to cover all the odorous compounds.

Crocker-Henderson System

Crocker and Henderson in 1958 reduced the basic odors to four: fragrant, acid, burnt, and caprilic—each having eight possible degrees of stimulation or intensity. Any four digit number from 0000 to 8888 could then represent a particular odor, the first digit giving the intensity of the fragrant component of the odor, the second the acid component, and so on. While the system appears to be quite artificial it has proved fairly reproducible in the hands of trained people, and is useful for cataloguing and reproducing odors. Operators work with a reference set of 32 standard samples which include representatives having each of the four basic components in each of the eight possible intensities.

There is some argument as to whether olfactory stimulation is caused by particulate matter or by some type of wave motion set up by odorous molecules. It seems likely in either case, however, that molecules of the odorant must actually get into the nasal chambers in order to be perceived. This implies that a substance must be volatile in order to be odorous, and such seems to be the case for all known odorants. It is true that some solid odorous substances volatilize so slowly that they show no apparent weight loss over many years e.g., some metals. However, we have already seen what a small concentration of many substances is required for stimulation, and it can be calculated that, for such materials, loss of the corresponding number of molecules even over a period of centuries would not result in a detectable weight change.

It is a common observation that hot foods are more fragrant than cold, that odors—pleasant and otherwise—are intensified in a warm room. This is certainly what would be expected, since the vapor pressure of any volatile substance increases with rising temperature. It simply means that a higher concentration of molecules enters the nasal chambers with each breath.

It also seems likely that in order to react with the olfactory cells, the odorant must be in solution. Both fat solubility and water solubility are necessary to some degree. In a homologous series, the lower members, which are relatively insoluble in fat solvents, and the higher members, which are relatively insoluble in water, are less odorous than the intermediate compounds which are fairly soluble in both water and the organic solvents. Contrary to what might be expected, however, if solution of the odorant is indeed necessary, introduction of solutions of odorous substances to the nasal passages inhibits rather than aids olfaction.

As with the other senses, the olfactory apparatus is subject to fatigue. After sufficient exposure to a constant odor, one is no longer able to perceive it. The time of adaptation is dependent on the strength of the stimulus, but is of the order of a few minutes for most moderately strong odorants. The adaptation is gradual during this period—that is, a stronger and stronger stimulus is required to elicit the same response. The fatigue persists as long as the stimulus is present, but if the odorant is removed recovery takes place also in a matter of minutes. As previously mentioned, fatigue for one odorous material lessens acuity for other similar acents, but does not impair perception of unrelated smells.

Certain pairs of substances, each odorous by itself, are inodorous together. That this masking is due to some mechanism in the central nervous system, and not to chemical reaction between the odorants or to interactions of the receptor cells, appears to have been proved by Zwaardemaker, who obtained the odor neutralization even when one member of the pair was introduced into one nostril and the other into the other nostril. By this technique he was able also to measure the ratios of the two substances necessary for masking.

Masking of unpleasant odors is not usually possible, since relatively few of these neutralizing pairs are known in any detail. More frequently the technique of "drowning" the undesirable smell with stronger, but more pleasant odorants is resorted to.

Another surprising olfactory phenomenon is the effect of dilution on some odorous compounds. Many of the components of perfumes—civet, ambergris, many aldehydes—are quite unpleasant in concentrated form. Indole is partly responsible for the odor of feces, but is also the principle constituent (in more dilute form) of jasmine fragrance.

Smell, Odor Identification

Just what is involved in odor identification? Start with the qualifications of the judge: (1) physical qualifications and limitations: (2) mental qualifications and mental limitations, especially prejudices; conditions of making smell tests.

The Time Factor in Flavor Perception

To perceive a flavor is not a simple process. Observing your own tasting process you will see that there is an important time factor in it. When do I taste the food in question? I am influenced when I first see it coming in on the dish, when I first smell it, etc.

Then other questions arise when you think about the process: How long does a flavor last? How long do I taste it? (These are not quite identical, as you will see.)

Let me bring out the features of this subject with a sidelight from a field allied to that of flavor judging—the rating of perfumes. Some experts use a two-fold method: first, sniffing the perfume from a drop placed on blotting paper; and second, placing drops of the perfume on his wrist and forearm. Each test is necessary, and each brings out different properties of the perfume. The first allows him to analyze it for its various "notes." For instance, when he first places the drop on the paper, he sniffs it to catch the initial "top note." Several hours later he sniffs it again to get the basic scent ("heart") and again after twenty-four hours for the "end note." This part of the test allows him to *classify* samples of different perfumes according to their *basic character,* placing all the "floral" types, for example, in one group.

In the second part of the two-fold method the judge evaluates the quality by comparing all the perfumes in one such group for the qualities each has of proper blending of odors, for "volume" (extent of dispersion in the air), for strength or intensity, and for lasting quality. Although most women do not expect a perfume to last longer than eight hours, he observes the test drop after 24 hours.

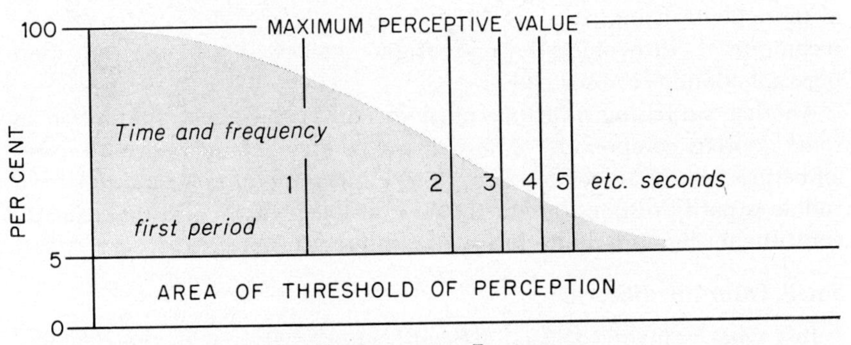

FIG. 5. OLFACTORY PERCEPTION

Realization varies as: kind, intensity, time, and frequency of exposure.

Perception of an odor involves anticipation (sometimes), detection or realization with or without recognition, time or frequency. The physical factors involved in perception of an odor are kind, intensity and *time* of exposure to it.

The aesthetic factors are anticipation (sometimes), specific realization, and identification. Appreciation requires recognition—usually by association with past experience.

Returning to the field of the flavor judging of food, you can now see that the processes are similar. That is because of the similarity in the way flavor of food and scent of perfume "register" with human beings. A perfume has a *basic odor* which depends upon the basic oil used, such as rose or jasmine "absolutes." The basic odor also changes according to the kind of fixative used (ambergris from whales, musk from musk deer, etc.), as well as what synthetic aromatics have been added. Perfumes usually have thirty or more different components.

In food, all flavors have *basic characters:* animal, vegetable or chemical. Most flavors are complex mixtures of taste, smell, and feeling. In your own experience you have noted that you do not get the "whole picture" of a flavor all at once, in many if not all cases. When is a lemon drop "tasted?" When you first become aware of the sharp tang, or later, when the heavier "aftertaste" remains? Why this variation over a period of time? One must be aware of several variables before he can answer that. I have divided them into six propositions which follow. First, he must recognize what is involved in the *approach.* He must understand, for instance, in what manner the peeling of an orange affects his perception of its taste when later he places the section in his mouth.

Second, he must observe the *instant* or the *condition* in which exposure to a taste or flavor experience is possible for the individual. E.g., what amount of sugar is needed in a solution before he can perceive sweetness? This is called the "threshold." Here the differences between individuals are highlighted.

Third, he must be aware that there is an *interval* between the initial exposure to a flavor experience and its *perception.* A man is blindfolded and a small, hard object is placed on his tongue. He closes his mouth. There is an interval before he recognizes it as a lemon drop. There is an interval between detection of the *low note* of a flavor and its *high note* within which period the flavor *may* be identified; but it is probable that identification does not occur until *after* the flavor experience has *peaked.* You may or may not identify the pepper before you start to reach for the glass of water. The interval under discussion is measurable in milliseconds!

Fourth, he must see that *perception* introduces the complexes of (1) awareness of a particular *kind* of flavor ("it is peppery"); (2) identification of *varietal* components ("cayenne"); and (3) judgment of intensity values–deciding about gradations of *individual qualities* ("raw cayenne!"). This is parallel to the perfume judge's two-fold method.

The time within which a flavor is classified varies according to its *intensity.* This in turn varies according to its concentration in a specific medium or carrier. Within this factor is the bulk of man's *qualitative* flavor determinations. ("Too much pepper!") Herein is the epitome of whatsoever the individual has of apprehension of flavor values.

As a fifth consideration, it must be understood that no single element of flavor is constant in the human mouth–or, broadly considered, the organs within the oral cavity. A flavor *peaks* and then subsides–it trails away. One of the reasons why we do not perceive a flavor at once, fully and constantly, is that the receptors become *fatigued.* The cardinal tastes remain most nearly constant, but even they, after the initial perceptory grasps, descend in what may be termed a "falling fatigue scale." We have pointed out in previous chapters that receptors responding to different flavor elements are located in different areas of the physical equipment. These become fatigued in varying lengths of time. The sense of smell is probably the most delicate of our physiological mechanisms. We assume that because of its extreme "sensitivity" it is the sense most subject to rapid fatigue. *The element of time dominates it.*

The sixth proposition to be kept in mind is that no flavor is absolute; no flavor, *per se,* is directly perceived. What are technically termed "flavor absolutes" such as essences, essential oils, etc., are sensorily perceptible only as *diluted by body fluids.* A process of physiological transfer is involved—through the mouth or the nose. We taste by *direct* contact with the food in the mouth; we smell *indirectly* the odor of the same food simultaneously. Both sensations fade with time due to fatigue.

Even chemically pure salt or sugar is organoleptically perceived in saliva-modified degrees. If the tongue were dry we could not taste it. Olfactory reception of aromas is highly variable. The variation starts with individual nasal conditions. Likewise, all flavor appraisals are contingent upon individual physiological chemistry; they vary accordingly. It is therefore implicit that there can be no direct, absolute taste or flavor evaluations.

Basically, all perception is *indirect.*

The questions we asked in the beginning of this chapter can now be answered—rather flippantly, it seems, but with real accuracy—by saying, "*it depends.*"

When do I perceive a flavor? It depends on my capacity, on the material tasted, and on the time factor. *How long does a flavor last?* Again, it depends on those things. *How long do I taste it?* Now you see that individual variation is as important as the variation of the substances tasted.

In other words, from now on, when you think of tasting food you will remember that *flavor perception varies with the individual, with the matter and with time.*

You put this knowledge to work by devising a set of procedures for testing flavors, which will take into account each of the six factors discussed above. The procedures will turn out to be something like those used in the judging of perfumes: similar samples, subjection to substantially identical tests, classification according to type, qualities, etc., and further tests in which lapse of time is the principal factor.

As the perfume judge uses closely similar amounts of perfume on reasonably identical pieces of blotting paper, keeps all samples in the same place and observes all samples after the same period of time in the same manner, so the food judge must have a definite plan in order that the judgment may be a comparative one. The word "compare" (L. *comparare, cum,* with or together—*parare,* to prepare) is the key to the process. Standardized comparison must form the basis for evaluation. Judging foods for yourself, you will need a systematic process beginning with selection of samples (similar in age, size, etc.), parallel preparations of the several samples (e.g., cutting into similar sized slices) and including actual tasting in the mouth, feeling with the tongue, and so forth.

Of course, each type of food to be judged will demand its own procedure; no one set of steps could be followed for coffees and for oranges. However, the particular plan in each case must embrace all the six propositions given above. This is the only way to obtain any degree of objectivity in the judgment. The awareness of the six elements is an aid to insuring that the conditions (including changes in the judge) have not varied between tasting one sample and another. Knowing that flavor fatigue is an influence upon your judgment, you will not expect to judge fairly between varieties of peppers by tasting them one after another in quick succession. You will endeavor to re-create the proper conditions with a fresh tongue, so to speak, for as many times as it is necessary to cover the samples.

Although there are standard processes in use by professional tasters of various kinds of food, a particular method will not be suggested, since the tests will not be made in laboratories. You will need to devise procedures for each comparative judgment you need to make. Notice the words *need to make,* because comparative judging by samples is a necessary step in the larger process of both understanding and using the fundamentals you learn by reading this book.

Work out your own procedures, then, based on the knowledge you have gained here. I give you just two rules: *Be systematic. Be aware.*

FACULTIES VS. SENSES

One of the most common fallacies is reflected in our reference to the "sense" of humor, and what may be the worst of all, "common sense."

In the meaning of perception, there is no such thing as a "sense" of humor; "common sense" taken in that meaning is equally non-existent. What is implied by the term "sense" of humor is a *faculty,* a phenomenon of the operation of what is sometimes called the "mind," but it is not connected with any organ. We have no *organ* of humor.

A good question for the cephalist is, "Is there a seat of playfulness in the brain?" Here it is pointed out that this is one of the faculties shared with other animals. The young of most animals are playful, but it seems that only man and porpoises retain faculties of playfulness into the adult stages.

"Common sense" just isn't. What is implied is definitely not sensory. The idea which the term conveys is judgment resulting from experience. This is within the field of aptitudes, which are widely variable; and anything approaching a high average, such as is implied by the term "common sense" is uncommon.

The application of what we call "common sense" to the selection of foods possibly provides us with our greatest pitfall. We tend to continue making the same mistakes; we don't learn, which is certainly a condition not implied by development of "common sense" in our food behavior. The majority of people drop into a groove and follow it, develop lifelong habits of what they think of as "common sense" in their eating habits.

"Common sense" implies "common knowledge" of a fact or facts upon which it can be based; therefore, if there is no "common knowledge" of a fact, though true, there can be no "common sense" about it. "Common sense" then will not help in thinking where the knowledge required is specialized, because specialized knowledge is by nature uncommon. A knowledge of food and the eating thereof is within the field of the sciences; and a knowledge of even any one of the fields of food sciences is not within common ken. Consider: how much knowledge is commonly held?

CHAPTER 4

Psychosomatics

PSYCHOSOMATIC NATURE OF FOOD EXPERIENCES

Sensory experiences cannot be shared, because they cannot be accurately described.

(1) They must be measurable to be describable.

(2) The individual must know virtually all there is to be known of each factor and phase—the impossible project of getting to know all about himself.

(3) He must be in complete control of (a) all of his faculties, his body and his conscious activity, and (b) his circumstances, the conditions surrounding a sensory experience—physical and social.

You don't share your taste with anyone. You can't because you don't know enough about your tastes to describe them accurately, so how can you share what you can't describe? You can share experiences, pleasures and displeasures, enjoyments, but your own sensory reactions can be shared with others only to the extent to which you are able to communicate them *exactly*, and the ability of others to *receive* and *comprehend* what has been transmitted. You have never equally shared a flavor experience with anyone. You have shared many meals and many food experiences. The portions and the food may have been equal, but the tastes and flavors—positively *no!*

Have you ever shared a meal? Before you blurt a hasty answer, pause for consideration of the subject and define what is involved for yourself:

(A) What is involved and implied, the notation and connotation of "a meal" as a food experience.

(B) "Shared," implying equal apportionment of a food experience which requires equal aptitudes in food behavior. Identical dining in everything—including extra-sensory perception.

Our tastes are our most closely held secrets. At most our tastes are only partially revealed to others and then only on rare occasions, because the matter of taste is largely concealed, unknown to today's greatest experts in the field.

Such experts daily realize they know less and less about more and more.

Comprehension of what is involved in taste, or consciousness of flavor values, varies from moment to moment and time to time, according to individual factors of receptivity:

(1) Qualifications of the individual: age; sex; education.

(2) Circumstances, physical, place, conditions and time. Social, people, atmosphere.
(3) The time factor—periodicity.

Memory of a *taste* experience is a composite memory of the appearance of a table setting and of food seen and/or conversation and background music (good or bad) or noise which accompanied a meal, but note particularly that only rarely, and then with additional distinct effort, is anything of the odor memory of the food experience reconstructed. Our odor memory is particularly weak, deficient, and in certain directions, nonexistent. In other words, we have little or no odor memory.

Some people will object that the odor memory is stronger than and precedes the other sensory memories of a scene. As an example, the smell of peppermint gum held up by a child against the hot isinglass of a Franklin stove is a vivid odor memory to that child grown up. The feeling that the odor memory is strongest and the first to be recalled of that scene is entirely average. You think about peppermint gum, and mull over the experience involved, and come out with a conclusion. This process is depicted in Fig. 6 on page 49. You go in, you circle around, and you come out. In that process occur all the experiences shown in that chart. In comparing odor memory with visual and audile memory, something engenders or stimulates the thought: peppermint gum—stove—scorch—and then comes the construction of the smell. You didn't get that first. You had to get the stove picture, you had to get the scorching recollection before you started to get the smell.

An odor memory can be recalled in two ways: first, by smelling something now which is similar to the odor recalled. The memory will then bring back the earlier scene. The other way is to have the scene recalled by something which happens now, and then the memory fills in the odor from the earlier scene.

It may be that there are certain scenes which stand out in the memory, like the example of peppermint gum held against the stove. In recalling these outstanding scenes, the odor memory returns quickly and strongly so that it seems almost to be a *direct* memory. But to recall a scene less pointed in the memory, complete with odor—say, a Sunday dinner at which Aunt Sophie was present—requires effort, if it succeeds at all.

Visual memory, on the other hand, is very frequently—most frequently —*direct*. The others are all *indirect*. Visual memory does not have to be reconstructed but comes to the memory unbidden. For illustration, if I ask you for your favorite composer, you may say, Bach. I ask you for a favorite piece of his. The moment I ask you for a favorite piece, then you have to *reconstruct* what it is, whether it is an Air in G, or something else. Having decided which it is, then you come to the melody itself. And

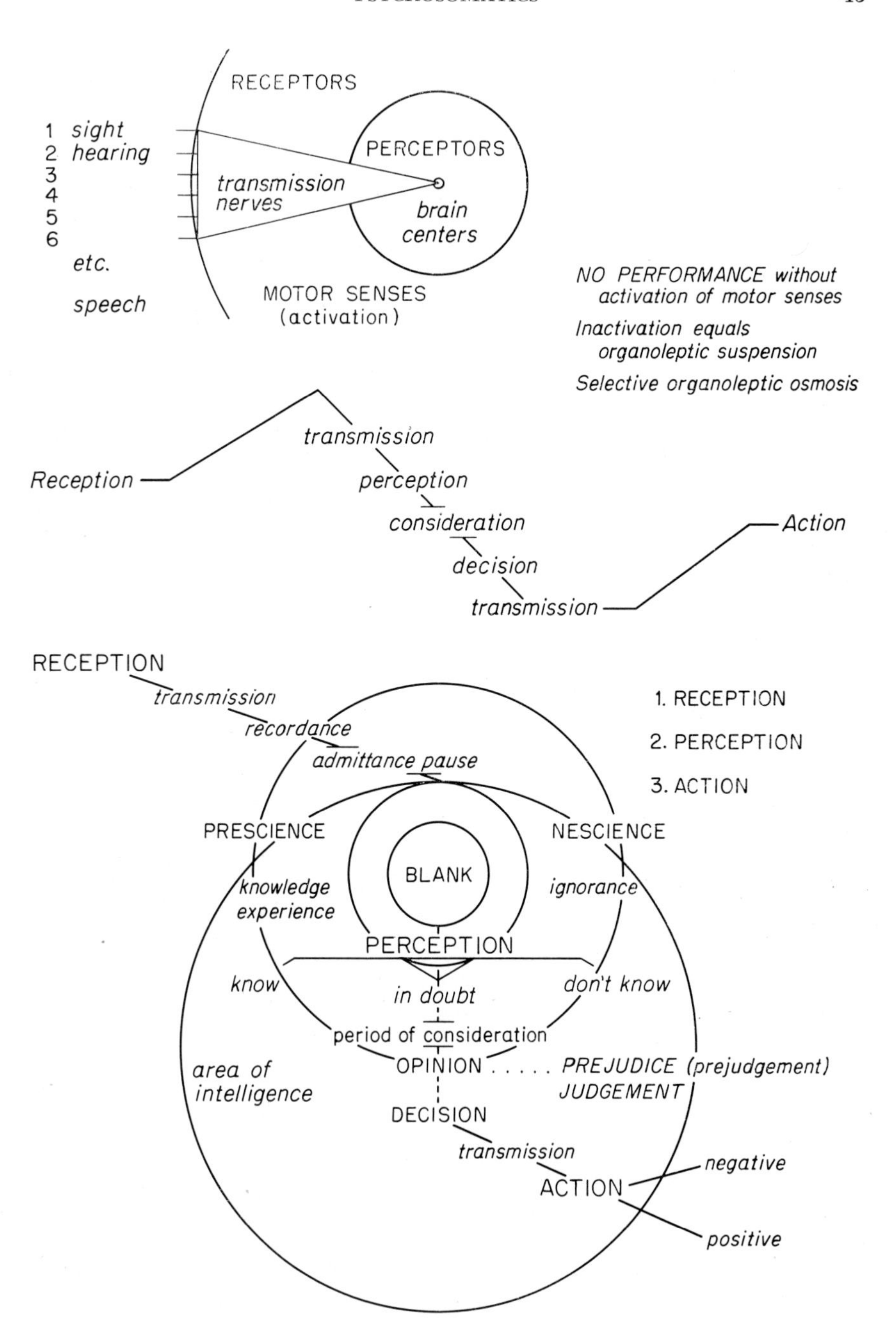

Fig. 6. Sensory Mechanics

Hypothetical flow sheet traces sensory reception, transmission, perception, and action, if any.

No performance without activation of the motor senses. Inactivation equals organoleptic suspension. Selective organoleptic osmosis.

then that part of the melody which you prefer. But it is some time before you identify the passage in Bach that you like. And it is never *direct.* When I ask you whose music you like and you say, Bach, what comes to mind? A visual memory: heaps of music, or the likeness of the composer himself, or the word "*Bach*"—a visual memory. A direct memory.

The odor memory is weaker, and must be recalled indirectly. I can think of Spain directly, but I have to have something to suggest Spain first. The moment I think of Spain, my mind goes flitting around a whole string of suggestions—all of which I *see.* I can slide around Spain in a sweep and see a hundred pictures instantly within a second from Madrid around to Barcelona and Valencia, and so on. It is a direct vision.

But if I am asked to name what I had at the seashore restaurant outside of Valencia, then I visually construct the restaurant, and I construct the kitchen and I have to labor to think what I had that night, and then to the kitchen itself, and the cook and what he was working with.

The weakest memory of all is that of *flavor.* It is slower to return. It grows weaker and slower with age. While visual memory also becomes weaker with age and distorted, it yet remains strongest of the sense memories.

All memory images distort with time, in the absence of recently repeated experiences. The big difference in all memory is the element of dimension. Things that are seen after a long period of remembering are farther apart, bigger, or smaller. All this is very critical in our considerations here, because it accounts for misconceptions—which they are—of *flavor dimensions.* These are discussed a little later on in this chapter.

Such misconceptions of flavor dimensions are "mother's hotcakes," "grandmother's cookies," "the stew we had here," or the "goulash we had there." Time lends enchantment, and it glosses over with an aura of desirability in many cases, and undesirability in others. I am in England and Scotland at least once a year on visits. I can walk into a certain house in Scotland and get to my room almost blindfolded, because I know my way. But if I postponed my visits for ten years, I might stumble because I would forget where certain steps were.

You go to San Jose and have a hamburger, and the same cook uses exactly the same ingredients and the same procedure year after year. The first time was under desirable circumstances, and the lights were good, you were hungry, and so forth. And many people will say, "Well, I had a hamburger there, out of this world." So you go there again, after 5 or 10 years. Meanwhile you have had other hamburgers "not as good as that one in San Jose." When you go back, it's the same cook, same time of day, etc., but the hamburger is terrible. The reason is that in the meantime you have had better ones.

You have learned to discriminate between meats. You don't like the smell of that hamburger. You don't like the way the cook did it. You say, "Is this what I thought was out of this world? Well, it was the wrong world!"

Now, to explain briefly what is meant by "flavor dimensions." The Gustametric Chart, Fig. 25, in Part II of this book, is naturally, two-dimensional: vertical and horizontal. It is subject to almost any kind of statistical representation, including plane geometry. Now, many flavors have *third* and *fourth dimensions,* primarily *depth.* All of the flavors vary as to *time.* Then, all of them vary with *ambience* of service, and all of them vary with *temperature.*

Part II goes into detail on this subject, but here is an example of what I mean: chervil and coriander, when young—3 or 4 inches high—have almost identical flavors. They are on the same *flavor profile level.* Chervil, however is very light and coriander is, comparatively, heavy. Yet you can't say that coriander has higher flavor, because it hasn't. It is the same flavor. It isn't sideways, because sideways they are identical. It is that coriander has greater depth than chervil.

All onions have the same flavor, but red onions have a deeper onion flavor than yellow, and yellow deeper than white. Using the same amount of concentration of essential oils, red, yellow, and white onions are identical; raw, let us say they rate at 350. But the red onions have greater depth, but not *more* onion flavor.

A still better example, closer to home, is beef. The flavor of the foreleg of beef is the same in flavor level as that of top round, we will say, or bottom round, or the rib section or the loin—exactly the same. But in flavor valuation it will be found markedly different. The foreleg meat of all animals—like smoked shoulder of pork, has a deeper flavor registration than the ham. The shoulder of mutton has a deeper flavor registration than the leg of mutton. Ratingwise, they are the same level.

FLAVOR APPRECIATION

Time-to-Taste Factors

To savor takes time. It may be said that one instantly recognizes some specific flavor. However, not only is there an appreciable time interval between exposure and perception, but in the majority of even analytically critical taste experiences the factors involving time are many, and their workings are little understood. It should be emphasized that the *time-to-taste factor* should not be thought of as instantaneous, but as an interval of time which radically varies in duration from exposure to perception according to stimuli and circumstances.

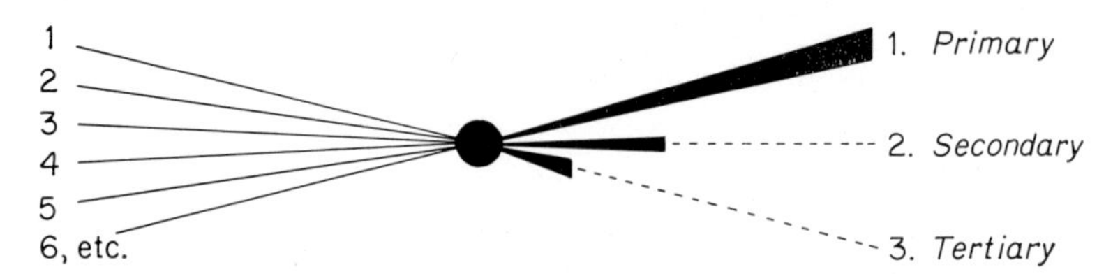

Each of the senses *tends* to require satisfaction of three factors:

1. The initial tendency is to focus on the Primary factor, (the focal point, the center of the specific sensory attention).
2. The next tendency is toward awareness of *secondary*, relatively one or more simple companionate factors.
3. The *tertiary* factor tends toward requirement of a compound base. May be considered the Atmosphere Factor.

The second and third factors may be considered as *the recessive phases of organoleptic perception:* they receded from the focal center of reference.

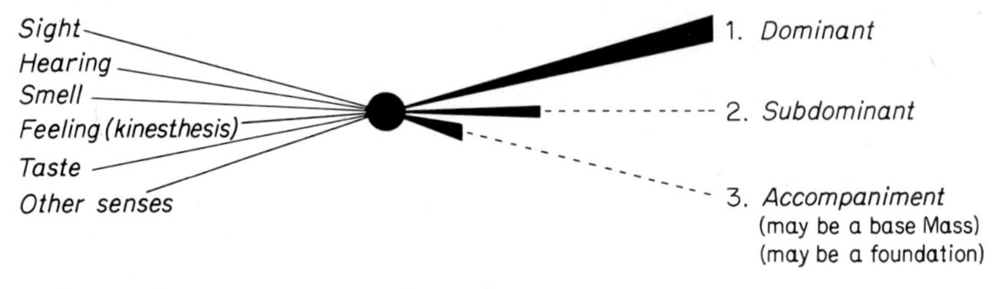

All organoleptic perceptions *tend* toward three phases: 1, 2, and 3.
Tendency toward limitation of any specific sensory perception to three phases:

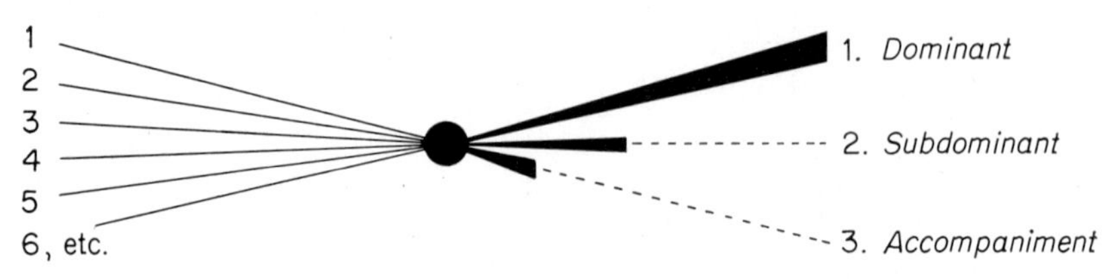

1. May be the *solo* part—*simple* or *single*,
2. May be the *counterpoint*—augmented or diminished,
3. May be the *orchestral base.*

Average perception may be focused on 1.
Average perception may be secondarily aware of 2.
Average perception may only accept 3 as background or base.

Only experience factors make possible awareness of *more than three* phases *simultaneously.*

FIG. 7. SENSORY DISCRIMINATION

The three phases of sensory mechanics.

The time factors of taste may be considered as having the dimensional and mass characteristics of a solid. This idea makes sense if we first recognize that taste perception is not, and cannot be, a straight line experience.

What happens when we approach and cross the threshold of taste perception? We are exposed to a flavor experience; we encounter what is always a new and unexplored threshold. Then we recognize a flavor. It is fair to say that every mouthful of food can be considered a laboratory experiment.

Flavor is far from being a simple thing. What is involved in flavor is one of the most complex masses of known and unknown factors of all that man is concerned with.

Flavor awareness varies with people and circumstances; above all, it varies with individual aptitudes, education, and training. Appreciation of food varies from zero to some degree approaching whatever may be complete comprehension within today's limitations of knowledge and experience. It can vary from the unconsciousness of preoccupation to the intensely concentrated savoring of an epicurean food technologist. Most individuals tend to have about the same acuity in all their senses.

Specifically this chapter is concerned with one of the fundamental considerations of man's food behavior—time and timing. It is probable that time is the most carelessly disregarded factor in our American food picture. Not only do we *not* take the proper time, but we push time, and our vital statistics clearly show the consequences.

We might use here the analogy of the modern food "traveler" to Mohammed, the ancient traveler. In the classic parable Mohammed jousted with the mountain and overcame it. But first he took the path to the mountain (the approach) then he recognized the characteristics of the mountain (the realization) which he studied (the exploration).

The average food traveler isn't interested in exploring the mountain; he goes around it, or if his figurative mountain is in capsule form, he tunnels through the mountain, or kites over it, with no realization of what he has missed. His taste experience of that mouthful, or mountain, of food, has varied from zero to insignificant. How often have all of us absent-mindedly eaten—and then become discomfitted on reproval by friend wife because we were not only unable to recall the flavor, but too often unable to recall just what we had eaten!

To carry on the analogy: The food traveler would require supernatural qualifications to (a) approach, (b) recognize, and (c) be willing *and able* to explore what lies inside the mountain. Taste experience may be represented as a volcano; the traveler must be qualified by knowledge and physical experience to explore and overcome his mountain. A food explorer *per se* realizes his hazards. He accepts or rejects according to his qualifications and training. Some food experiences, like volcanoes, might errupt in his face as when an inexperienced person tastes Mexican pepper for the first time!

The time intervals are directly concerned with the kind and extent of flavor exploration of the taste mountain. Assume the simplest taste experience as a plateau which requires a certain given interval of time to traverse.

The most direct and the shortest path over the plateau is not a straight line; it is irregular. It weaves both sideways and up and down; while the path can be represented as crossing a plateau, don't for a moment forget that the mountain has a root mass, which varies in width and contours according to the terrain. Like the mountain, the food mass varies in the nature of its components—in kinds and qualities, and, of course, in amounts.

There may be a rocky road of approach, a glacier, a plateau, an exploding volcano, and an abrupt tumble. There are such combinations in nature, and there certainly are plenty of them in food and drink.

In talking about the time element in taste perception, you must allow for the involvement of organolepses *other than taste and smell* when you are attempting to analyze what is involved in the timing of taste.

All we have been discussing emphasizes the very important fact *that presence of a specific kind of food varies in the individual's enjoyment only so far as he can and does perceive it.*

Now let's give this imagery substance by analyzing a few examples. With an orange as the food, consider it in different ways, starting with (1-A) picking an orange from the tree, peeling and eating it; (1-B) picking an orange from the tree, cutting it in half, extracting the juice and drinking it; by suggesting entry into an orange grove the approach of the taste experience is preceded by the highly important period which is designated as the *approach* (to the threshold of perception). The introduction of the orange grove idea provides a build-up to emphasize the combination of planning and anticipation that is part of much of what we coldly term the *approach* to the threshold of taste perception. (2-A) At the breakfast table we peel an orange and eat it, section by section; (2-B) We have a glass of orange juice. Within all of these taste experiences, even assuming the same orange, we have different qualitative and quantitative taste experiences, each one varying mainly as (a) time and (b) physical characteristics of the food.

Now, you can drink faster than you can chew; you can guzzle liquid food faster than you can gulp solids. But here is an important qualification: while taste experience can be more complete for liquid foods because of the time factor, yet because of the rapidity of our swallowing liquid foods, we tend to get more flavor from foods we chew. A flavorful liquid coats the tongue, and presumably is exposed to the majority of our taste buds. But that exposure is very short, as against lesser taste bud exposure with food chewed over a longer time.

Let us go back to reiterate that taste experience is preceded by a mental approach and then is exposed to both physical and psychosomatic factors, and realize that the physics of taste are just as real, just as applicable as the physics of inorganic matter. Time velocity, energy, matter—its kind and condition—are the dominant factors. The circumstances of application are secondary contributory circumstances.

Start comparing the orange experience with the simplest elements; orange juice and orange segments with granulated sugar and neutral syrup (granulated sugar and just enough moisture to make a syrup). Syrup tastes sweeter than granulated sugar. The sweetness of syrup registers much faster than that of sugar crystals. The sweetness of sugar crystals is retained longer than that of syrup. These phenomena can be technically expressed by saying syrup has a short period of approach and departure; sugar crystals have a relatively long approach, experience, and departure.

Now go back to the orange. Orange juice can be gulped, experienced while it is mouthed and the flavor fades away rather quickly after it is swallowed. Eating the orange segments takes a radically longer time than drinking the juice.

Here enter the important kinesthetic factors. The taste of syrup, like orange juice, goes on the tongue like paint; and too frequently faster than the swipe of a brush. The juice sacs of the orange must be crushed before any flavor is perceptible. Up to the moment of juice and aroma liberation by pulping forces in the mouth, there is no real flavor detection, but it is emphasized that the factors of anticipation, if realized, are important. But whatever loss of taste contrast that may here be at work, the organoleptic experiences involved in eating orange segments obviously make for not only more but longer flavor experience. In other words, anticipation, realization, and contemporary taste memory is longer and probably more intense—having higher enjoyment potential for the three phases—which can be considered as ascent to the flavor plateau, the organoleptic exploration and the descent experience.

Any consideration of these ideas will reveal that the possible variations of each of the phases are infinite, but the melancholy fact emerges from our shadowy mists of thought that the fascinating possibilities inherent in most of what we can visualize as latent are rarely experienced by very few people—and the majority of men not at all. Thoughts leading up to semitropical and tropical journeys, lands where oranges grow, the circumstances that would make possible gathering the fruit for oneself, the different steps, one by one, by which oranges are used—conjuring the feel of soft, warm air and the heavy fragrance of orange groves in blossom and in fruit. Trying to pick one orange from the many in sight and reach, the yank necessary to separate the fruit from the stem, cutting or tearing the skin and the first whiff of popping orange skin oil cells and the penetrating aroma of orange oil coated fingers, and then the first appreciative crunch of crisp orange segment. Wondering how much you feel like eating and if another orange is better than the one you have. Trial of two or three if you are experimentally inclined. If you are being competently guided, you will be told to avoid the windfalls and how to distinguish the partially ripe from the ripe fruit when they all seem to be the same color, and finally laughingly told that the best fruit is usually in the crown of the tree where it has the most sun exposure. And of course, factors of soil, humus, fertilizer, atmospheric conditions and all that, which go to make up the prerequisites for standard grades and finally, what is involved in the choice and show grades. Oranges and orange products, like everything else, will vary from 0 to 100 per cent. The lowest marketed grades as a rule have minimums and maximums of the rated factors—and to the uninitiated there are surprisingly many.

Lest we forget the descent from the plateau of flavor experience, of organoleptic experience of the whole orange—or it could be orange juice in a grove, possibly in a groveside stand—usually is very much longer and certainly more pleasing than any other kind of flavor experience descent or departure. It can be said that the element of prolongation radically differs from the sometimes only momentary flavor hangover from a gulped glass of orange juice.

Now let us probe further into the possibility of protracting a flavor experience by a different orange service. Let's peel and slice the orange into, say, six thick slices. If you pick up each of the slices in your fingers, your experience is involved in the approach and realization plus the kinesthetic factors involved in handling the slices. Then the kinesthetic process continues as chewing and swallowing.

Now cut the same orange into double the number of slices, twelve thin ones instead of six thick ones—incidentally if you take pleasure in cuisinary skills you will find that more than meets the eye is required to peel cleanly, round cut, and straight slice an orange—but as with all other given skills there will be the gratification in developing the skill *per se* and the pre-preparational enjoyment of working with a fruit as fragrant and as satisfactory to handle as an orange. If the prospect of this pre-preparational procedure does not pleasantly impress you, this may serve as an unfavorable index of your given aptitudes. To put it bluntly, if you don't like the idea of getting your hands into and onto food in the pre-preparational steps, you will probably be well advised to stay out of the kitchen. Continuing, while it doesn't take twice as long to eat twelve thin orange slices, and it may not be double the pleasure, the factors are almost in that relationship, with some qualifications for the time and flavor fatigue factors.

Now try after trimming the orange free from the outer skin of the segments, cutting the ball into quarters and then each of the quarters into approximately ten slices, arranging each of the sliced quarters as 90° spokes with a bit of green, perhaps a crown of fresh mint, in the middle. Now you have a service that involves eye appeal and to all but the hastiest (not the most preoccupied—he is feeding, not eating; after his departure from the table he may find it difficult to the point of impossible to tell you what he ate) is submitted one of the longest possible exposures to savoring an orange. Here realize that if the slices are to be picked up one at a time, there are forty pick-ups involved. Hurrying the process will substantially reduce the number of operations but here even with haste, the eating experience can be hurried only so much. This, as in many other carefully planned food experiences, can only be shoveled in so fast. Anyway it is the kind of service that discourages feeders who use forks as shovels.

The slow treatment can also be applied to orange juice: here the juice is served in a clear, preferably fishbowl shape glass (see the reference section for service of aromatic beverages) with one or more ice cubes floating therein. Service may be on a gray-green plate with transverse slices of whole orange riffled around the base of the glass and the service is made at the moment when the bowl is frosted outside and before the ice cubes lose their shape by dilution. A sprig of fresh mint is used for color contrast as well as its aromatic companionship.

The object of all these word pictures is to point out the variations of time influence on flavor appreciation—particularly the *term* of the time of each of the phases of organolepsis. It doesn't seem possible that anywhere in man's experience is the expression "haste makes waste" so graphically illustrated as in his food behavior.

A page or two back it was remarked that the variations of application of the ideas presented were infinite. Let's go further with the use of orange products to emphasize just one short probe into infinity: orange products in sauce. Here note orange products are indicated, not orange juice; the discussion is not limited to orange juice because skin components varying from orange oil, freshly scraped skin, besides slices and chips of cut oranges can be part of sauce preparation as well as final sauce service (here refer to the section on the make-up of sauces). For simply flavoring an orange sauce the most common expedients turn to orange oil, orange juice—natural or canned—and particularly frozen orange juice concentrate.

As condiments there are orange segments and slices and compounds from the simplest up to elaborate pastries. These are all examples of part or all of an orange in or with a food. Now here is emphasized the very important fact that presence of a specific kind of food varies in the individual's enjoyment only so far as he can and does perceive it. To get the full implication of this assertion requires recapitulation of this section. Flavor awareness varies with people and circumstances, their attention and above all their individual aptitudes, education and training. Appreciation of food varies from zero to some degree approaching whatever may be complete comprehension within today's limitations of knowledge and experience. It varies from the unconsciousness of preoccupation to the intensely concentrated savoring of an epicurean food technologist. When we comprehend that these extremes of perception exist we then naturally come to realize that the food behavior of man, like almost everything that he does, is probably subject to the same laws of averages that seem to work out in almost everything.

Flavor Fatigue

Flavor fatigue may be considered as a short-term phenomenon. The term is misleading in its denotation if it is applied to long-term experiences. At issue is individual maintenance of a given level of flavor-intensity-perception for the period of a single food experience. Our taste buds seem to tire quickly of any specific flavor exposure. The phenomenon might be considered as taste-bud short-term fatigue, not long-term physiological wearying.

For extreme philosophical contrast, bear in mind that man has not only far more taste bud and olfactory receptors in infancy, but also the involved senses are more acute; but nevertheless by the processes involved in everyday living he develops and educates the fewer taste receptors left to him through maturity and into his declining years to the point of demonstrating in a fair proportion of population much greater flavor acuity than was true of his younger years. Though equipped with far *less* sensory perceptive receptors, the sensuist has educated what little he has left so that it more than counterbalances the potentialities of youth. It amounts to just that: the potentiality of youth versus the accomplishment and skill of age. It demonstrates that possession of equipment does not necessarily qualify for accomplishment. He who has does not always get. Being blessed with eyes does not assure seeing. By far the great majority of people do not taste what they eat!

Sensory perception of a flavor tends to decline with time. We tend to require satisfaction in quantity of agreeable flavors. After an initial taste of a cherry we want more cherries. Having sniffed the first strawberry we appreciatively mouth and savor it; then we tend to gulp a handful to satisfy our taste of the moment for those strawberries, but with each successive mouthful our appreciation tends to decline—the factor of *taste fatigue* operates. The last swallow never equals the first taste. The last rose of summer never equals the first bud of spring.

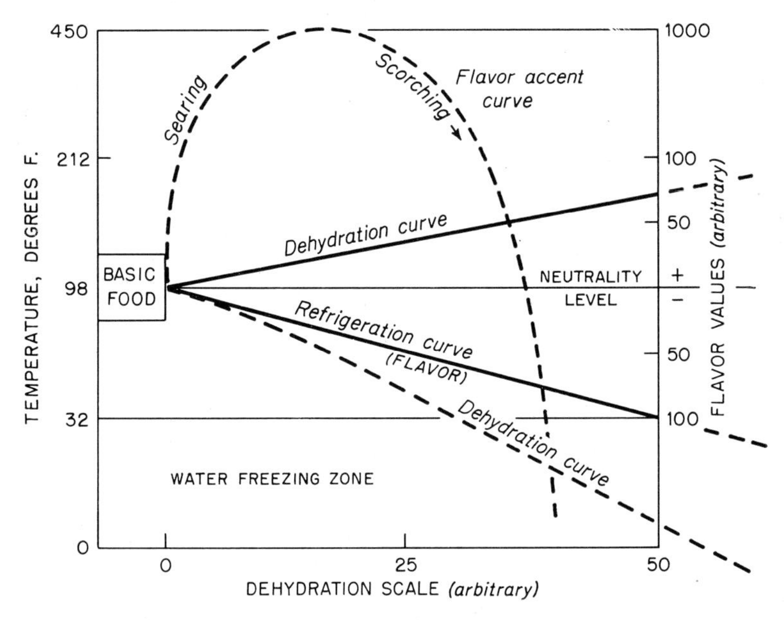

FIG. 8. FLAVOR FACTORS OF TEMPERATURE AND DEHYDRATION

To offset the decline of a falling curve of flavor experience we tend to require continued satisfaction of a flavor craving, to maintain the qualitative scale. Having developed a taste for a flavor we tend toward requiring it to reach some measure of specific intensity: first, to satisfy the acquired taste to the degree in which it was first established, then require intensification of successive flavor experience to approximately equal what we apprehend as a normal weight of flavor of a specific kind.

Flavor Variants

The flavor factors of food vary with their temperature, as our ancestors discovered when they ate their first hot food. Most flavor factors tend to rise with heat and to go down with cold. Thus, hot bouillon requires less seasoning than bouillon over ice.

Basic Assertions in Flavor Perception

1. 98.6° F. is the temperature at which all human factors of flavor are in balance.
   a. Flavor perception is out-of-balance below or above 98.6°.
   b. Input temperatures below 98.6° F. (down to almost 32° F.) are in the under-balance phase.
   c. Input temperatures above 98:6° F. (up to about 145° F.) are in the over-balance phase.

2. There is no flavor perception at or below the freezing point of water.

3. The threshold of flavor perception is above the freezing point of water.

4. The threshold of flavor perception is within the thawing phase of water.

5. Flavor perception is deficient below 98.6° F.

6. Flavor perception is aberrational above 98.6° F.

7. There is no taste perception above the point of scalding the taste buds of the mouth.

8. There is no smell perception at or above the point of scalding the olfactory receptors.

9. In appraising flavors allowances must be made for the time-of-temperature-stabilization-interval-factor.

   a. TtSIF at 98.6° F. = 0.0%
   " ± 145.° = −100 %
   " ± 32.° = +100 %

10. There is deficient or no flavor perception under circumstances or conditions of organoleptic shock; traumatic or psychological.

11. Flavor factors lag as temperatures drop to about 32.° F.
    Flavor factors shorten as they approach and reach about 145° F.
    Flavor-perception-time-factors probably lag directly as temperature falls below 98.6—with mathematical configurations of the mass. May be said to recede in inverse ratio (minus) as temperature falls below 98.6° F. configuring the mass.

    Minus 98.6° F., FPTF/m = Minus N
    Plus 98.6° F., FPTF/m = Plus N

12. Flavor perception fatigue factors
    a. probably vary inversely as temperature falls below 98.6° F.

$$\text{FPFF} \; // \; -\left(\frac{32}{-98.6}\right)$$

    b. probably vary directly as temperature rises above 98.6° F.

$$\text{FPFF} \; // \left(\frac{-145}{98.6}\right)$$

13. Flavor perception factors vary with the nature and temperature of a mass.

$$FPF\ //\ M_n + t$$

14. Coefficients of flavor-perception-factors can be establised for:
    a. gases
    b. liquids
    c. solids
    d. combinations

15. A. Flavor-perception-factors of gases vary with:
    1. temperature
    2. nature and amount of solid inclusions

    b. Flavor-perception-factors of solids vary with temperature and composition.
    1. Temperature
    2. Composition

	of vegetable matter
Volatility	mineral "
Solubility	Animal "

    c. Flavor-perception factors of liquids vary with:
    1. temperature
    2. nature
    3. Quantity of solids in solution and suspension

16. No flavor perception is possible if there is no dissolubility.
    a. Flavor perception exists only as a function of dissolution:
    chemically—decomposition,
    physically—disintegration.
    b. The flavor-perception-factor of an undecomposed solid is zero.
    c. The taste-perception-factor of an insoluble solid is zero.
    d. The flavor-perception-factor of an insoluble or undissolved solid is zero.

17. The smell-perception-factor of a gas varies with its temperature, volatility and composition.

18. The smell-perception-factor of a non-volatile solid is zero. There is no smell perception if there is no volatility.

19. Flavor-perception-factors vary as ambient atmospheric conditions.
    a. Average physical discomfiture increases as temperature falls below approximately 68° F.
    b. . . . . median optimum humidity.
    c. Average physical discomfiture increases sharply as temperature rises above 98.6° F. and optimum humidity.
    d. Allow for marked organoleptic aberrations below 63° F.
    e. Allow for marked organoleptic aberrations above 98.6° F.

In Fig. 8, however, we are most concerned with temperature and dehydration as they are used as preservatives, and the effect of refrigeration and dehydration on the basic, original flavor of food. In this age of refrigeration, such a discussion has much relevance.

It is not usually realized how quickly foods deteriorate. Vegetables and fruits may begin to mold within minutes after they are picked. From the moment of an animal's death decomposition begins by enzymatic digestion and flavor values change. Hunters know that old and muscular game, cooked before rigor mortis sets in, will be tender, but if it is cooked the next day, it may be too tough to eat. Chinese gourmets prefer fish which they have seen taken alive and cooked immediately. Otherwise they are sensitive to changes in flavor and texture they prefer to avoid.

Few people can obtain food so promptly, and, perhaps fortunately, not all of us are as sensitive as Chinese gourmets. It is important, however, to know what effects our methods of preservation have upon food, and concomitantly how to overcome some of the changes in flavors.

As can be seen in Fig. 8, the effect of dehydration on the flavor values of foods varies from that of refrigeration or freezing.

As water is extracted from a food, its flavors usually become more concentrated. There are other changes caused by the processes involved in dehydration which will be discussed later. Thus, raisins are sweeter than the original grapes; dried fish is often fishier, usually thought of as stronger, than the fish was in its original condition.

There are other considerations, however, beyond simple strength of flavor; otherwise we would probably have continued to dry all our foods and might even have preferred them to fresh foods. Raisins may be sweeter, but they are not as attractive, not as juicy as fresh grapes. And who would prefer jerky to steak as a regular diet? Also, flavor is volatilized along with water.

Consequently we are resorting more and more to freezing for preservation because we believe, apparently, that to preserve the appearance and the original texture of a food is of prime importance. It should be definitely understood that there usually is a *definite and continuing* loss of flavor values in frozen food. Meat may become rancid if not properly packaged and if held at temperatures above 0°F. for too long. Fish and poultry deteriorate more quickly. Frozen fruits and vegetables gradually change. The experienced cook knows that they require more seasoning or different processing than fresh foods. These facts are important for an informed cook to know so that he can compensate for loss of flavor values in frozen foods by the use of seasoning or various carriers, and perhaps also so that he will not neglect dehydrated foods which in some instances actually retain so much more of their original flavor values.

Flavor perception varies with: (a) temperature, (b) time, (c) mass, and (d) surroundings. The assertions which follow are meant to be objective and do not take into account personal prejudices or subjective psychological factors.

Basic assertions:

(1) There is deficient or no flavor perception under circumstances or conditions of severe organoleptic shock, traumatic or psychological.

(2) A temperature of 98.6° is that at which all human physiological factors of flavor are in "temperature balance," in equilibrium. This is commonly understood to be the average normal blood temperature. Actually, normal temperature varies with when and how and where it is

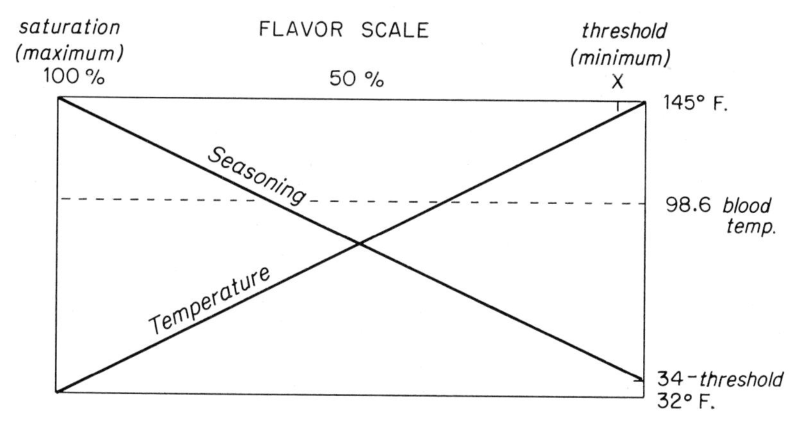

Fig. 9. Taste Perception Varies As Temperature

Seasoning requirements may vary directly and in inverse ratio to temperature rise from 32°F. to approximately 145°F.

taken—from about 97.5° to 99.5°. The point to be stressed is that foods which are normally eaten at higher or lower temperatures can best be judged for flavor qualities at normal body temperature, because no physiological compensation for temperature is required if ingestion occurs at that temperature.

Professional coffee tasters, for example, make coffee with boiling water and then "cup" the coffee for critical flavor blending determination at a temperature at or near lukewarm. (Lukewarm is defined as "body or blood heat.")

From the assertion just made, it follows that: (a) flavor perception is strengthened by temperature above 98.6°F.; (b) it is weakened by input temperatures below 98.6°F. (down to almost 32°F.); (c) flavor cannot be perceived above about 145°F.

(3) There is no flavor perception at or below the freezing point of water. Ice cream actually is not tasted until it melts in the mouth. It is better for the cook to taste the ice cream mixture before it is frozen, when it is at body temperature; however, it will taste too sweet.

(4) The threshold of flavor perception is above the freezing point of water.

(5) The threshold of flavor perception is within the thawing range of water.

(6) Flavor perception is deficient below 98.6°F. For example, take a piece of smoked salmon cold from the refrigerator. It will taste fairly mild. Leave it until it reaches room temperature, and then taste it again. It will taste much saltier. At lukewarm it may be so salty as to be unacceptable. By this example it will be realized that most all salt fish should be served at least cool and preferably cold (see separate chart and notes on use of salt, Fig. 15).

(7) Flavor perception is aberrational, i.e., more intense above 98.6°F. To continue the example above, if smoked salmon is fried or broiled it will have a salinity flavor above the acceptance of the majority of tasters.

(8) There is no smell perception at or above the temperature at which the olfactory receptors are scalded.

(9) There is no taste perception at or above the temperature at which the taste buds are scalded.

(10) In appraising flavors, allowances must be made for the time-of-temperature-stabilization-interval factor. All after-tastes develop at body temperature, and allowances must be made for time for hot or cold food to reach this norm so that reliable taste reactions can be realized.

(11) Flavor factors lag as temperatures drop to about 32°F. Flavor factors accelerate as they approach and reach about 145°F. Flavor-perception-time-factors (FPTF) probably lag directly as temperature falls to 98.6°F. and increase directly as temperature rises above 32°F. A kind of sliding-scale variance in flavor perception changes by temperature could be expressed by this formula:

(m equals mass, N equals normal)
Below 98.6°F., FPTF/m equals less than N
Above 98.6°F., FPTF/m equals more than N

(12) **Flavor Perception Fatigue Factors.**—The phenomena of flavor fatigue are remarkable. We usually critically taste for only a short time—the first sip of a glass of wine is tasted; the rest is gulped. In this first instant we recognize a flavor and savor it. We can, however, be trained to sustain flavor perception for longer periods of time, as professional enologists do. Sooner or later, however—usually sooner than is generally

realized—we reach the saturation point, just as when we turn on a radio and, having adjusted the volume to a given point, no purpose is served by turning it higher. Although we have comparatively little voluntary control over flavor fatigue, certain assumptions can be made about it.

Fatigue factors probably vary inversely with temperatures both above and below body temperature.

Example: a person can taste iced coffee for a longer period of time than he can taste hot coffee, and drink more of it.

(13) Flavor perception factors (FPF) vary with the nature and temperature of a mass. Foods frequently have different textures at different temperatures, and texture affects flavor perception. A baked potato differs in texture from a raw potato or a boiled potato—baked, it is granular and has less moisture. Presence of moisture usually improves taste perception because liquids coat the tongue and perception is more nearly complete. Ice cream can be tasted only when it has been reduced to a liquid state. This principle can be expressed in a formula:

$$FPF = M/n + T$$

Where M is the mass present, n is number of taste buds in action, t is temperature and T represents time.

(14) Coefficients of flavor-perception factors can be established for (a) gases, (b) liquids, (c) solids, and (d) combinations.

Mathematical formulas can be established for variations of gases, liquids, etc., according to their conditions and circumstances.

(15) (a) Flavor-perception-factors of gases vary with (1) temperature and (2) nature and amount of solid inclusions.

(b) Flavor perception of solids varies with temperature and composition, and according to the (1) volatility, and (2) solubility of vegetable, mineral, and animal matter.

(c) Flavor-perception factors of liquids vary with (1) temperature, (2) nature, and (3) the quantity of solids in solution and suspension. When brandy is tasted in a snifter, it is first warmed so that it can be tasted more satisfactorily. Its flavor factors vary with its alcoholic content and by the nature and qualities of its other constituents.

(16) No flavor perception is possible if there is no dissolubility.

(a) Flavor perception exists only as a function of dissolution. Chemically this dissolution can be termed solution as when a child licks an all-day sucker and the sugar dissolves. Physically, the dissolution of the all-day sucker can be termed disintegration.

(b) The flavor-perception-factor of an undecomposed solid is zero. Consider, for example, a piece of horn and an ice cube. At normal temperatures horn is tasteless; its flavors, such as they are, can only be detected when, as, and if it is melted or dissolved. Flavors frozen into an ice cube are not discernible until the ice cube starts melting.

(c) The taste-perception-factor of an insoluble solid (like marble) is zero.

(17) The smell-perception-factor of a gas varies with its temperature, concentration, and composition.

(18) The smell-perception-factor of a non-volatile solid is zero. Salt is non-volatile. Salt has no smell. The odor of "salt air" at the seashore is due to other substances than salt.

(19) Flavor-perception-factors vary as ambient atmospheric conditions.

(a) Average physical discomfort increases as temperature falls below approximately 68°F.

(b) Average physical discomfort increases sharply as temperature rises above 98.6°F.

(c) Hence, allow for marked organoleptic aberrations below 68°F. and above 98.6°F.

Time

The element of time, if it is not the most commonly disregarded factor of our food behavior, is at least one of its fundamental considerations (see also p. 81). In this writer's opinion the time symbol—T—should be printed somewhere on every chart (and that includes menus) and every paper where foods and food values are to be listed or appraised. The factor of time should be a required consideration for most thinking about food.

Calculations involving time and velocity may be said to begin with the mathematics involved in calculating hypothetical wave lengths of sensory perception to the common clock-and calendar arithmetic. What is thought of as instantaneous recognition of a taste or smell involves a complex physiological circuit with psychological overtones. The physiological path is sketched as a graph representation of a hypothetical circuit within which the time factor involved in the duration area of physical perception—which implies that recordance probably varies between four-tenths and eight-tenths of a second for what we think of as average sensory experience. Those time intervals may represent the gap between exposure and recognition of basic tastes. Here realize that transmission of sensory impressions from organic receptors is by the nature of nervous-system electronics very much faster—in terms of electronic wave lengths than our reactions. Varying from mental recognition to physical performance they are very much slower, probably approximating one-tenth of a second as the fastest period of reaction. In other words stimulus and resulting electronic impulses may vary from dull to sharp and low to high, but our recognition and what we subsequently do must be expressed in terms of comparatively longer times.

Savoring takes time. Most flavor experience is comparative which brings in considerations of what is involved in deliberation as we brood over a transient flavor exposure.

For the moment we are concerned with sensory detection and physiological weighing of the evidential values of flavor. As we proceed it will be apparent that time—T—should be considered as an ever-present factor, some values of which are to be included in most appraisals.[1]

Kinesthetics

All foods are ratable on a chart of physical compositions of foods but the specific placement of each varies with its condition, in most instances mainly with moisture and temperature.

Most fluid or soft foods can be converted to from firm to hard, and most firm to hard foods can be inverted to from soft to fluid by altering their composition of liquid or solid. The simplest change of condition is effected by adding or removing identical liquids or identical solids. Then the next variation is with the addition of congeneric liquids or solids. These additions progress from agreeable to disagreeable.

Reduction by dilution of foods in the kinesthetic scale varies with proportionate addition of liquids and modification of particle sizes of solids and variation of temperature.

According to such a chart the physical composition of any food is variable, or *can be adjusted* for its kinesthetic factors. A liquid or a solid food can be made firm or hard and vice versa. We can accomplish those ends by taking from or adding to it less or more agreeable solids or changing temperature conditions.

All of which is not very exciting unless we translate the plain arithmetic of such statistical representations to kitchen action with an example that may stimulate imagination. Let us take the so-called lowly potato and project its kinesthetic factors according to the chart. For purposes of this illustration such a chart proportions only liquids and solids.

Experiment with "Instant" potatoes (Simplot).—By varying quantities of solids and water and according to different conditions of cookery, results will vary from imperceptible potato perception in a watery suspension to a dry mass; from bland potato in broth to dry cake; from mashed potato consistency to potato fritters.

[1] This is to be continued in the direction of notes emphasizing the time factors in food selection, the time factors in cookery, the time factors in service and in eating and particularly in the time factor in relaxation.

Up to the *threshold of perception* the addition of potato granules to hot water only affects the viscosity of the broth. Beyond the *threshold of perception* the production will vary from broth through soup to purée to different consistencies of potato cake.

Now if we superimpose a curve for dry cookery on that chart starting with the median line, another set of variables comes into the picture; in our concern with surface hardening the technical phrase "case hardening" may best apply here: implying a hard outer case and some relative degree of inner softness.

Up to this point only variation of quantities of potato granules have been considered, but now we approach the secondary purpose of the chart; the possibilities involved with variation of other kinds of liquid and solid foods by temporarily limiting our consideration to kinesthetics. The addition of solids will vary just as the curve indicates from soft to hard and from vegetable to animal, from agreeable to disagreeable. The cook plans for an agreeable companionate result. But here it is emphasized that not all companions are agreeable.

Since we are still considering only textures, we will limit our first study to the effects of a vegetable inclusion in, let us say, potato cake and potato fritter. Here again, we start with the texture of a congeneric tuber: puréed sweet potatoes, then ground sweet potatoes, then diced or chipped sweet potatoes.

Then follow the same procedure with some of the leafy vegetables—chard, for instance. Adding meat products, ranging from meat broth through adding ground, chopped or diced meats will vary both consistency of mashed potatoes and potato cakes according to cookery procedures. By these processes the basic nature of the potato mass has been modified and the kinesthetic composition changed. All of this amounts to kinesthetic elaboration. It is obvious that the additives allow a range of chewing experience from soft to hard, from something slightly differing from the basic potato mass to something to be chewed or crunched.

Now let us introduce what may be the most important consideration for most of us, low modification to high change in the flavor profile. Now we combine the kinesthetic with the other organoleptic considerations. If potato granules are added to hot water, the resulting mass can only have whatever flavor is inherent in the solids; at best, pretty insipid broth. But if *Instant Potato*[1] is added to vegetable or meat stock both the consistency and the flavor are modified upward. So the addition of potato flour or *Instant Potato* to broth adds to its body as well as modi-

[1] *Instant Potato* is the trade name of the J. R. Simplot Co., Caldwell, Idaho.

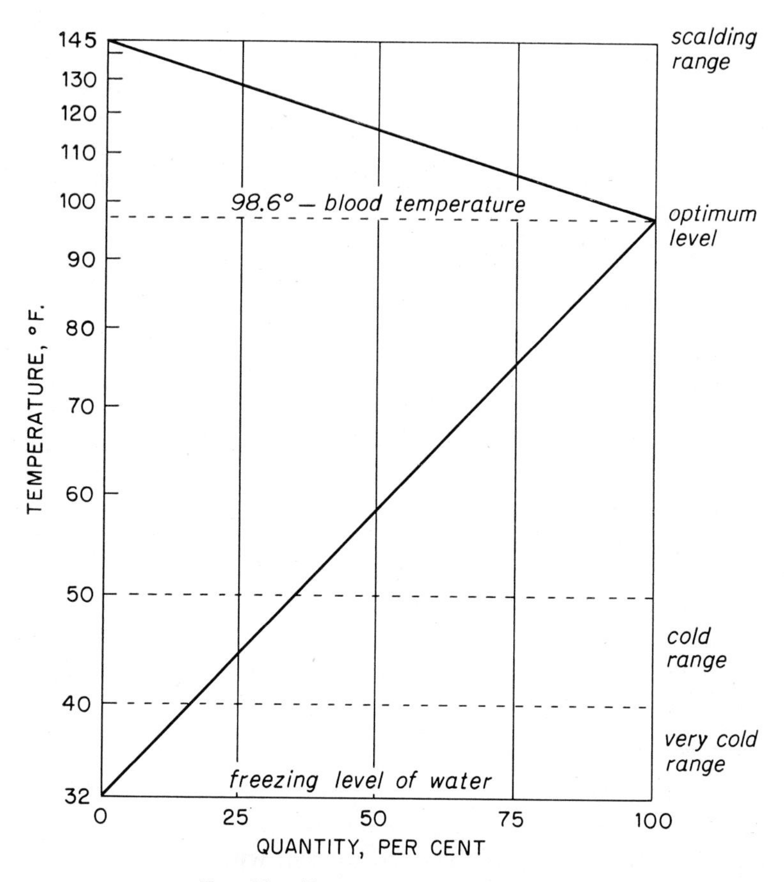

FIG. 10. TEMPERATURES OF INGESTION

Bearing in mind that 98.6° F. is the temperature of optimum flavor judgment: beverages of high flavor rating must be drunk below 98.6°F. for maximum quantitative ingestion; cool to cold, but not "ice cold." Consequently, quantity tasted and velocity of ingestion varies as kind and temperature.

Note that ingestion of foods and beverages in the range of cold to frozen is metabolically limited: in the lower ranges—approaching freezing, metabolically hazardous.

fying its flavor. Here it must be remembered that potatoes and other kindred vegetables exercise a flavor-sponge-or-blotter characteristic (see Vol. II).

Simplot directions suggest half water and half milk as the carrier for the dry potato granules which when properly compounded results in what may be termed a neutral mashed potato norm. The addition of a pat of butter will agreeably raise the flavor while very slightly modifying the texture of the resultant "mashed potatoes." If, instead of water we use a vegetable or meat broth, the flavor and the color will be changed as well as adding an imperceptible difference in texture. If the basic milk, water, and *Instant Potato* formula is modified to include 1/4 inch onion chips, minced parsley, and the right amount of butter, instead of relatively tasteless mashed potatoes, you have a serving that is far more agreeable in texture, in flavor, and in appearance. All that remains is to serve it forth molded by a spoon or cornet to make the difference between an unappetizing glob and something gastronomically interesting.

Naturally another step with the same last formula for the production of a fritter would provide a variation of both physical and kinesthetic factors. Remember that light cookery of onions dissipates almost all their pungency so their inclusion in the mashed potatoes or the potato cake or fritter should result only in the addition of a mildly sweet and crunchy component. Onion fragments lightly browned on the surface add an olfactory factor.

Incidentally, heat treatment dissipates most of the bitterness of parsley which, surprisingly enough to most people, will be found to have an agreeable sweetness when fried. If you want to raise the onion flavor without including too much onion pulp add a pinch of garlic powder or a few drops of garlic juice.

Temperature Factors in Seasoning

Here the basic thesis is that organoleptic perception varies with temperature. This must be considered as self-evident. All seasoning matter has different rates of flavor registration varying with:

(A) The physical condition, training, and aptitude of the consumer and ambient atmospheric and other physical and aesthetic conditions.
(B) The temperature of ingestion.
(C) The nature of the food, real and imaginary; *per se* and psychophysiological.

Not generally realized is the incontrovertible fact that regardless of what the food is or how it is ingested all of it is metabolized (we hope) at 98.6°F. Let's not quarrel about how accurate 98.6°F. is. For all men the temperature norm for flavor registration is 98.6°F. This is a physical invariable. It is in aesthetics that the tastes of men differ.

Realization of these concepts is essential to judgment of flavors in foods, the use of seasonings. It is a strange fact that most cooks pass on the flavors of seasoning components at room temperatures or below—

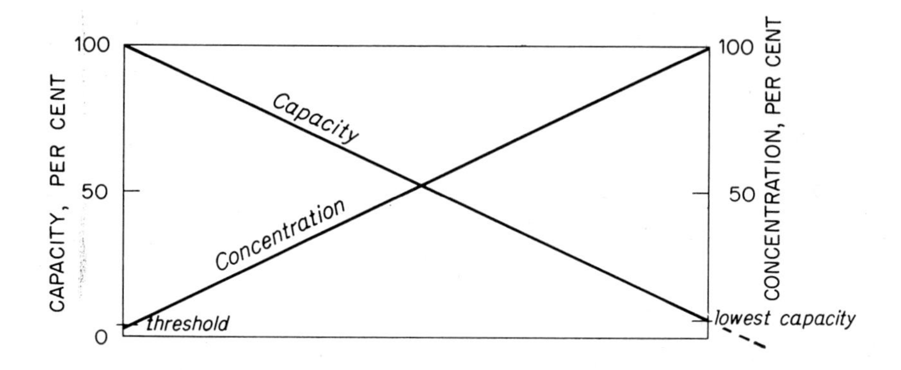

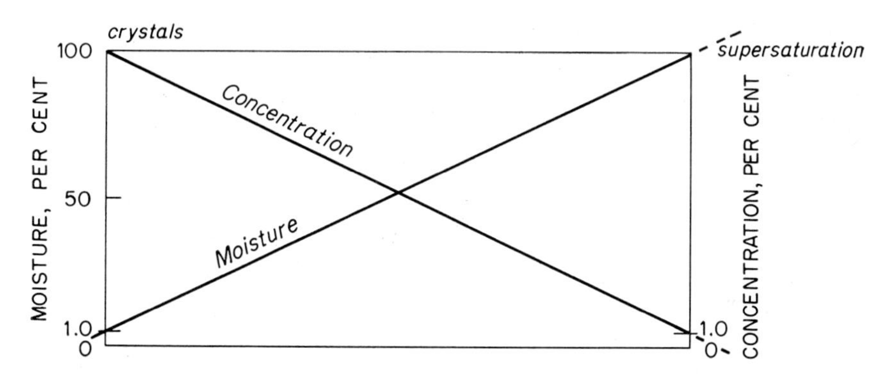

FIG. 11. FLAVOR PERCEPTION AND CAPACITY VARY AS CONCENTRATION

Example: Sugar or Salt.

Individual capacity is lowest at point of flavor saturation (100 per cent concentration)—and highest *below* his threshold of flavor perception.

Individual capacity probably varies directly and in inverse ratio to flavor concentration.

sampling foods out of the cooler or refrigerator. Certainly over a period of time by experience they learn how much of a given seasoning they find best in the finished product. But some components of seasoning are rarely correctly estimated because of the cook's failure to appraise them according to their effect at a temperature other than those in which those flavorsome foods are usually sampled. One large group of flavor contributors which are almost universally wrongly appraised are fruits and beverages used in cookery, because those foods are usually in a fresh warm condition and beverages are served cold. The moment you stop and think about it you see what happens. A fresh peach with its flavor judged at room temperature acquires a somewhat different and higher flavor profile when it is cooked. Not so apparent and much more radical in flavor and result are the wines. A light white wine, a chablis, chilled to 50°F. would be rated as a very bland wine with a quite low flavor level: raise the temperature to 98.6°F. and the wine becomes surprisingly "strong."

FACTORS AFFECTING VARIATION IN TASTE PERCEPTION

Taste Perception Varies as:
1. Temperature (including dehydration)
2. Moisture
3. Structure. a. physical
   b. chemical

Percentages of flavoring matter should be varied as temperature.
Adjustment of pH should be varied as temperature varies.

Food materials with moisture:
a. Supersaturated
b. Neutral or natural water balance.
c. Below natural moisture content.

Food materials without moisture:
1. Inorganic; a. Hydrate (draw moisture)
   b. Dehydrate
2. Organic (dehydrated) Must be hydrated to approximately natural balance, or sufficiently for metabolic processes.

All foods have numerical water-balance values.

The sweet, sour, and astringent components are now very marked. Go a step further and raise the temperature to 125°F. whereupon, it is so strong you virtually can't drink it. A cabernet may be rated as a light red wine at room temperature, assuming 68°F. Now raise that to 98.6°F., and it will have as high a flavor as you will want to have in a red wine. If then you mull the wine and heat it to about 125°F., you may be one of the many people who will vote it as "much too strong." The conventional recipe for mulled wine would call for just a little addition of sugar and a trace of cinnamon, but realize that that is not what would make you pass the heated wine. It would be the inherent flavors of the wine which have been made so very strong by the simple process of raising its temperature. What all this amounts to is that when the wine is cold you like it and when it is hot you don't.

So in seasoning you use one quantity for a cold food and a different quantity for a hot food. As a generality, the quantity of seasonings will vary inversely with the temperature.

Concentration as a Flavor Variant

Example: ***Cheese Dressing.***—The amount of cheese flavor in a dressing or a sauce varies with the kind and quantity of cheese as well as sev-

Assumed average capacity per hour:

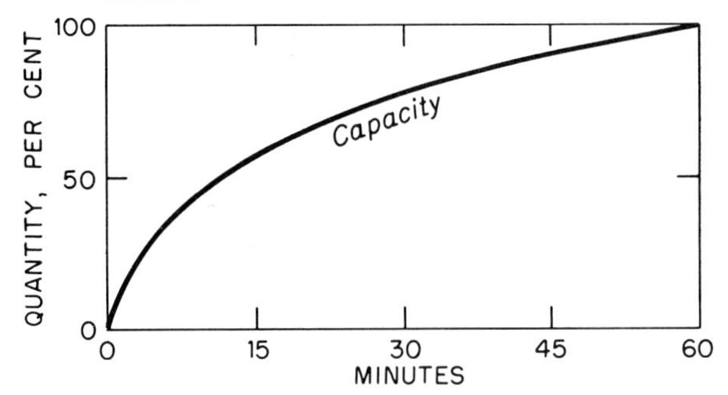

Assumed average capacity of first fifteen minutes:

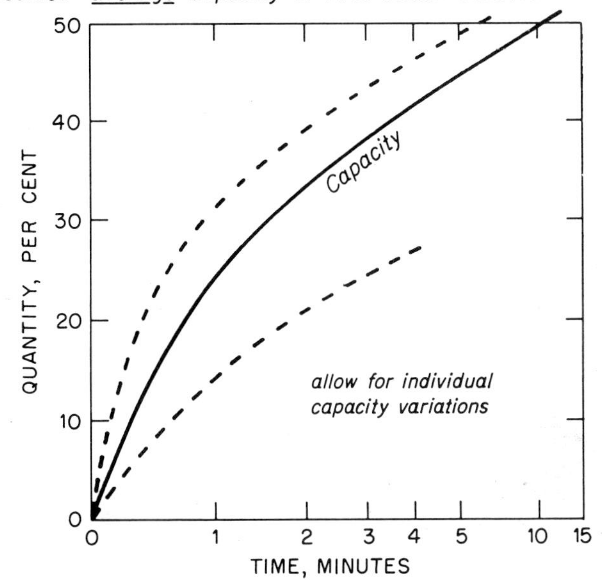

FIG. 12. CAPACITIES FOR MOST TASTES/FLAVORS—FOODS/SEASONINGS

Capacities for most flavors vary as: temperature, concentration and time.
Every living thing has capacity limits of quantity and quality in terms of time.
Quantity limited by organoleptic and time factors. Physical capacities limited by:
size (dimensions), individual tolerances and time of a. ingestion, and b. digestion.
Capacity *per hour* varies with time of ingestion-cph/T.

eral other factors: physical—such as dispersion, temperature, etc. To put it crudely, the cheese flavor is according to how much cheese is used. A valid criticism of most cheese dressings is that there is not enough cheese flavor present. Something like the proverbial clam chowder: the cook

(*text continues on page 81*)

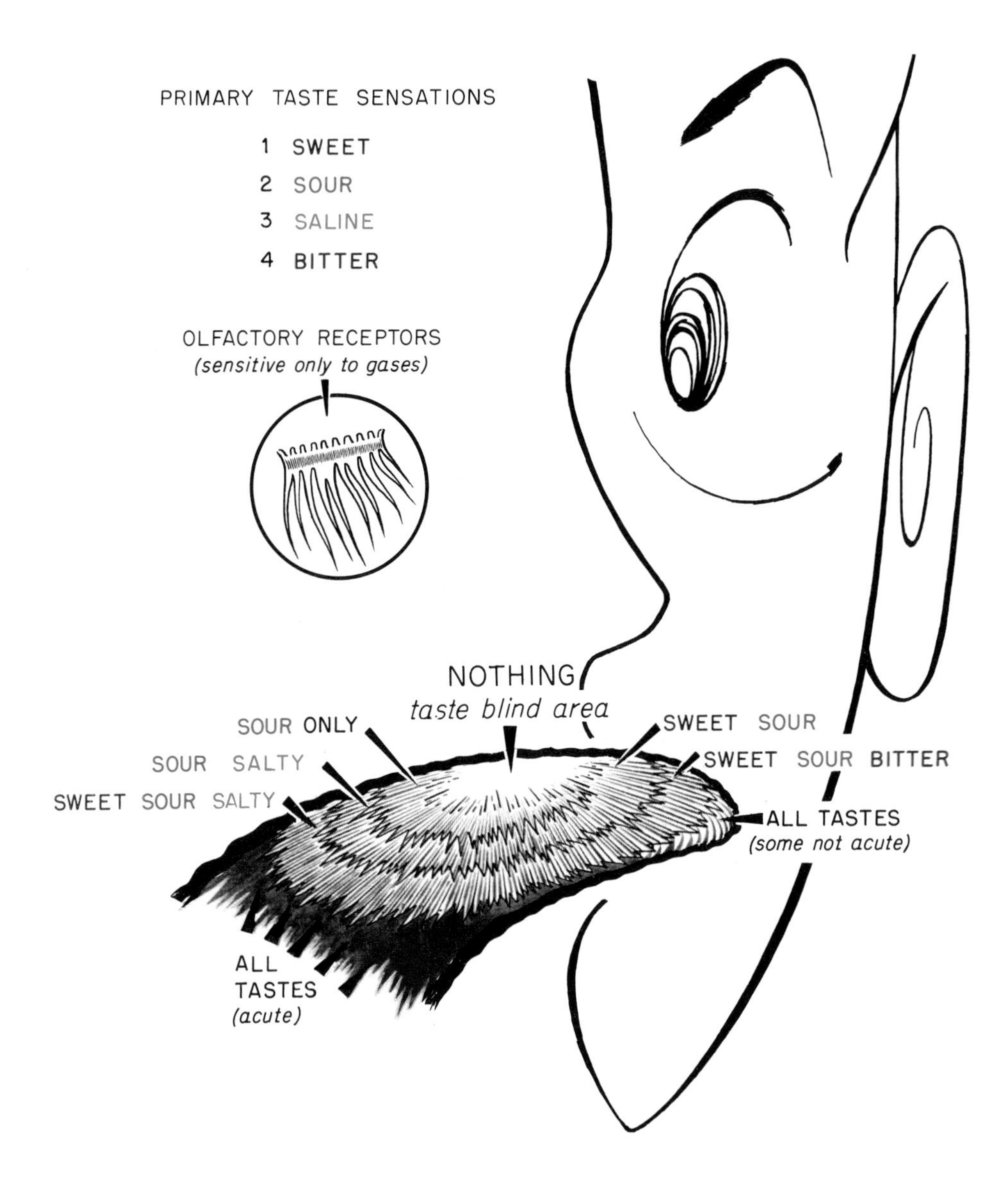

Fig. 13. The Tongue and Olfactory Receptor Areas

This cartoon is presented to emphasize some of the limitations of taste *reception* by the tongue, and that olfactory reception is entirely separate. The sketch approximates the areas of the tongue sensitive to each of the four cardinal tastes, and the separate olfactory receptors. The two are not proximal; they are relatively distant. *Flavor* is *perceived* when *both* taste and smell receptors are stimulated.

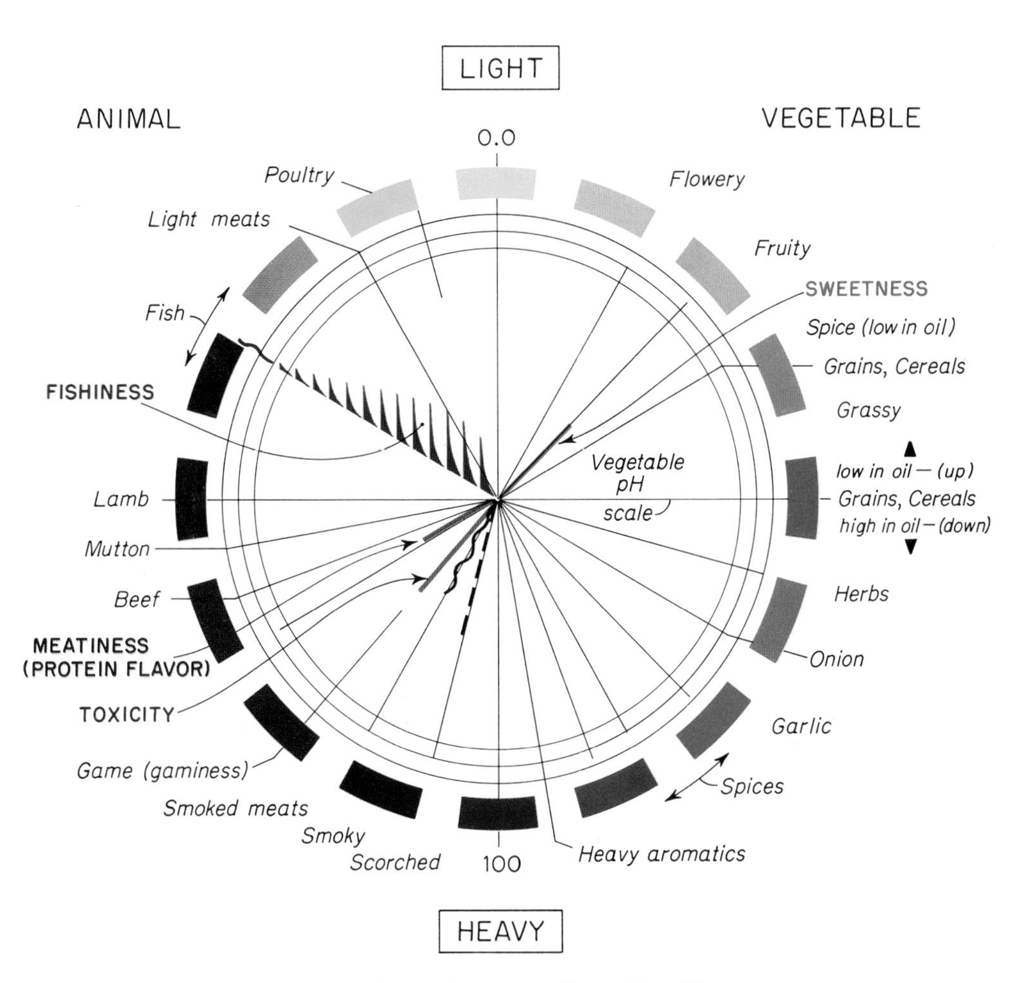

FIG. 14. THE SMELL FACTORS OF FRESH FOOD FLAVORS

This circular comparator plots the relationships of fresh animal and vegetable smells, and suggests some schematic graphs to represent specific factors.

Lines or curves radiating *out* from the center or *in* from the rim shall by their length or other variation represent proportions or percentages.

For example, the *green* line representing sweetness in the above chart, if extended from center to rim, would show a sweet (or sugar) saturated solution or condition. A similar salt line would indicate a salt saturation.

The same applies to other charts in this series.

Supersaturation (chemical or physical) would be shown by extending the line *beyond* the rim of the circle.

If two or more constituent-factor-lines are to be shown for a food or preparation, the dominant factor lines may be heavier, wavy or eccentric.

Red may be reserved for indicating heat or toxicity factors.

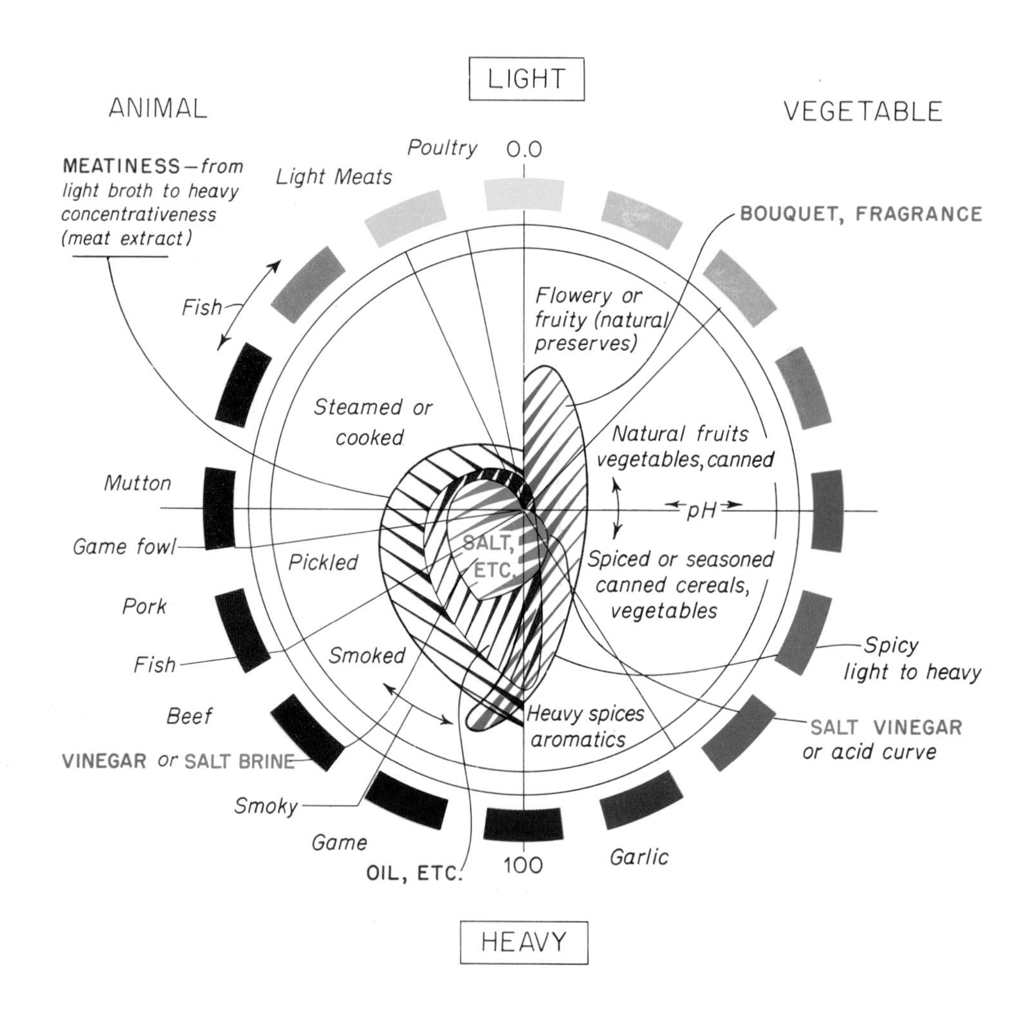

Fig. 15. The Smell Factors of Preserved Foods

Circular comparison of relationships of the smells of preserved foods, and some methods of representing components.

Oil, etc.: Toxic properties of some fats, mineral and chemical constituents; bacteria and fungi; physical deterioration, chemical decomposition; adulteration; contamination.

Salt and other natural or chemical preservatives: Allow for allergies and hypersensitivities. Allow for differences of temperature and other considerations.

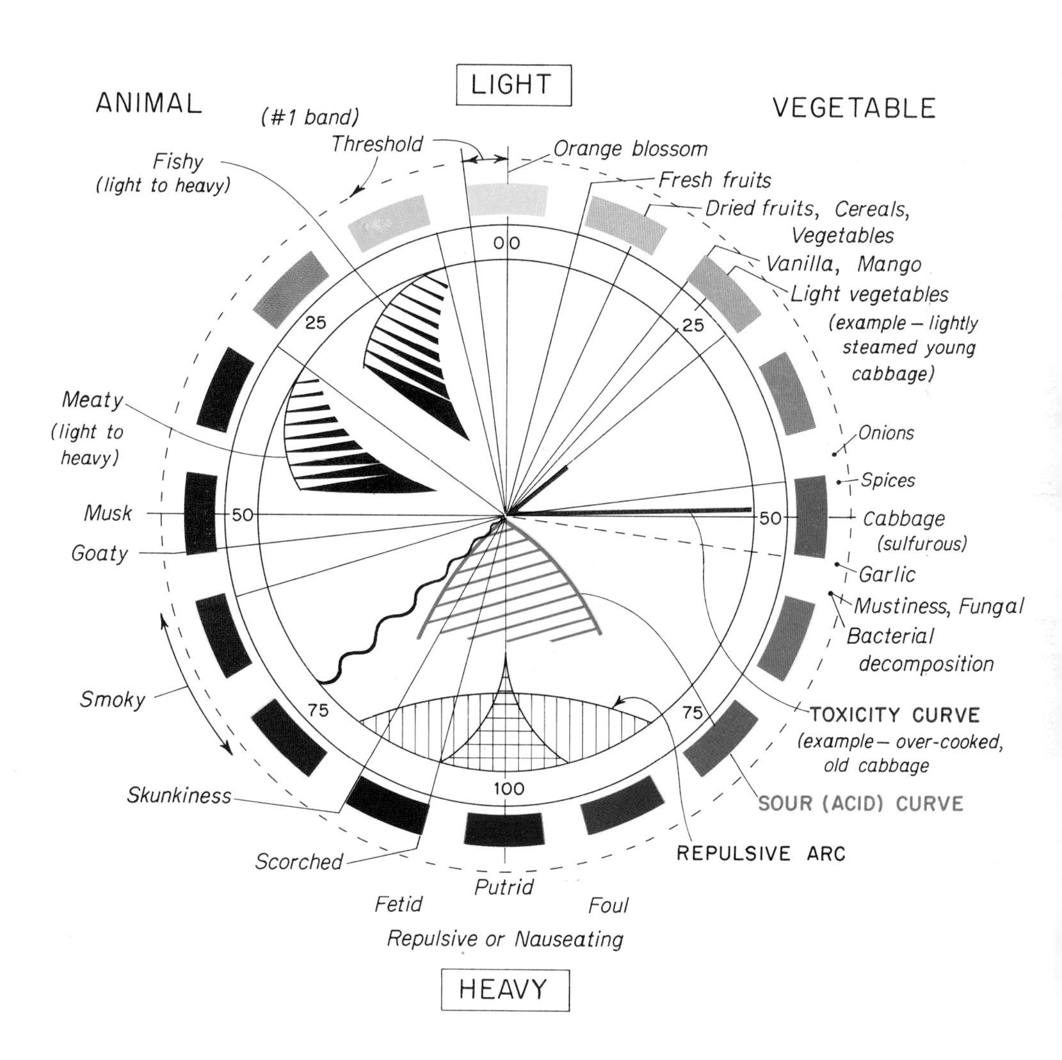

Fig. 16. Some Smell Factors of Animal and Vegetable Foods

This circular comparator suggests methods of representing smells of animal and vegetable foods from the threshold of perception to repulsion, from agreeable to disagreeable.

Allow particularly for temperature variations.

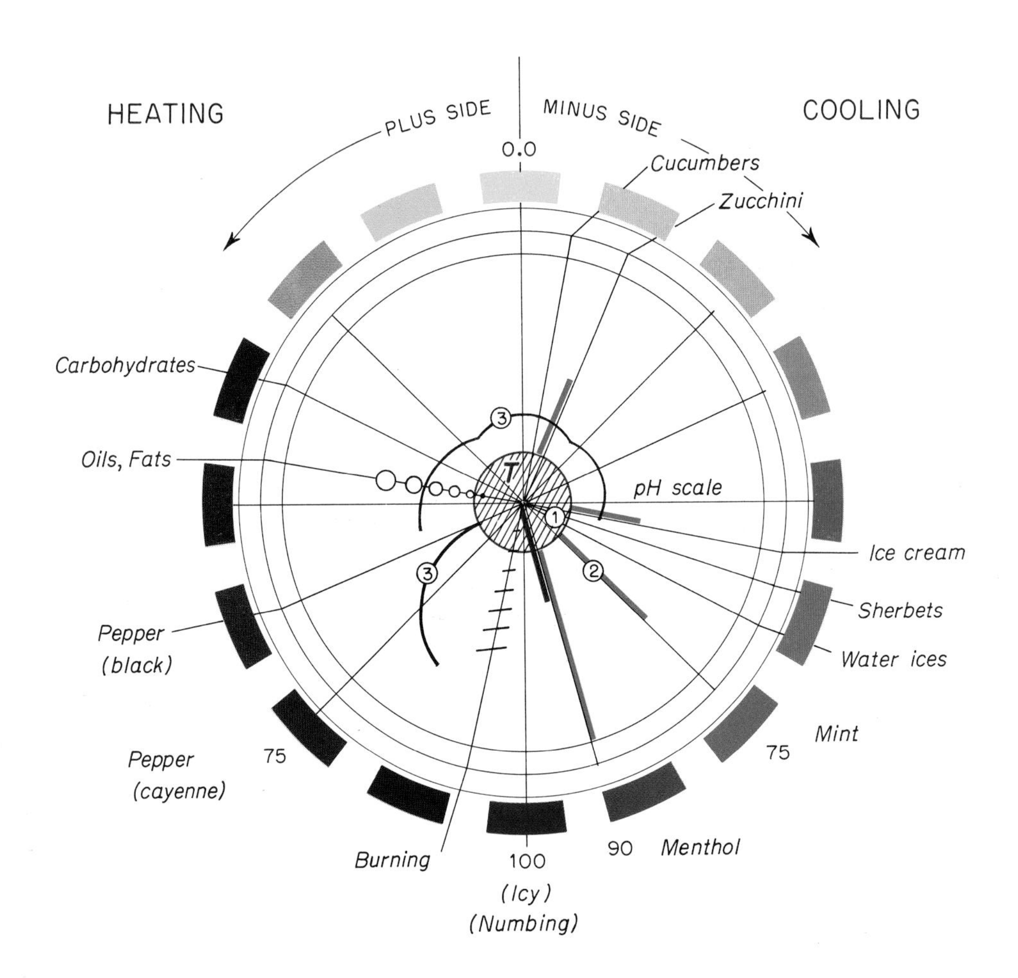

Fig. 17. Heating or Cooling Sensations

Suggesting color-wheel relationships applicable to *contact*, then consequent organoleptic perception of temperature factors.

The different physiological factors can be graphically represented like the area (1) and curves 2 and 3.

1. *T*—*T*oxicity
2. Relative cooling effect (apparent to actual)
3. Delayed action effect (after-taste, after-feel). Examples: ice cream—immediately cooling, subsequent heating. Black pepper (whole)—biting to burning.

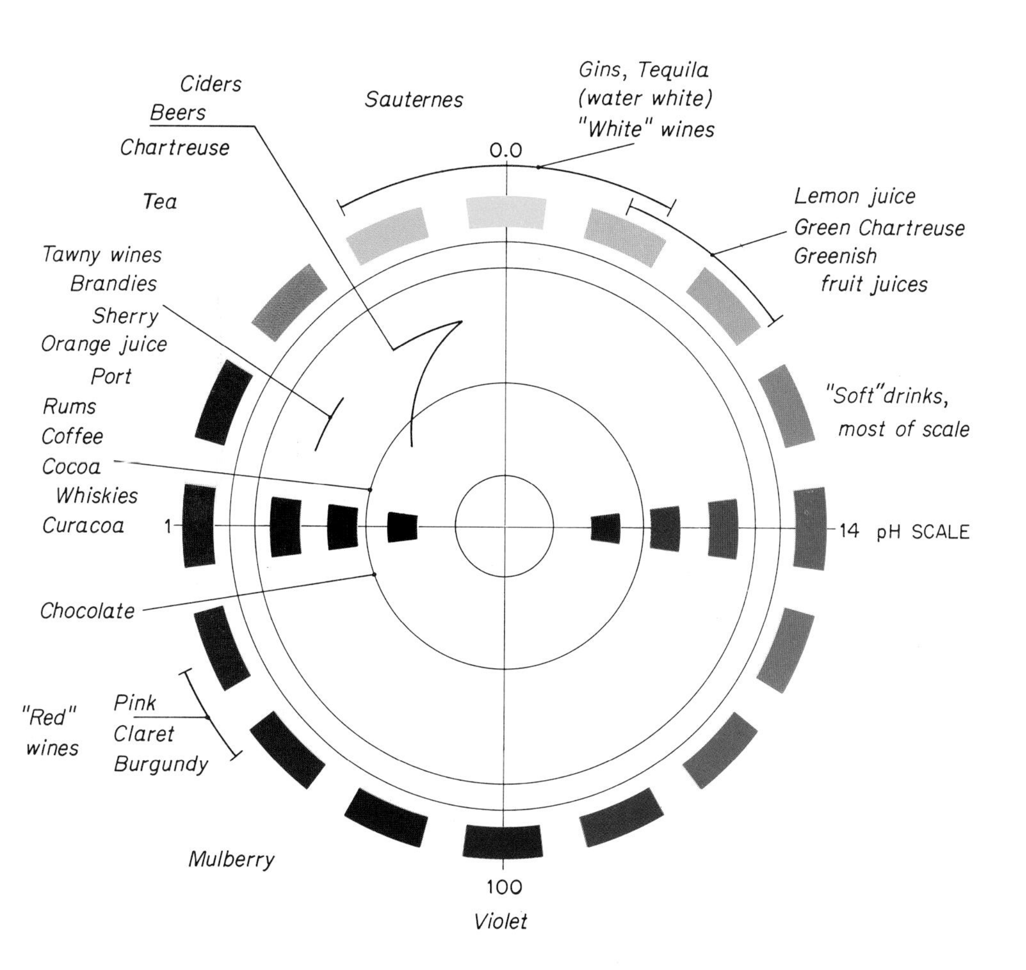

FIG. 18. WINES AND LIQUORS (COLOR SCALE)

Qualification: Popular color designations applied to wines are not accurate; i.e., white wine isn't white and red wine isn't red.

The blue group and some of the primary band colors can be approached by use of light color wines and liquors or juices in colored glassware.

Glass and liquids, especially clear color combinations make for depth and luminous illusions.

Curves can be shown for each liquid: Caloric values vary as alcohol, by percentage.

Toxicity factors: Chemicals–residues, artificial coloring and flavoring, alcohols and bacteria, fungi, acids.

H_2O by percentage. Ash by percentage.

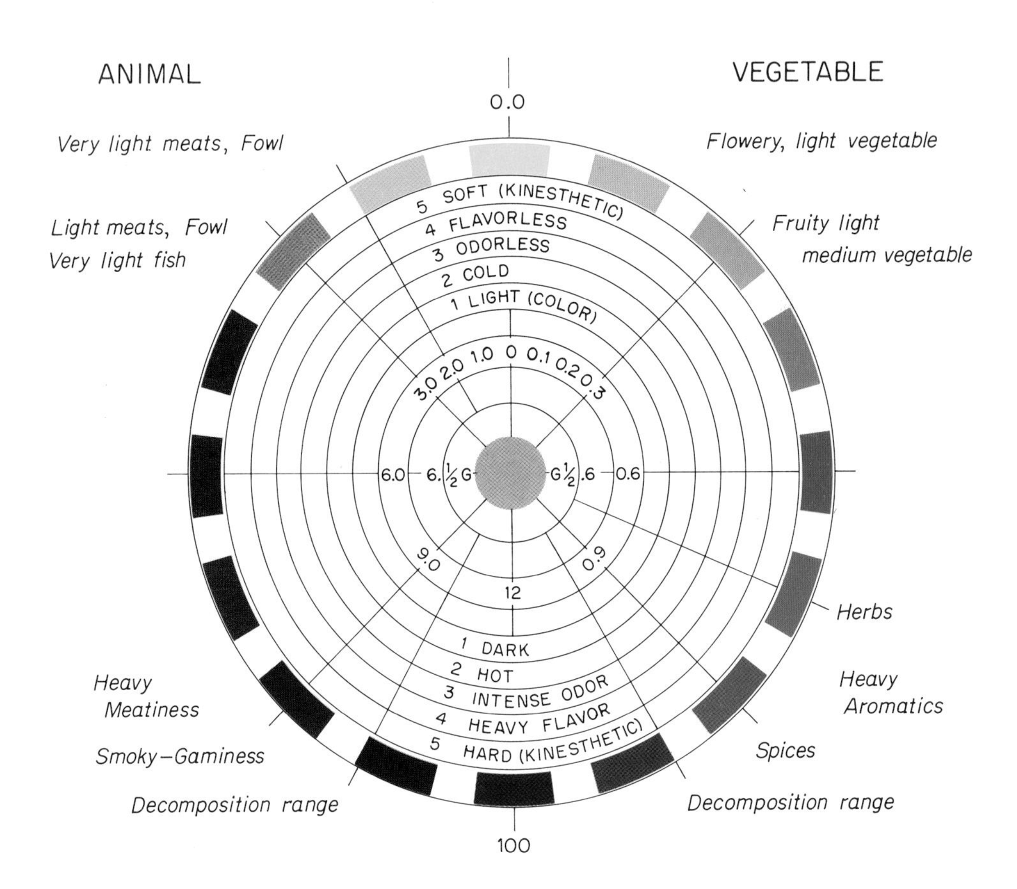

FIG. 19. ORGANOLEPTIC ASSOCIATIONS AND RELATIONS

Circular comparator; suggesting color-wheel and numerical values for the principal associations and relationships involved in organoleptic perception.

The primary ideas are:

1. Flavors tend to vary (by association) with color (a dark-brown taste is more than a figure of speech) and from light to dark:

2. Flavor values (as exemplified on the Gustametric Chart) when plotted on a color wheel are susceptible to the same rules that apply to colors: variations of color values (hues and tints, tones and shades), analagous or adjoining, triads, sextads, complementaries, contrasts, etc.

dragged one clam through the chowder. So far as quantity of cheese used, many productions of cheese dressing are ludicrous, mainly because the dressings are compounded with no knowledge of what is involved in the elements of sensory perception. The cheese content is so low and vinegar and other seasonings so dominant in many productions of cheese dressing that their cheese flavor is almost or entirely imperceptible.

If the cook uses a standard commercial mayonnaise as the carrier and admixes, say, 15 per cent by weight of Roquefort cheese, the compound may yield a mild Roquefort dressing flavor norm; but then only if the Roquefort is strong enough to overcome the higher flavor of the vinegar used in the mayonnaise base. How much additional Roquefort he must add to bring it up to the flavor level which he may be in the habit of using will vary primarily according to the vinegar content of his base.

To illustrate what we have in mind, let us assume that the chef was running low on dressing and was compounding some more starting with the original batch or what was left of the original batch, and among other things added 1 per cent of malt vinegar, then it is probable that from 3 to 5 per cent more Roquefort cheese would be required to balance that vinegar flavor addition.

It must be obvious that there are key points on any flavor concentration curve. The first, the lowest, would be subliminal. The second is the minimum, call it the most delicate and agreeable flavor level. The third, the optimum, accents the quantitative factor. The fourth is the maximum tolerance, both qualitative and quantitative.

Between the second and the fourth levels occur the average norms of use—between high and low.

Capacity. Now note particularly that capacity probably varies inversely as concentration: Starting with a flavor concentration below the threshold of perception, it must be clear that one's capacity for food at that level of flavor is greatest. Then as the degrees of perception mount, one can take less and less.

Individual capacity probably varies proportionally and in inverse ratio to flavor concentration. Assuming a water solution, perhaps a beverage, any flavor concentrate would thus vary: e.g., sugar below a given percentage in tea or coffee. At a higher coffee concentration it is not strong enough. In strong coffee e.g., one needs more sugar.

What we can ingest in an hour varies with many things. Under the most favorable circumstances the primary factors of individual capacity and the rate at which food is ingested, assuming 100 per cent of capacity to be ingested within an hour, requires a rate of ingestion something like the hypothetical curve in the first drawing in Fig. 12, where 50 per cent may be consumed in 15 minutes—allowing for the preliminary urges of appetite and hunger, and the balance within the remaining time.

The second drawing of Fig. 12 suggests a higher input for the first minutes because allowance is made for the human urges of food desire. But here we should also allow for differences between the gourmet and the epicure, as suggested by the broken lines in the second drawing. Those two charts assume some importance when we consider the food behavior of feeders.

Note that in the first drawing the epicure has a very much lower angle of approach and his capacity curve does not meet the halfway mark for more than twice the time for the average. Finally, the epicure never eats to capacity.

It is manifest that the capacity of the human stomach and the upper gastro-intestinal tract has an average limit of capacity always measured with the qualification of time: c/T. The stomach (and the epiglottis, the latter for only a few seconds) has its limits of capacity at any given moment. No matter how hungry, the individual can only cram so much into it within the given time interval. An extreme example might be a commuter gulping a sandwich and running on his hectic way. Regardless of what he thinks of his necessity for haste, he can only jam the food down his gullet so fast—without gagging. If the performance is stop-watch measured, the elapsed time between reaching for the sandwich and cramming in the last hunk, surprisingly enough, requires between two and three minutes. (Here again refer back to the consequences of swallowing, feeding, discomfort and worse.) The commuters can get it in, but they can't get away with it indefinitely without distressing consequences.

Now, our hypothetical commuter in a hurry devours a sandwich in haste; and that is just about his capacity for several hours because of the gross rate and kind of input to his stomach. He did not have, or take, the time to chew, so he has a lumpy mass distending his stomach, which in turn requires overlong to be converted to the viscous consistency required for passage to the upper intestinal tract. If he had taken more time he would have eaten more slowly, but would have put the food to useful purpose more quickly.

In the first instance he had reached what might be a 30-minute-or-longer-capacity within three minutes. But bear in mind that under those circumstances the amount of food ingested may have been less than 25 per cent of his one-hour capacity. In the second instance he may reach something like 30 per cent of his capacity, but if he allows 15 minutes he may consume a meal approaching 50 per cent of his hour capacity.

Going further in time, a 30-minute meal period may allow ingestion of three-fourths of an individual's capacity, but it must be clear that it is not physically possible for any person to ingest the quantity of food that is his capacity for one hour under ideal conditions in less than one hour and hold it down. Even the Romans didn't circumvent that.

A number of things happen or start happening in unfavorable or disagreeable directions when optimum time requirements are not complied with, or as some would say, when we try to "push nature around."

Capacity vs. Time Factor—Vary as Concentration

Let us give another example: a beverage high in alcohol. Bear in mind that the average metabolic capacity tolerance of alcohol is one-third of an ounce per person per hour. Then a single martini sipped during one hour is his capacity, assuming that the martini is up to standard (if there is such a thing). If that martini is gulped within a few seconds or a few minutes it will have side effects. Within those few seconds or few minutes, the individual has assumed his metabolic load-limit-per-hour capacity. Any additional alcohol ingested thereafter *within that hour* exceeds his metabolic tolerance. Physically, he has exceeded the rate at which alcohol can be metabolized, and the side effects begin peaking. The current expression is, "He is getting high." His inhibitions go down as his spirits go up for a short period of rise before his fall. The curve of tolerance can be shown to drop sharply to a drooping tail. Incidentally, refer to Volume II on *masks* and *sponges* which point out that while we can physically disguise and postpone a food effect, especially in the case of alcohol, the workings of metabolism are unalterable and the payment therefore inescapable. The piper must be paid. The martini may help him escape his mood, but not the toll.

In the case of the martini there are some factors that are elusive and some readily apparent. The quantitative factors of alcohol are assumed to be apparent with very little explanation required. The qualitative factors involved in flavors are in the field of intangibles and require much consideration.

Let us start by agreeing that a martini is not a drink. It is a beverage that because of its components is, or should be, sipped. We distinguish between a beverage to satisfy thirst, which is assumed to require substantial volumetric satisfaction, whereas a beverage like all cocktails does not satisfy thirst. It would be far more proper to say that the individual wanted a shot in the way of a cocktail akin to a shot in the arm, as an escape mechanism, which both are, but not to satisfy his thirst. It isn't his thirst he is satisfying, but his taste and his desire for a momentary escape, for "getting high," for lifting his fagged or depressed spirits, which is a psychosomatic appetite. The cocktail hour is almost peculiarly an American social phenomenon. It may be considered a left-handed cousin to English tea time.

In the flavor components of the martini it can fairly safely be assumed that the flavor level is so low, both as to quality and quantity as to be almost disregarded. They may be just at the threshold of perception of the average imbiber for the first slug, but because of the nature of the alcohol and its effects as a carrier, flavor fatigue probably develops so rapidly as to dull to the point of deadening subsequent or successive taste bud exposures to the same flavor; that is, assuming successive exposures within a short time-interval between shots. There is, moreover, an individual limit to the number of olives and onions—none of which appeals to an epicure.

Capacity for Most Taste Flavors

Coffee can be ingested at rates varying with the temperature as well as concentration and some other factors. At maximum temperature-tolerance, hot coffee can only be sipped without scalding the taste buds, sipped at a very slow rate: warm coffee at a much higher rate. The maximum possible rate of ingestion occurs at body temperature $\pm 98.6°F$.

Gulping of ice cream is usually immediately attended with a dull headachy kind of feeling in the sinuses.

Inadvertently mouthing a too hot chunk of meat requires its explusion to avoid a scalded mouth.

All food and drink is normally ingested between the extremes of too cold and too hot. It should be realized that the nearer a food is to what is our normal body temperture, the greater is our capacity for all factors of organoleptic perception as well as metabolic capacity.

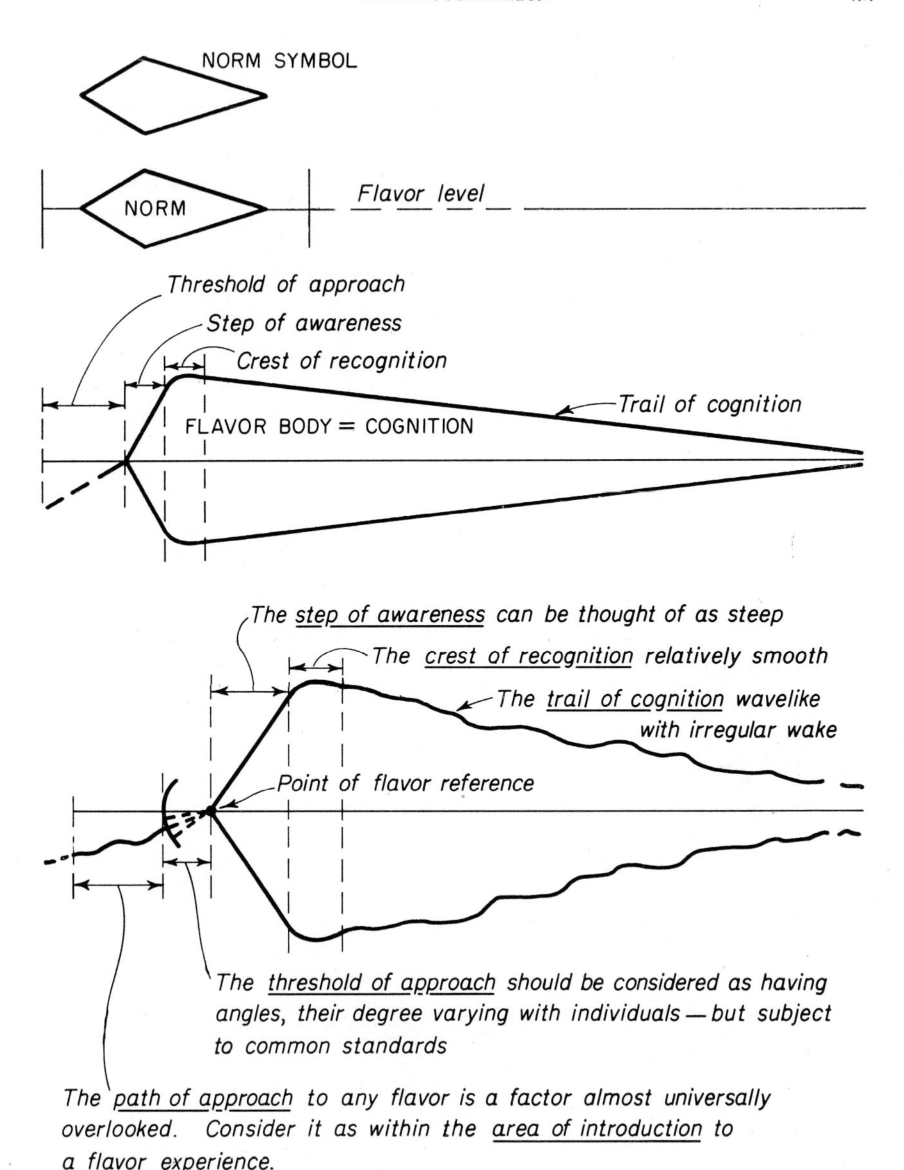

FIG. 20. FLAVOR PERCEPTION IS NEITHER INSTANT NOR CONSTANT

The flavor level of a given norm may be considered static only for purposes of evaluation: organoleptic cognition is virtually never on an even keel.

A norm's Center of Flavor Reference is the scale graduation assigned to it (e.g., Beef, 45).

All phases of flavor recognition and appreciation vary with individual aptitudes of organoleptic perception.

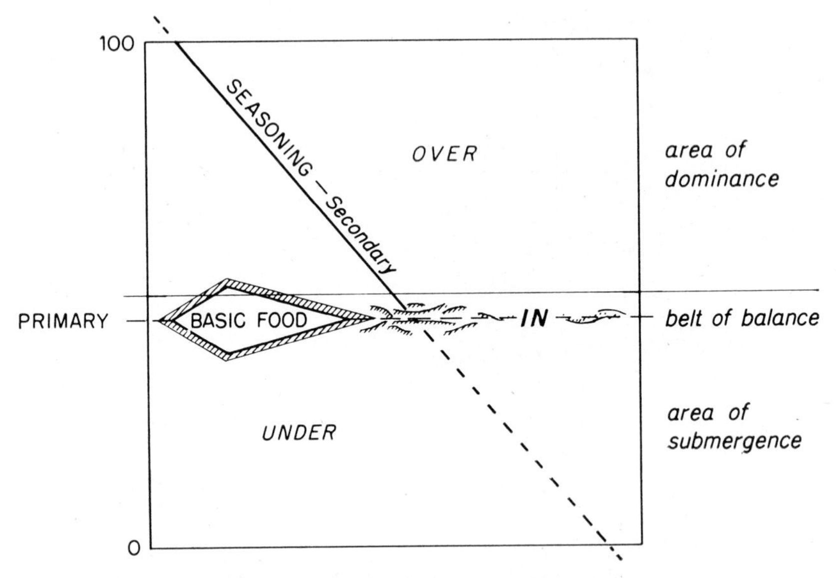

FIG. 21. THE PHYSIOLOGY OF FLAVOR—1

Relationships of the flavor curve of accompaniments—secondary flavors, to that of the primary, basic food.

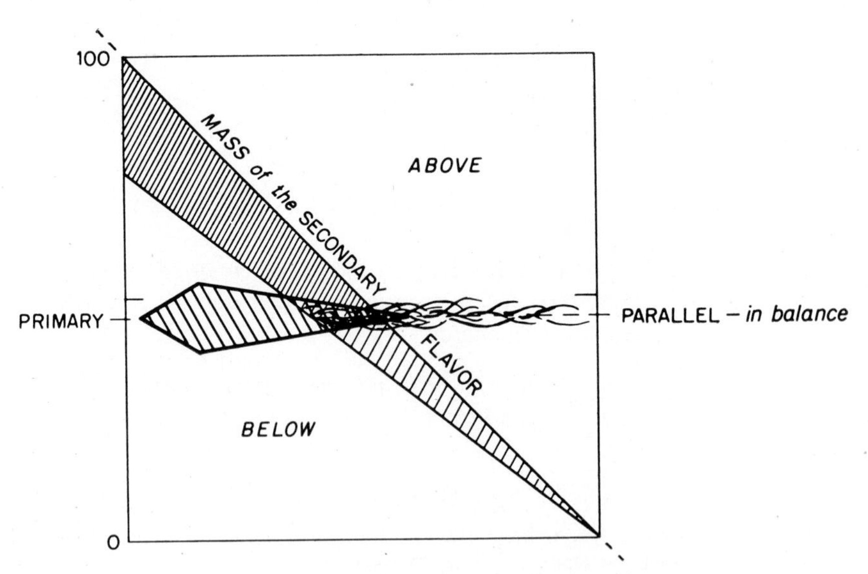

FIG. 22. THE PHYSIOLOGY OF FLAVOR—2

Relationships of the flavor curve of accompaniments—secondary flavors, to that of the primary, basic food.
Representing flavor-curve of accompaniments as mass.

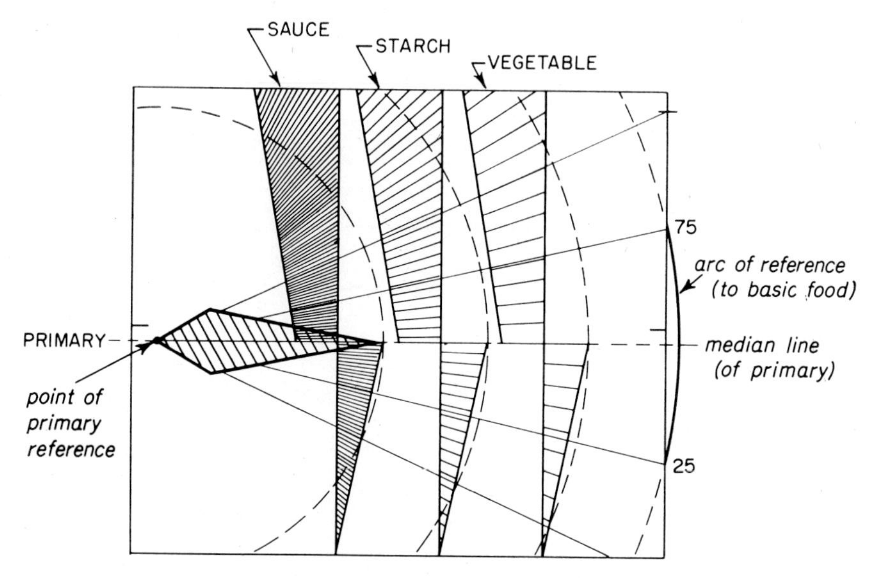

FIG. 23. THE PHYSIOLOGY OF FLAVOR—3

Relationships of the flavor curves of supplementary foods to that of the primary basic food. Shown as accompanying masses.

A food eaten without an accompaniment has a single flavor profile. A second food successively eaten is influenced by the trail of aftertaste of the first.

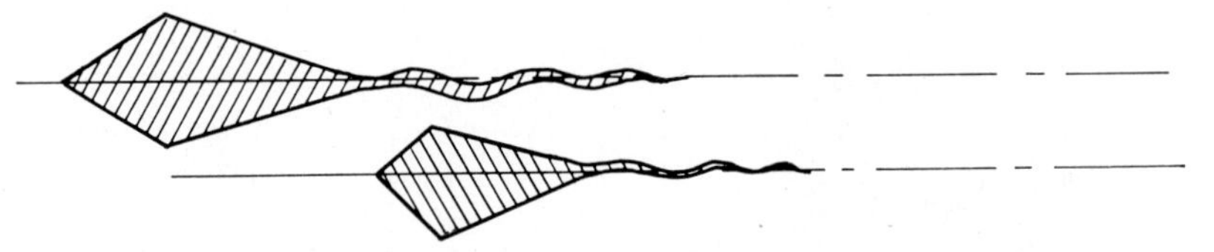

Two foods eaten chainlike together may be said at their conjunction to entwine their flavors, to weave or to braid, and to curve according to their organoleptic characteristics.

The mixture of two foods—without an absorber, will result in an ascending flavor curve.

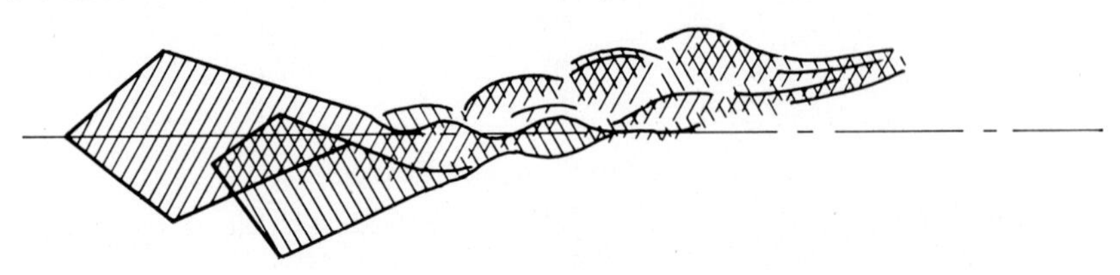

Admixture of an absorber, by flavor dilution inverts the curve, forces it downward. Consequent interweaving of flavors may alternate or blend them. Alternation here means intermittent peaking or cresting of individual flavor waves; one crests while the other submerges. Blending of flavors would suggest more-or-less uniform merging.

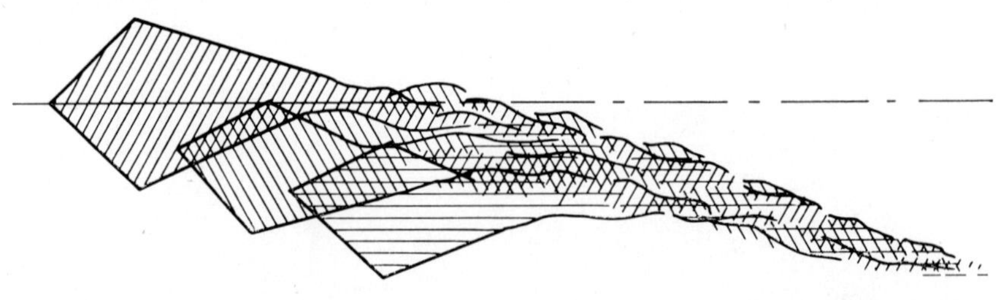

Incidentally; while flavors twist and churn—or merge, kinesthetic factors tend to maintain individual characteristics—they resist binding or weaving together. The texture of one food resists amalgamation with that of a structurally different other food. Flavors flowing together can behave like streams of pigment, mixing as they join, and under favorable conditions *blend.*

Considering for a moment only those kinesthetic factors of food normally requiring chewing; granules, fibres and chunks virtually *never* amalgamate in the mouth—but their *flavors* do, dispersing as they go.

FIG. 24. FLAVOR PERCEPTION VARIES AS AND WITH ACCOMPANIMENTS

Bibliography for Part I

ANON. 1958. Flavor Research and Food Acceptance. Reinhold Publishing Corp., New York.

AUBERJONOIS, F., and OSBORN, R. 1955. Taste: views on taste, pertinent and otherwise. Scope, IV, *8*, pp. 10–15.

CAMERON, A. T. 1947. The taste sense and the relative sweetness of sugars and other sweet substances. Scientific Report Series 9. Sugar Research Foundation, Inc., New York.

CORN INDUSTRIES RESEARCH FOUNDATION. 1958. Corn Syrups and Sugars. Corn Ind. Res. Fdn., Inc., Washington, D.C.

FOX, A. L. 1932. The relationship between chemical constitution and taste. Proc. National Acad. Sci. *18*, 115–120.

HENNING, H. 1916. Smell. Barth. Leipzig, Germany. As quoted in Moncrieff, R. W. 1946. The Chemical Senses. John Wiley and Sons, Inc., New York, N. Y.

LANGLEY, L. L., and CHERASKIN, E. 1954. The Physiology of Man. McGraw-Hill Book Co., Inc., New York.

Moncrieff, R. W. 1946. The Chemical Senses. John Wiley and Sons, Inc., New York.

WHITTAKER, SIR E. 1952. Eddington's Principle in the Philosophy of Science. American Scientist. *40*, 45–60.

ZWAARDEMAKER, H. 1895. The Physiology of Smells. As quoted in Moncrieff, R. W. 1946. The Chemical Senses.

PART II

The Selection and Combination of Foods

CHAPTER 5

Foods—Factors of Their Selection and Combination

Introduction

The second section of this book has been developed around the Gustametric Chart (facing p. 88). To begin with, the author wants to emphasize that the placements of the different foods and food substances on the Gustametric Chart are *qualifiedly* scientific. The chart is constructed according to the author's own ideas of taxonomy, his own conceptions of (1) an orderly arrangement of the foods of man according to classes of foods, and (2) listing the different foods in each class according to how they, *in his judgment,* rate as to flavor intensity. Here the reader is referred back to p. 13 in Part I, which explains Eddington's Principle in the philosophy of science, because the Gustametric Chart is the product not of orthodox scientific confirmations but findings in the author's own laboratory procedures and the judgments of his cookery class panels and many of his collaborating (and often long-suffering) friends.

The author became engrossed in the study of food flavors early in the 1930's. He began laboratory experiments with foods, combining literally thousands of different foods, cooking, testing, tasting them, and juggling combinations. Over a period of 30 years he studied his own taste reactions, those of his friends and people he encountered in his travels. He visited many of the market places of the world, checked the different foods of each area, and in one way or another tasted the foods with which he was not familiar. He probably spent more time in domestic and commercial kitchens than in dining rooms. He studied and compared the food preferences of various peoples and compared them with cookbook writings.

In his International Cuisine classes at Mills College in the fourteen 4- to 6-hour sessions on the selection, combination, preparation, serving, and participation of intra- and international foods, class reactions were panel-checked and recorded.

Thus the Gustametric Chart is the result of what every cautious investigator will concede is according to limited, often narrowly restricted and sometimes arbitrary judgment. The flavor ratings of the different foods on the Gustametric Chart are based on two theorems: (1) it is possible to produce a scale of flavor *intensity* whereby any given food would be assigned an arithmetic flavor value; (2) if all the foods of a certain class are placed on one scale, one or more foods would be at the bottom of the scale and one or more foods would be at the top of the scale. In other words, for each class of food, the flavors range from low to high. With this part of the theorem there can be no disagreement. Where all the other foods flavor rate on a specific scale would be according to subjective determinations, and about each one of them there could be much disagreement. It is the relative placement of a given item that is subject to question and experimental determination. Example: in the class of dairy products, Column 4, there can be no question but that skim milk is at the bottom of the flavor range and Limburger is at the top. Placement of the other cheeses and dairy products is subject to speculation as to their exact intermediate positions.

On the Gustametric Chart all the basic food groups are rated on a numerical basis from 0 to 1000. The numerical figure appearing opposite each item represents the level of flavor intensity of that particular food when the chosen food is prepared in its simplest form. In the case of cooked foods, the process must be *steaming* under controlled laboratory conditions. That figure is referred to as the *Flavor Norm* of a particular food. It should be emphasized that the establishment of the flavor norm for any given food must begin with that food in its ideal condition. The resulting flavor can be charted as the *norm* or the *standard flavor* for that food. Other methods of cookery will cause the flavor norm to increase or decrease—up or down the chart. Thus the flavor of any food can be diminished or increased, submerged or overpowered.

At the top of each of the columns of the Gustametric Chart is a symbol for that particular classification of food. The categories of food have been arranged according to the order in which man normally reaches for his food. As man has always been primarily a carnivore and secondarily an omnivore, meats (fish, fowl, and beast) are listed first. Dairy products come second; foods which may be used as substitutes for meat. Next come starches, cereals, and legumes, which have been the mainstay of agricultural man, particularly in time of want. Then there are the fruits and vegetables, many of which are comparatively new developments.

Next come liquid carriers, which include meat stocks, fats, oils, milk, and water; then the beverages, the seasonings, and the condiments—those foods which, while not always nutritionally necessary, are psychosomatically satisfying.

The chart then consists of the graph listing first the *categories* of food, and second the *numerical rating* of *flavor norms* for each food included.

From the standpoint of cookery, it enables one, by means of a straightedge, to select a group of foods that are compatible with one another.

The Gustametric Chart contains only the bare minimum of foods and should in time be greatly expanded. The listings have been restricted to more or less well-known foods. It must be realized that there are many more foods than such a relatively small single chart can show. Separate charts are provided to show some of the varieties in a single classification. Used as a foundation, the Gustametric Chart can have endless ramifications.

Self-determination of Flavor Rating

Since any system of flavor rating must be *comparative* and all scaling methods must be established according to *relative* values, flavor rating trials may be made at will and according to the foods at hand and circumstances as one proceeds.

Bear in mind as a prerequisite for any fair weighing of flavor values you must observe the requirements of laboratory procedures. However, even in the absence of ideal conditions you should weigh flavors as you eat, if you are to consider seriously the subject matter of this book. For accuracy you should have peace, quiet, and *time,* although many worthwhile organoleptic observations can be made without them.

Start with the simplest comparisons: compare whole wheat bread with white bread, at room temperature. Compare light, medium, and dark toast with a control slice, but be sure to savor all four at the same temperature, preferably 98.6°F. Then lightly butter half of one of the toasted slices and compare it with the other. Repeat the trial by first buttering the bread and then toasting it in the broiler. Then record what you estimate to be the resultant flavor levels of the different trials. Here realize that two different classes of food have been combined: the bread is vegetable and the butter is animal. Incidentally, the toasting process is a phase of dry cookery. By pan-frying finely minced onion in a little butter and then toasting the bread in that, you can go to a much higher flavor level.

Later compare different combinations of breads and cheeses; some cool, some hot. Evaluate a medium cheddar on plain white bread contrasted with the same cheese on light, medium, and dark toast. Repeat the procedure and compare the flavor of the cheese broiler-melted with that of the cold cheese on toast as a control sample. Then go a step further and sprinkle a little crumbled herb on the cheese before melting it.

Follow this laboratory procedure with each individual food and then with combinations. Judge the effects of the different kinds of cookery, wet and dry, with identical foods, always maintaining equal trial conditions. In the classification of seafood you might start with a radical contrast of fish low in the scale compared with one that is above 50 intensity units. Try a low-fat fish, such as one of the bass group, with one of the high-fat flat fishes, such as sole or flounder. Then contrast fish of the same genus, perhaps cod versus haddock or lobster versus crawfish. Then differentiate between organoleptic considerations involved in savoring two different parts of the same fish, some of which have substantially different flavors as well as kinesthetic values. Examples would be codbelly versus cod backmeat, and the dark meat of tuna versus light tuna meat. Compare sand dabs with flounder and pink salmon with red salmon, which are two different species of salmon.

As we proceed through the different classifications of the Gustametric Chart there will be new comparisons of the different foods by kinds and varieties, singly and in groups, and some allusions to variations in cookery techniques. However, it is emphasized that the techniques of cookery are covered in more detail in the section on cookery in Volume II.

The concept of a norm of any given cooked food is based on the enclosure of the specimen in a package or vessel, creating temperature conditions that will heat the mass of food for just long enough to cook it; then sampling the result, both solid and liquid, when the temperature is reduced to 98.6°F. Without laboratory equipment and conditions such results can be approximated by using parchment bags or metal foil envelopes, either of which can be heated to temperatures ranging around 185° to 210°F. in a closed vessel atop the stove or racked in an oven where the temperature is controlled within the required range. Obviously any such procedures must be performed by the individual to meet specific requirements. As neither bags nor envelopes are ordinarily hermetically sealable, there will be some vapor escape with some flavor loss. Under careful procedure, however, the results should be fairly satisfactory.

Obviously other types of cookery would raise or lower flavor values. Steamed lamb is rated at 50. If it is water-cooked (two parts lamb to one part water) its valuation drops to about 40. If the lamb is roasted, the flavor rating, an average of the seared outside and the cooked inside, will rise to about 60. If it is cut into steaks and fried, it rises to about 75. If it is broiled, the rating goes to about 85, primarily because scorching takes the surface to over 100. Similar observations can be made for other meats. Sole is rated at about 62 when steam-cooked, using the entire fish; poached in water, its rating drops to about 50; deep-fat-fried it is about 75; pan-fried in fat it is about 85; broiled it is around 95. However, fillet of sole from which the skin and bone have been removed has a valuation when steamed of only 25. This is because most of the fishy flavor is in the skin or alongside the bone. The most frequent preparations of sole fillets, and most other fish fillets as well, involve frying techniques without the cook's realizing why.

Establishment of a flavor norm for any given food must begin with that food in its ideal condition and cooked by the steaming process indicated earlier. The resulting flavor can be charted as the norm or the standard of flavor for that food; the flavors resulting from any other methods of cookery can be plotted up or down on the same chart.

A flavor sample is always understood to be at 98.6°F. Thus the ideally steamed lamb starts with a rating of 50 but served cold at 60°F. it might rate ten points lower; sampled at 125°F. it would rate nearer 60.

There are still other ways of changing the flavor rating of a given food. Using beef as an example, start with the arbitrarily assumed flavor norm of 45 (see Fig. 29 on p. 101). The *inherent* flavor is represented by the horizontal line and the flavor gradient is represented by the line at an angle.

Here it is obvious that the flavor curve starts below the threshold of perception and goes to infinity, passing the upper reaches of dominance. The flavor curve below the median line represents flavors and seasonings *under* that line of the basic beef norm; and the flavor curve above the median line represents flavors and seasoning *over* the basic beef flavor norm. Only a little pondering of that chart will reveal the startling fact that the ideas thus represented can be considered as basic assertions, probably applicable to all the foods of man. The flavor of any food can be diminished or increased, submerged or overpowered, and both the matter and methodology are represented as straight line progressions from lowest to highest.

Pressure-cook one pound of finely ground meat in two pounds of water and the dilution of flavor is 1 part in 3, assuming no aroma loss in flavor. Slowly bake the same meat under laboratory conditions with equipment that makes possible entrainment of the aroma components that usually escape into the atmosphere, until it is reduced to one-third of its original mass. The flavor of one pound of finely ground meat is then concentrated in one-third of a pound, which naturally has three times as high a flavor rating.

The addition of *any* seasoning raises the flavor rating of any food, the degree varying with kind and quantity. In the small range of concentration usually employed, the seasoning's influence on the basic food will be directly proportional to the quantity added, assuming the same conditions of cookery

Salt may begin with so little as to be imperceptible as a saline taste: it is then below the threshold of perception of salinity, *but* the flavor level of the basic food is proportionately raised. Then as more salt is added it becomes identifiable as such. Beyond the median acceptance of salt we commonly say that it tastes too salty. And if it goes over 100

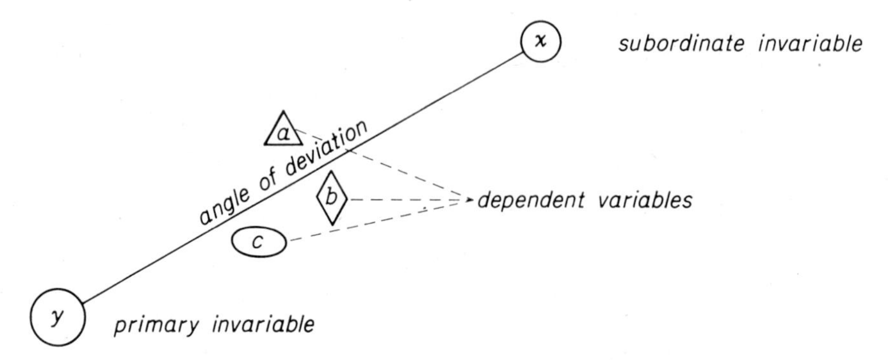

FIG. 26. PLOTTING NOMOGRAPHIC PROJECTIONS

When the flavor norm of the highest (or lowest) secondary accompanying food according to the seasoning of a given made dish) is determined it becomes (x) the *Subordinate* Invariable; the field point of reference for the nomographic Angle of Deviation (from the anchor point.)

The *Dependent* Variables (a, b and c) are the accessory foods that are coordinate with the (flavor) *Angle of Deviation.*

Once the BASIC point of reference (y) is (by selection of a given food and determination of its flavor norm) fixed, it is established as the *Primary* Invariable and anchor point of nomographic reference.

it becomes for the average individual intolerable. Bear in mind that three per cent of salt in solution in the water present in the food is rather generally accepted as constituting maximum average acceptance. Addition of salt to the basic food will have straight line taste characteristics. Granulated sugar, one of the few seasonings with no odor in low-temperature cookery and subject only to a taste curve increment, has straight line characteristics like salt, but we can take larger concentrations of sugar than salt before its sweetness becomes cloying to the average taste.

With white wine as a single seasoning additive to a basic food, beef in this instance, a little consideration of the flavor steps will reveal the same kind of results: at first not enough to be perceptible, then just enough to realize some flavor addition that may not be identified, then up the curve into the area where it is identified and liked as an agreeable foundation or background in the beef broth, which may then be called a sauce. At the median point the flavor of the beef and the wine should be in such balance that the consensus of judgment would be split on whether the beef or the wine was tasted. Any further addition of wine then dominates the basic food. Then, if the curve is pursued, it could be said that one could increasingly taste the wine rather than the beef.

The median flavor level of any solid food in or with a sauce tends to be organoleptically variable primarily according to the kinesthetic factors of the compound or food assembly. If the seasoning of a sauce is below

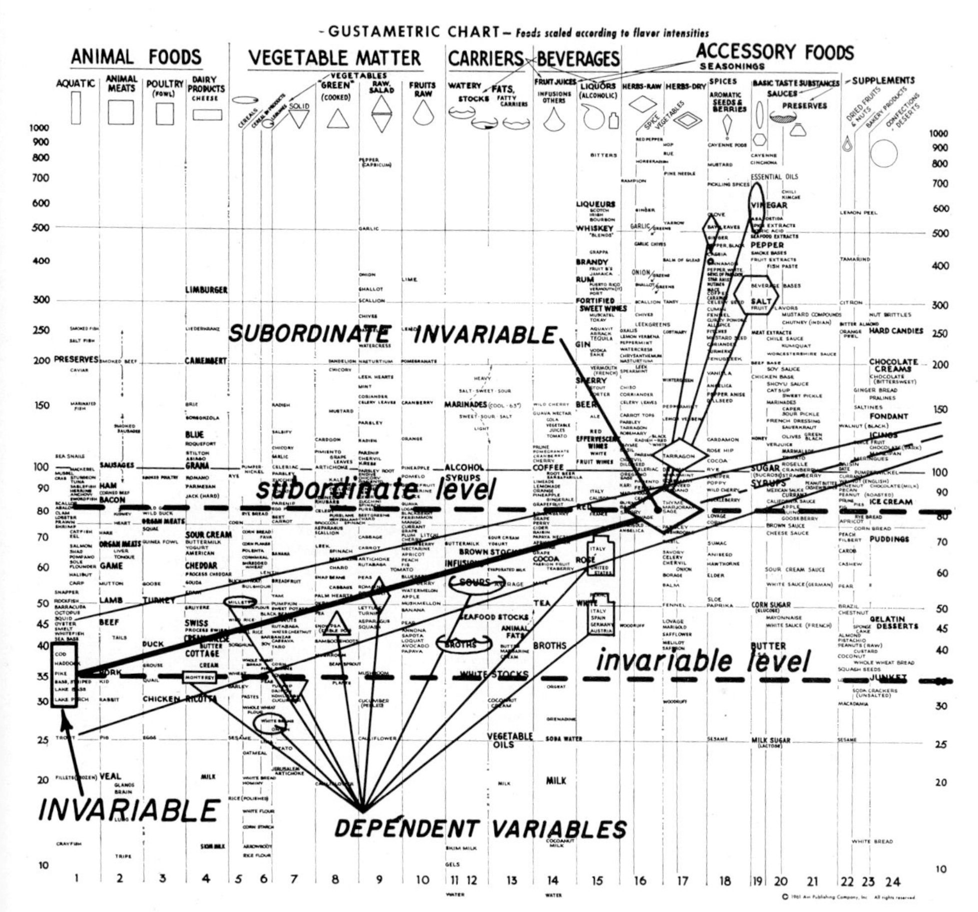

FIG. 27. USE OF FLAVOR EVALUATIONS TO ESTABLISH POINTS OF REFERENCE

Examples of Nomographic Operations. Prerequisite understanding: all basic terms refer to flavor values.
Examples: Invariable—Basic point of (flavor) reference; Invariable level of (flavor) reference; Subordinate Invariable—Field point of (flavor) reference; Subordinate (flavor) level of reference; Angle of (flavor) Deviation; Dependent (flavor) Variables.

the median line of the basic food, it can be thought of as a foundation or background which is dominated by the basic food. If the sauce is equal in flavor rating to the basic food, it parallels the basic food in flavor, and only kinesthetic variations are present. It is like a thin slice of roast beef submerged in its own juice; like fish steamed in parchment where just enough seasoning has been added in the preparational process to balance the inherent flavor of the fish. Finally, making the flavor rating

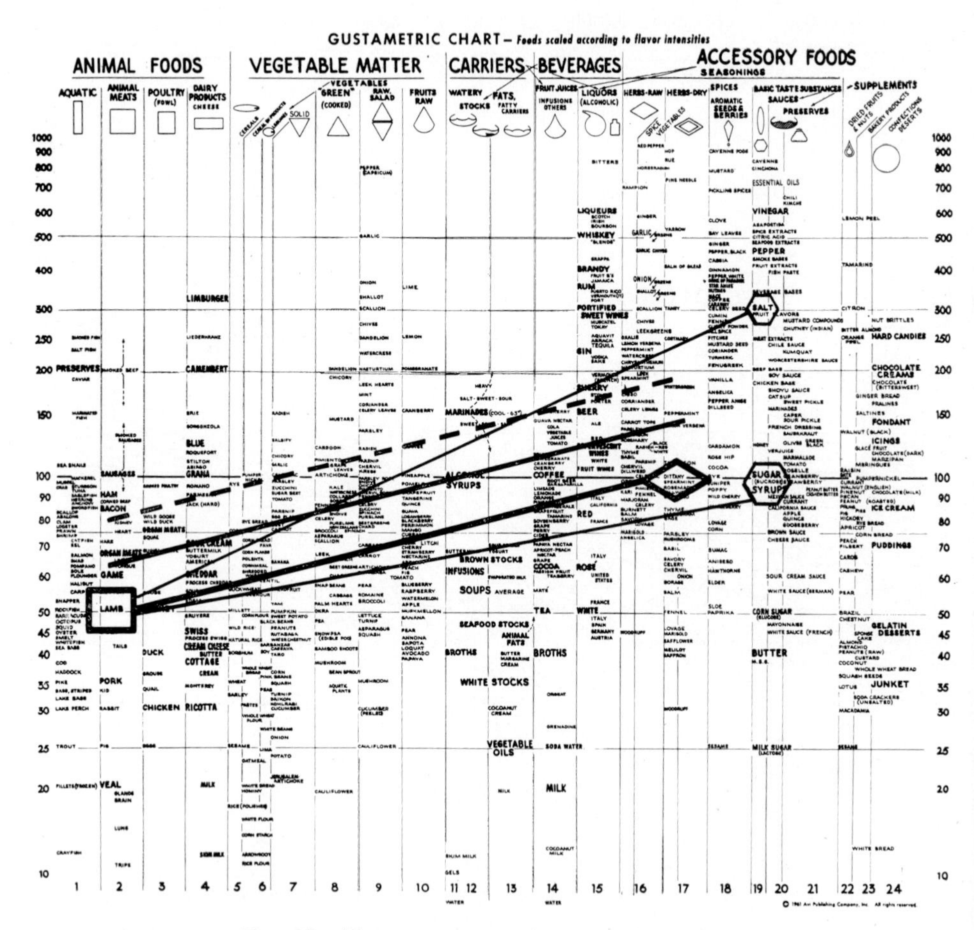

FIG. 28. ESTABLISHING THE ANGLE OF DEVIATION

The degree of the Angle of Deviation is fixed when the Invariable and the Subinvariable points of reference are established. The Angle of Deviation is constant if the Subinvariable (the dominant seasoning) is constant.

Changing the quantity or quality of the Subinvariable *will equally* lower or raise *both* Subinvariable and Invariable but will *not* alter the degree of the Angle of Deviation.

The degree of the Angle of Deviation may be (and usually is) altered *if the nature of* the Subinvariable is changed.

Example by this Nomogram:

A. Simply steamed lamb; FN 50.
B. Lamb steamed with average seasoning of mint, salt and sugar; FN raised to 60.
C. Lamb *baked* with the same seasoning; FN raised to 80.

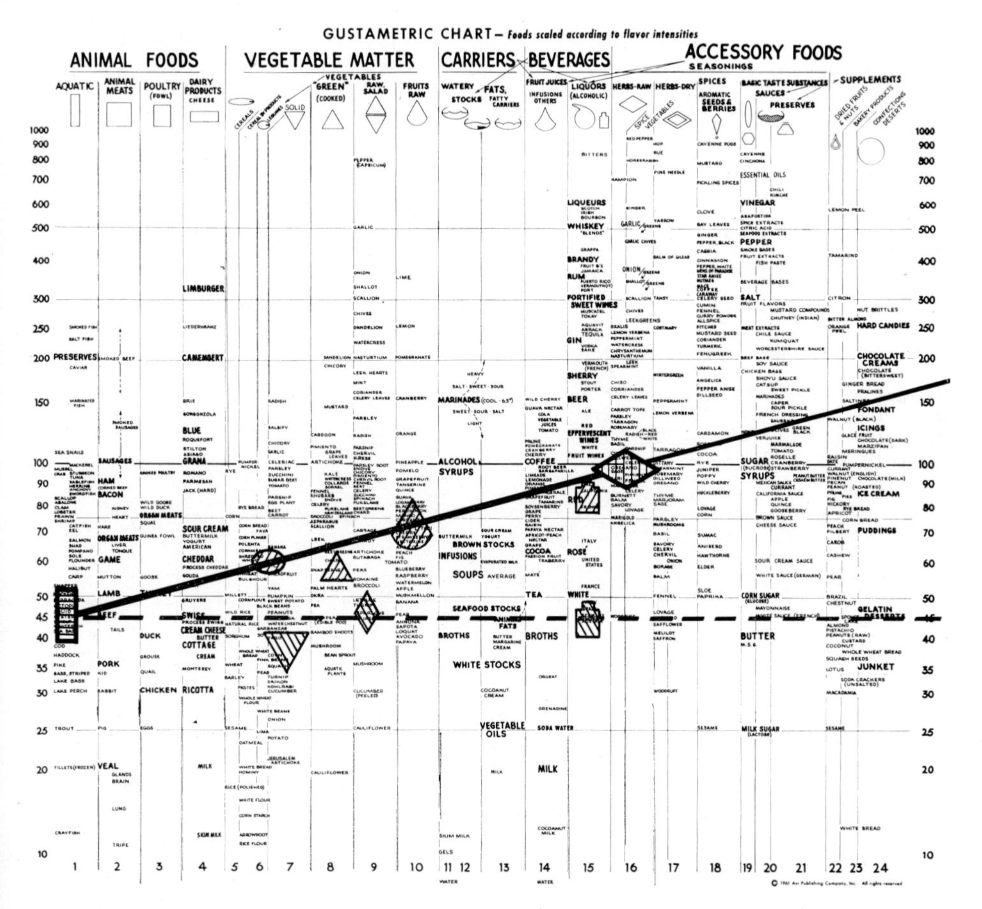

FIG. 29. ACCOMPANIMENTS OF THE BASIC FOOD

All of the foods along the Angle of Deviation are coordinate Dependent Variables of the Angle of Deviation (or coodinates of the Angle of Deviation).

All of the foods along the flavor level of the Basic Food Flavor Norm are coordinate Dependent Variables of the Basic Food flavor level.

of the sauce higher than that of the basic food means serving the basic food with a sauce that dominates it; like a beanery serving of a two-day-old slice of roast beef fortified with a motley paint-like sauce that alike disguises the condition of the base and the components of the sauce.

Thus far we have considered only individual foods, or at most single dishes on the chart. We come now to what is the primary usefulness of the Gustametric Chart.

Man does not normally tend to make a meal of a single item of food. Without really thinking about it, he doesn't consider a food experience

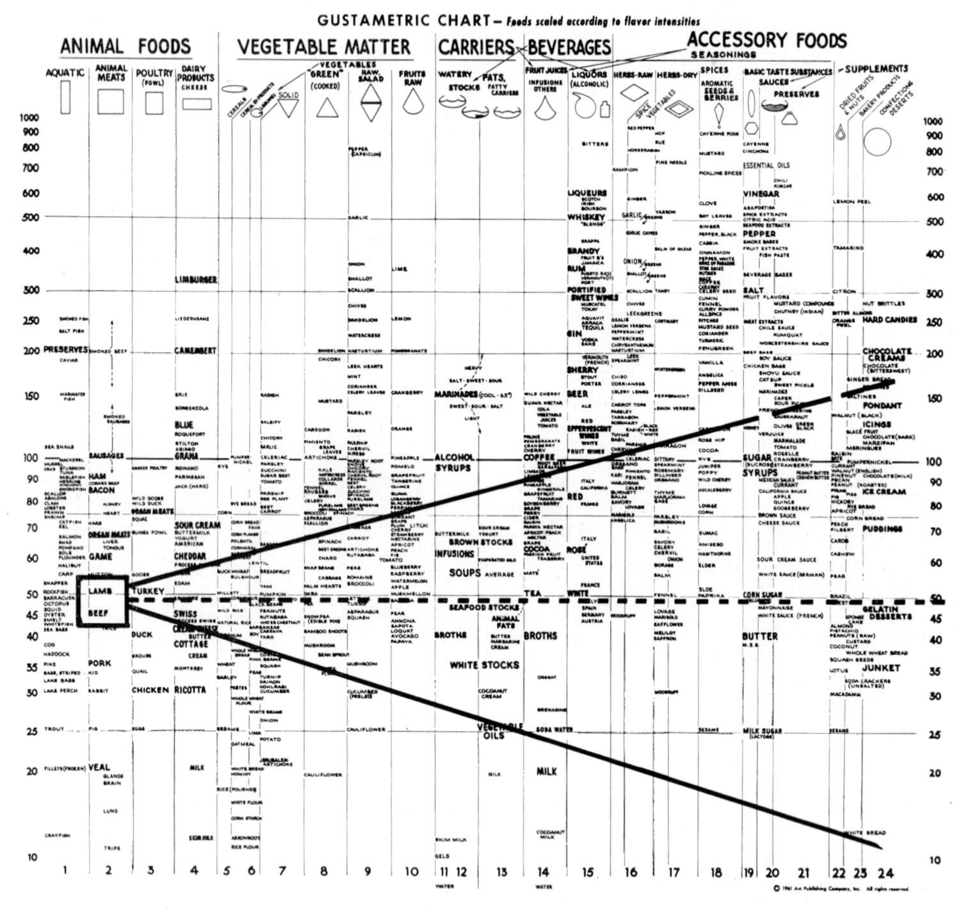

Fig. 30. Ascending or Descending Flavor Angles of Deviation

Ascending Angle of Deviation—All of the foods coordinated with its lines are *higher* in flavor than that of the Invariable.

Foods of the same flavor intensity as the Invariable (dotted line).

Descending Angle of Deviation—All of the foods coordinated with its line are *lower* in flavor intensity than that of the Invariable.

a meal unless it is in the way of a combination in some kind of order, of different kinds of foods, usually with different kinds of flavors.

The purpose of the Gustametric Chart and some of its supplements is to provide a food scale or set of scales by which foods can be flavor-evaluated on a comparative basis, for single dishes and combinations or assemblies up to complete meals. In its simplest usage, it provides an index for pairing companion dishes or accompaniments or a seasoning for a specific dish. The wider application graphically shows possible effects that may be new to the user. It will make possible an infinite number of effects different from everyday practices. Further, by following the procedure to be pointed out, this chart also indicates which combinations to avoid. It is like musical composition: given musical notation and a good sense of tonal perception, the means to compose music of variety and beauty are at hand.

How to Use the Gustametric Chart

Part I of the book sets forth in some detail the scientific factors influencing the experience of *tasting* a food.

Here we consider the food itself, in what may be called its *specific eating qualities,* which are found to be objectively measurable for the sensory experience of tasting them.

These factors are the following:

(1) *Nature* of the food—kind, physical structure and components.

  (a) *Breed* and *feed* (if the food is animal). *Variety* and *fertilizer-soil conditions* (if the food is vegetable).

  (b) *Maturity,* meaning stage at which the life process was arrested.

  (c) *Aging,* meaning time lapse after the life process was arrested until the food was cooked.

  (d) *Method of preservation.*

(2) *Mass.*

  (a) Bulk, form or volume related to mouthability.

  (b) Availability or readiness of edibility.

(3) *Temperature* of the food at the instant of ingestion.

(4) *Manipulation* required in the manual or mechanical handling or transfer of the food as it is eaten.

(5) *Kinesthetics,* concerned with tactile sensory experiences. This usually involves

  (a) *Densities,* surface and deep textures; and tenderometry, including measurement of its penetration and shear qualities; and

  (b) *Viscosity* of the liquorous parts. Because *tenderness* and *juiciness* are so frequently (often wrongly) coupled, such couplets may well be considered *kinesthetics.*

Other factors influencing flavor are discussed in other parts of the book. For example: factors influencing the eater himself, such as his physical equipment and condition.

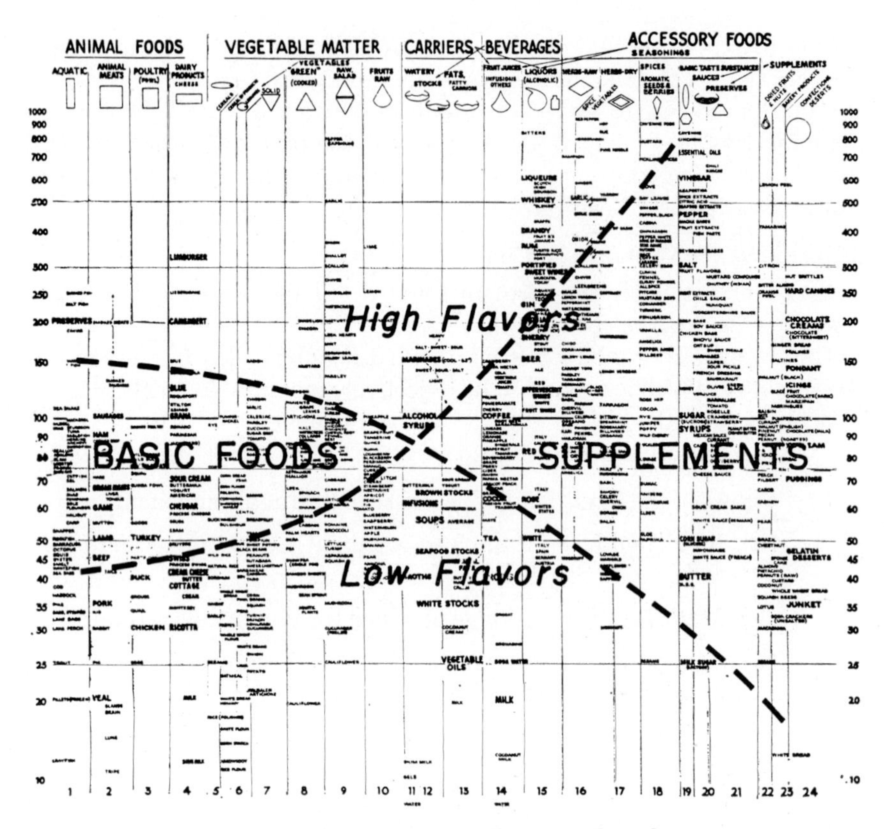

Fig. 31. High Versus Low Flavors in Plotting Food Combinations

With *any additive* a simple food becomes a composite food; a preprocessed or composite food becomes an elaborated food. Its flavors alter according to the nature and quantity of the additive, time and processing.

Wine Accompaniments

Symbiotic. Coordinates of the level of the Invariable: A light red wine; claret or cabernet sauvignon *or* a strong rosé; corignane or aleatico.

Complementary. Angle of Deviation *up* (the flavor of the wine slightly dominates that of the basic food); a strong red wine.

Angle of Deviation *down* (the flavor of the wine is subdominant to that of the basic food; a light rosé; *or* a strong white wine.

Contrast. Angle of Deviation *up;* an effervescent wine. Angle of Deviation *down;* a light white wine.

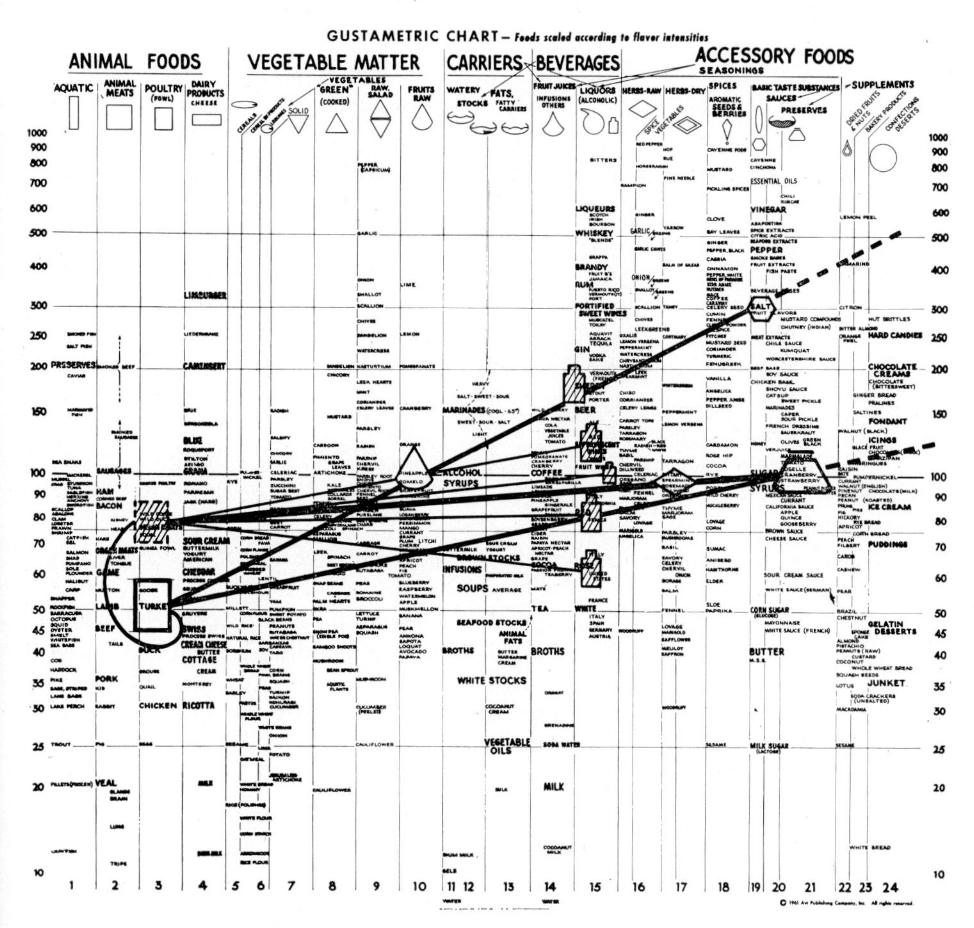

Fig. 32. Beverages Accompanying a Food Vary According to the Flavor of that Food

Beverages accompanying a food are plotted with relation to their flavors, (*not* their colors).

Invariable. FN 50. Basic food, *turkey,* before addition of dominant seasoning (Subordinate Invariable), pineapple; and the subdominant seasonings—spearmint, sherry and salt.

Invariable FN raised to 75 by roasting and seasoning.

Alternative

Invariable. FN 50. With dominant seasoning of oregano or thyme, and subdominant red wine and cranberry juice,

Invariable FN raised to 75 by roasting and seasoning.

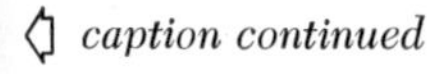
caption continued

Uses of the Gustametric Chart

The Gustametric Chart is a nomograph, an alignment chart that enables one by the aid of a straight-edge to read off the value of a dependent variable when the values of two invariables are given.

For nomographic purposes, once the flavor rating of the main-dish food has been established it becomes the invariable *point* and level of basic flavor reference.

The angle from the *invariable* point of reference to the point of reference of the dominant flavor rated accompanying food substance (the subordinate invariable) is the angle of deviation. Once the invariable and the subordinate invariable points of reference are fixed all the coordinates or options are variables dependent on the straight-line projection between the invariable and the subinvariable points of reference or the *flavor level* of the invariable.

All the dependent variables (optional foods or food substances) are relative to (1) the flavor level of the invariable or (2) the flavor angle of deviation.

There are no independent variables in a consistently ordered level or angular flavor profile.

To illustrate, take the case of lamb with mint. Lamb represents one invariable factor, mint the other. Now draw a straight line between the two. In the band (plus or minus about five points) connecting the two will appear the foods which will be agreeable with the lamb and mint and from which the cook can form a suitable "flavor profile" for the meal. Those foods directly in the path of the straight line represent the *dependent* variables. In the case of lamb with mint, on or near the straight line will appear such vegetables as snap beans, spinach, and chard, with French dressing for salads. These foods are compatible.

The Rietz *Gustametric Chart* is a graph that covers all of the foods of man in five divisions and twenty-four classifications, and which is subject to nomographic relationships.

Nomo- (Greek) Laws: *Graph.* A diagrammatic representation of a system of connections (Century). (Diagram. A line drawing for scientific purposes.) (Webster)

Nomograph. A graph on which appear graduated lines for all variables in a formula, arranged in such a manner that the value of one variable can be read on the appropriate line from a knowledge of the other variables. (Blakiston)

Nomogram. (The author's definition for purposes of application to the Gustametric Chart.) A graph that enables one by the aid of a straight-edge to read off the value of a dependent variable when the values of invariables are given.

CHAPTER 6

Aquatic Foods

COLUMN 1

Introduction

Aquatic Foods encompasses both animal and vegetable matter, all or part of whose life cycle is associated with a water habitat. The chart at the beginning of this classification subdivides aquatic foods into animal, mineral, and vegetable. Column 1 of the Gustametric Chart lists the majority of the most familiar seafoods.

Only botany exceeds ichthyology in the enormous number of families and relations. There are not only more fish in the sea than there are animals on land, but there are many, many more species of fish than there are of animals.

The majority of people have never tasted really fresh fish. The term *freshness* as applied to fish must start with the condition of fish slaughtered immediately after removal from the water. Other requirements for proper evaluation of flavor in fish are careful butchery, and if heat-treated, simple and low-temperature steaming immediately after trimming.

Visual Considerations.—Visual appraisal by itself is not to be relied upon except for differentiation between kinds and varieties and as a basis for superficial judgment. Failure to investigate *what does not meet the eye* is fraught with more hazard in the selection of seafood than in any other classification.

Distinguishing between fish high in fat and those with low fat content is of primary importance. There a visual judgment can be relied on in choosing kind and variety for fat content. Visual appraisal should include appearance of eyes and gills and surface factors that are readily apparent. Distinguish between male and female, young and older fish when there is an option. In the reproducing seasons the females are almost invariably soft, sometimes to the point of flabbiness. The smaller, younger fish of many kinds and species, are preferred to the larger and older ones for over-all qualities.

Note that the seafood column in the *Gustametric Chart* is also subdivided. The so-called lean fish start at the left margin, and the fatty fish are indented. The relative fatness of fish should always be borne in mind not only in selection but in preparation. Selection should be dependent upon the intended method of preparation.

The seafood column, like many of the others, indicates in some instances one member which is representative of a family. In other cases two or more members of the family are listed for purposes of emphasis or because they are known to most Americans. In the mackerel family only two members have been listed: mackerel and tuna. Bonita and skipjack are omitted. In the herring family only herring and anchovy are listed, but sardines are not, nor are the very large group of relations in the herring family. Clams, crabs, and lobster are all listed only once, though each has many family relations.

It is especially important to realize that flavor factors vary not only by variety but according to sources and, of course, the seasons of the year. There are radical differences in flavor, texture, and other organoleptic factors between crabs, from the Alaska King crabs through the Pacific Dungeness and the Eastern Blue crabs, and the Cuban and English huge rock crabs.

Only in the last few years has the public been exposed to the great differences in qualities of shrimps and prawns, not only by kind and variety but by area, and of course type of preservation. There is much difference between fresh prawn and that which is refrigerated.

Some of the larger fishes and other seafood, particularly clams and oysters, have tissue characteristics that are generally judged less desirable than the smaller and younger members of the same kinds or varieties.

Feeling—Primarily Touch.—Probe for tactile perception, but realize it is not a good index for a hard-frozen fish. The simplest test for texture should provide an index of condition by relative density and characteristics of individual seafood solids.

Seasonal Variations.—Concentrate some attention on appreciation of seasonal variations of specific species of fish. There are several books limited to just this phase of the subject. There seem to be more of Teutonic origin than any other, with Britain a close second. American authors lean toward *fishing* as a sport, and their treatment of fish as food is incidental. The fisherman may not care for fish as food. Many trout fishermen know practically nothing about trout eating. Conversely it is probable that the majority of trout epicures never fished for trout and know practically nothing about the fine points of fishing.

Fish Parts.—Parallels between the flavor characters of different parts of fish may be drawn on the basis of comparison with parts of warm blooded animals. First it will be observed that there is less difference in flavor *per se* between different parts of a fish than between different parts of beef, but greater differences in the kinesthetic factors of the different fish parts. The intrinsic flavor of cod tongues, cod bellies, and cod meat will be judged fairly close together, more or less similar, but the textures are radically different; whereas the flavor of beef tongue is much higher on the flavor scale than the muscle meat of beef from the same animal, and the differences in the texture scale are substantial.

One of the startling observations of international food behavior is that sections of fish and other seafood are more frequently preserved by salting, smoking, marinating, in both domestic and commercial packing, abroad than are animal meats. The reason is obvious: man has used aquatic foods and developed discriminatory tastes for them and what he considers the tidbits or specialties much longer and on a much broader scale than he has done with the warm-blooded animal meats.

Comparison of domestic and foreign usages and practices of preservation of the different kinds of fish "in the round"—dehydration, salt and smoke curing, marinating—is a rewarding field of exploration for the individual self-educator.

Preservational Practices Applied to Selected Parts.—Fillets, roe, livers, milt, tongues, and bellies of some fish, particularly cod and salmon, are used for preserving, as are cod and salmon collars.

Fins of some species of shark, dehydrated, are used almost exclusively for soup in the Orient. The gelatinous threads of "shark fins" are practically tasteless but are prized for the kinesthetic character.

Dehydrated squid, cuttlefish, and octopus, commonly used in the Orient, are relished for both flavor and texture.

What may be the outstanding tidbits of every fish, and it is generally overlooked, are the two cheek muscles, which are frequently too small to justify probing for them, but in the larger fish, particularly cod and salmon, amount to fair-sized chunks, each weighing an ounce or more.

The larger fish heads are frequently specially prepared and served abroad, usually cut with the collar intact. Salmon is particularly relished for practically all soft parts of the head, with the cheek usually going to the head of the house.

In appraising the flavor characters of the different sections of a fish, while there will be little difference in flavor *per se* between the back and the underside meats, the difference in texture is substantial in all fish. There is almost as much difference between the strip of meat near the fin and that on the underside as there is between the breast of chicken and the thigh. There is more difference in flavor between some of the parts of a fish having both light and dark meat, like some of the mackerel family.

The Japanese are just as selective in the use of different parts of a fish as we are in the different parts of beef. They will pay double the price for some sections of tuna, which they usually eat raw (*sashimi*) but dipped in a specific sauce, just as we will pay more for a fillet of beef.

Both the Japanese and the Chinese are very exacting about the specific section of practically all kinds and varieties of fish.

There is an easily recognizable difference between the upper and lower fillets of all the flatfish. Many fish, like carp, that are high in "boniness" have tissue meats of fewer bones in the back section, compared with more below the middle line.

Flavor Ratings in General.—The majority of the low-fat fish are rated below 50. The majority of fresh-water fish are also rated below 50.

Fish sticks, which are usually marketed frozen and ready to use, may be rather high because of inclusions of fat and salt. The present United States standards provide that "frozen fried fish sticks shall contain not less than 60 per cent by weight, of fresh meat." Obviously if 40 per cent of a fish stick is not fish, it is something else. What is it? And what does this "something else" taste like? The additives (which are usually bread crumbs and fat), the process by which the fish stick has been modified, and the length and type of storage, bring about a conversion not only from the original physical form but from the organoleptic factors of the original. The original texture of the fish has been altered to the point of radical change. The additives have affected just about everything involved in flavor.

Salient Influences on Flavor of Fish

(1) The flavor of "fresh" (unpreserved) fish is best if used *immediately* after catching.

(2) If not to be used immediately (within one or two hours) the fish should be *immediately* eviscerated.

(3) Storage of fish adversely affects flavor, according to (a) conditions of storage, primarily temperature, (b) surrounding influences, and (c) time.

(4) Chemical decomposition of intestinal contents will generate a gas which permeates the body meat far more rapidly than is generally realized. In some cases it can be organoleptically perceived within one hour.

Commercially, fish are not usually eviscerated and cleaned immediately after catching because of (1) local custom, (2) labor costs, (3) appearance (a fish *looks* better before evisceration, beheading, etc.), or (4) ignorance of the fact that gas generation from decomposing viscera will spoil flavor. It is such commercial practices which cause the use of heavy sauces found in most commercially cooked fish. A mask may sometimes be necessary to cover the strong flavors of decomposition.

Preparation of Fish for Market or at Market.—Definitions:

In the round—the whole fish, eviscerated or uneviscerated.

Half-round—the fish is split, the backbone remaining in one half, the other half without the backbone.

Eviscerated—only the viscera are removed.

Dressed—eviscerated, beheaded and fins, tail, and scales removed.

There are two kinds of *fillets*: with or without the skin. Example: Finnan haddie is generally marketed in three ways: in halves (but trimmed), half-round with fillets left on the skin, and skinned fillets.

Foods Listed on Aquatic Chart

Everyone knows that crab and lobster, clam and oyster are edible, but the majority ignore most of the monovalves (the one exception seems to be abalone) including conches, whelks and other sea snails, particularly the small ones. Beach and rock-combers seem unaware of some real delicacies in shellfish they ignore as the tide recedes. Some of the new books on ichthyology, particularly paperbacks, cover most of the creatures commonly found below high tide. If there is any criticism of those books, it is that little or nothing is said about the edible qualities of such shore life. The aim here is to point out some of those qualities.

A separate chart for the *Aquatic Foods* is provided as Fig. 33 (in Appendix I) first to show many more kinds of aquatic foods than could be listed in Column 1 of the *Gustametric Chart;* second, to provide classification. It will emphasize that these foods are *aquatic,* not terrestrial. This is formulawise important because pre-preparation and cookery techniques applicable to seafood and game—usually involving seasoning and supplements—apply to all the foods on this chart. For example, wild duck, an aquatic food, should be processed with consideration of its possible fishiness, beside using procedures applicable to game.

Fish in the Aquatic Foods Chart

There are thousands of different kinds of fresh-water, brackish-water, and salt-water fish, so those listed are representatives of many sub-classifications. Emphasis is on those fairly well known in the United States.

Crayfish (12)

Crayfish is the common name of a fresh water crustacean, *Astacus fluviatilis,* which resembles a small lobster. It should not be confused with crawfish, also known as spiny lobster, which is a different genus (*Palinurus*) and is rated at 78 flavor units.

Simply steamed, they will probably be considered uninteresting; hence they are usually prepared with a rather high-salt marination, or served with savory dips. They are interesting for the kinesthetic experience of picking the meat from the shell.

Crayfish on the Atlantic Coast is *Cambarus.* On the Pacific slope and in Europe: *Astacus.*

Crawfish is *Cambarus pellucidus* (the blind crawfish of Mammoth caves).

"Dublin Bay prawns" are crayfish in Scotland, and called "scampi" in some of the Mediterranean countries.

Fillets (Frozen) (10–40, av. 20)

This refers to commercial packs where the fish are processed by washing, brining, and packing. If steamed just as packed, such fillets will have a low flavor rating. It is by subsequent seasoning and the different methods of cookery, wet or dry, that such frozen fillets can flavor rate higher.

Trout (10–50, av. 25)

The real rainbow trout (*Salmo shasta*) of the fish culturists is also called *Salmo irideus* by Kingsley, who says it is nearest to the European *Salmo fario,* and that *Salvelinus fontinalis* or American brook trout is of the same genus (*Salvelinus*) as that known in England as *charr.*

There are more than a score of trout of the genus *Salmo,* all closely related and difficult to distinguish. For example the so-called "rainbow" of our western coastal streams are simply young steelhead trout (*S. gairneri*). Such trout, the salmon-meated kinds, are flavor rated with salmon, the flavor norm (FN) of which is 68. For convenience, ichthyologists regard the trout of western America as falling into three more or less distinct groups or series: the cutthroat series, the rainbow series, and the steelhead series.

Simply steamed, trout flavor rates surprisingly low, which is an observation that applies to most of the fresh water fish, and particularly in their off-seasons when they are insipid and flabby. Much of the interest in trout is related to romantic backgrounds associated with conditions and places where they are caught and who we catch them with; and of course, campfire cookery under which conditions we tend to relish anything. Let us be fair and concede that what is in the pan beside the trout—the bacon and the bacon gravy and the biscuits that go with it, and a beat-up coffee pot—are considerations. But a surprisingly large number of trout fishermen never eat any part of their catch.

Lake Trout (29) (*Cristovomer namaycush*)

Lake Perch (30) (Genus *Perca*)

In England and Europe: *Perca fluviatilis,* in America *P. americana* or *P. flavescens* is the common yellow perch of North America.

Lake Bass (33)

There are many varieties of fresh water bass living in lake, pond, and river. Small and medium size fish taken from cold and running water in the cold seasons of the year are generally the best. The niceties of difference in flavor between small-mouth and large-mouth bass are certainly debatable, but when similarly cooked it is questionable whether they can be distinguished in a blindfold test.

Bass, Striped (35)

Striped bass (*Roccus saxatilis*) taken from ocean waters at their seasonal best rate at 33 or a little higher. But taken in harbor and some inland waters they, with other fish caught in those waters, are particularly susceptible to picking up off-flavors such as from petroleum by-products.

Pike (37) (*Esox lucius*); ***Pickerel*** (37) (*E. reticulatus, E. americanus, E, vermiculatus*)

Some of the related fresh water fish are also in this range.

Pikes and small pikes, called pickerels, belong to the family *Esocidae*.

Haddock (38) (*Melanogrammus aeglefinus*)

See Cod, FN 39.

Cod (25–35, av. 39) (*Gadus morhua*)

The codlings possibly flavor rate the lowest in this group; then the tomcods, then the haddocks, and above them the pollacks and blue and green cods.

What is frequently marketed as "kippered cod" or "smoked Alaska cod" is not the Alaska codfish (*Gadus macrocephalus,* Tilesius) but the sablefish which is in the Anoplomidae—the skil-fishes (see Sablefish, FN 90).

The group of cod, haddock, and hake flavor rate close together whereas the ling cod of the Pacific Coast, the blue and green cods, flavor rate near 50. With the exception of those that are contiguous to the fish piers at which the fresh catches are delivered, very few people have the opportunity to get prime cod, which is of course, an observation applicable to all fish. But it is particularly emphasized in speaking of cod, because that is one of the most widely marketed fish, and to meet marketing requirements most of the fish are eviscerated at sea, packed in ice or otherwise frozen and subjected to time delays before reaching the consumer. That, combined with the retail marketing factors, results in the consumer usually getting fish the flavor of which is really far from the flavor norm.

Another relation, the cusk (*Brosme brosme*) is a valuable food fish allied to the cod, found on the coasts of Northern Europe and America, which is readily filleted.

Sea Bass (30–50, av. 41) (*Centopristes striatus*) (*Family Serannidae*)

This may also be the name of the *Cynoscion nobilis* (Tressler and Lemon 1951).

There are about 75 genera and over 400 species of bass, most of them marine, but there are several fresh water genera. There are 29 genera and about 100 species in United States waters. Vernacular names are striped sea bass, white lake bass, rockfish, white perch, yellow bass, jewfishes, and groupers, and many colloquial names.

Whitefish (20–60, av. 43)

Whitefish (*Coregonus artedi*) are members of the *Salmonidae* family. They are possibly more widely distributed than the different kinds of trout; in rivers and streams, but more commonly known as a lake fish. It ranges in physical characteristics from quite small to examples weighing over 20 lbs. Average may be between $^3/_4$ and $1^1/_2$ lbs.

Here note that many of the lake herrings are ciscoes (*Leucichthys dyboski*) sometimes called "whitefish." An example of the confusion of ichthyological nomenclature is a "bloater whitefish," which is also known as "bloat," "longjaw," "silver whitefish," and sometimes "cisco" or "ciscoette" around Lakes Ontario and Michigan. This may serve as an example of the need for standards of identity; for one of the most confusing—bewildering to the point of frustration—aspects of intra- as well as international food studies is this factor of one food being known by many, many different names in the same country, added to the confusion of the foreign language difficulties, where the same situation exists in practically every foreign land. This kind of nomenclature constitutes the substance of the Food Tower of Babel.

Silverside Family (44) (*Atherinidae*) (*Osmerus eperlanus*) (*Atherinopsis*)

Common names: smelt, jack smelt, horse smelt, top smelt, grunion.

The smelts are among the best small fish but perhaps more than any single group of fish they are particularly susceptible to parasitic worms. They should be carefully inspected before cooking.

Oyster (15–125, av. 45)

The lowest ratings are for oysters gathered in brackish water during warm periods, under unfavorable conditions; the highest ratings for those possessing a "chemical" taste, which is a character of many of the European oysters, particularly the greenish ones, most of which are judged unpalatable by Americans, who are accustomed to our much superior oysters. The author has yet to sample any European oysters that he would rate higher than 50 on the qualitative scale.

Oysters, clams and most of the mollusks, if eaten "on the half-shell" immediately after opening, have a characteristic appearance and texture. Visual factor is one, texture is second, flavor characters third. It must be realized that the oyster or clam immediately after opening is *still alive* and when you eat it on the half-shell, you're eating a living animal. If you look very closely at the liquid in the shell, it is pearly in appearance rather than muddy; there are small particles, some of which appear to move but if the oyster has been removed from the shell and washed before replacing in the half shell, the liquid will be water clear. The live oyster is plump and resilient as against a dead oyster being flat and flaccid. As with clams, the flesh of the muscle parts is characteristically solid and life-like when served quickly after opening, which is true of practically all fish, in that the flesh has a characteristic firmness which it rapidly loses with the passing of time.

Broadly considered, there are three kinds of American oysters: the principal one, which varies in form and size (and there are varietal differences), is the one which is common to the Gulf and Atlantic Coast states (*Ostrea virginica*). As marketed they vary in size from around three inches to more than twelve inches in length, from rather narrow to broad, shallow to deep, and lean to "fat." Oyster fanciers discriminate between points of origin as well as size.

The principal flavor difference between prime oysters is in what is described as "saltiness." Most discriminating users reserve the large oysters for cookery and the smaller oysters of good appearance for raw service and some in-the-shell cookery.

The second kind of oyster is the so-called Pacific or Japanese oyster (*Ostrea gigas*). Since only the very small indigenous oysters propagate in our Pacific waters, the Japanese spawn is cultivated to maturity primarily in the Pacific Northwest. The result is generally considered inferior as oysters go, particularly in the softness or flabbiness of the flesh, which seems to be a characteristic regardless of their size, which ranges in the shell from three inches to longer than dinner plates. It is usually considered suitable only for cookery, which is an example of man's sensitivity to extremely small differences in food textures; the acceptance with enthusiasm of "eastern oysters" and a highly qualified tolerance of western oysters.

The third class of oysters is the very small species (*Ostrea lurida*) which is found distributed along our Pacific Coast, but which seems to be commercially raised in only one area, contiguous to Olympia, Washington. Freshly gathered, shucked and immediately used under the right conditions, and in the right ways, they may rate a grudging 15 points. To those who know oysters, they are judged insipid and low in flavor characters.

TABLE 1

COMMERCIAL EDIBLE OYSTERS

Ostrea virginica Gmelin	American oyster of the Atlantic Coast
O. edulis, Linn	European edible oyster.
O. (gryphaea) angulata Lamarck	Portuguese oyster introduced into France
O. commercialis Iredale and Roughley	
O. angasi Sowerby	from Australia
O. denselamellosa Lischke and *O. gigas* Thunberg	from Japan (introduced to Pacific Coast of the United States)
O. cucullata Born	in India
O. chilensis Philippi	found on the coast of Central and South America
O. lurida Carpenter	so-called Olympia oyster of the Pacific Coast of the United States and Canada
O. taurica Krynicki	cultivated in the Black Sea, Russia
O. (gryphaea) rhizophorae Gmelin	from West Indies

Squid (47)

The Latin name of the common squid (*Loligo opalescens*, Barry) is given.

It belongs to the devilfish family; and is a favorite among Oriental peoples. Squid is sold fresh in most of the important fish markets of California, Oregon, and Washington, and in some Atlantic Coast markets. It is one of the best seafoods.

Octopus (49)

There is a small trade in octopus on the Pacific Coast. The most abundant species is *Polypus hongkongensis;* small individuals of this mollusk are found in shoal waters and much larger ones in deep water. Some are caught in Puget Sound and along the California Coast, but sold chiefly to Orientals.

Mullet (30–70, av. 50)

This family (*Mugilidae*) contains about ten genera and 100 species. The mullets are far more appreciated abroad, particularly in the Orient. Because of its combination of physical as well as flavor characters, it may be the favorite of Chinese epicures. It has long been pond-propagated in the Orient. Too, it was probably more frequently propagated in ancient Roman aquaria than any other fish. Some of the most fascinating chapters of Roman gastronomia have details of appreciation and elaborate usage of the many different mullets they used. In particular they rhapsodized about the red mullets.

Tortoise (50); **Green Turtle** (30–80, av. 50) (*Chelonia mydes*)

The only true marine "turtle" that is commonly eaten. Small ones (under 100 lbs.) "cows" with yellow or immature eggs are marketed at higher prices than those of greater weight with the white or mature eggs; the bulls are degraded. The meat of the flippers and legs is pink to reddish, but the tissues next to most of the inner shells is muddy to muddy-gray-green, which when cooked yields the light seaweed green characteristic of "green turtle soup." The term "green turtle" is something of a misnomer, since the shell is distinctly brownish and only the flippers have a greenish cast. The green color of "green turtle soup" can be naturally produced only if the scaly shell of the flippers is cooked long enough to leach its color. Some of the belly fat and tissue that in life is light olive becomes grayish, not green, in cookery. The gelatinous components are derived from cookery of the flipper hide and the matter surrounding the bony structure of both the flippers and some of the internal connective tissue.

Tortoise steaks and scallops (or *scaloppini*) of green turtle meat in the raw state resemble rather darkish veal, and when cooked can taste like veal with just a faint overtone of something marine about it. On a blindfold trial it is almost impossible to distinguish between turtle and veal. The average person, unless forewarned, could be served green turtle *scaloppini* in place of veal and wouldn't know the difference.

Snapper (53)

The snapper group (*Lutianidae,* Simon) is one of the best of ocean fish in form, texture, and flavor. The smaller ones resemble rock cod but are finer in texture and usually more delicate in flavor.

Carp (30–55, av. 50)

Of the sucker family (*Catostomidae*) the carp is a member of the genus *Carpiodes.* The buffalo fishes, among which are some of the largest and coarsest of this family, reaching a length of three feet and weight of around 50 lbs., is the genus *Ictiobus.* The carp-suckers are the genus *Carpiodes rafinesque.*

The common carp is *Cyprinus carpio.*

A smaller species is *Carpiodes carassius,* a subspecies of which is *C. carassius auratus,* the goldfish of the Orient.

The carp family may be the largest single exception to the generality that all fish are carnivorous or cannibalistic: the carp are mostly vegetarians. They prefer a diet of aquatic plants. They are one of the few fish that will go for a chunk of boiled potato as bait.

Their muddy habitat and diet, most noticeable when taken from warm water, account for the inherent muddy flavor of carp, which in turn accounts for the high FN: 55. Extreme examples may flavor rate at 80 or more. This muddiness can be minimized by skinning and filleting. Most of that muddy flavor is residual in the skin and the fat and in the gel alongside the bones. Soaking for three or four hours in a dense brine will largely remove the muddiness.

European epicures relish the carp roe far more than the body meat. It is an odd fact that Orientals rate the carp—even some of the carp-suckers—second only to mullet, perhaps because it is easily pond-bred, domesticated, and kept alive for long periods, and thus amenable to their preference for *live-fresh* fish; contrariwise the Chinese cure and preserve carp in more ways than any other fish. It is the fish they most frequently use as a compressed, more or less dehydrated, salt snack as an accompaniment with other foods, particularly vegetable dishes.

Halibut (25–65, av. 55)

Note that halibut (*Hippoglossus hippoglossus*) is, together with other fish, indented in Column 1, which arrangement is intended to differentiate the fat from the lean fish. All fish have some fat, but for practical purposes lean fish are generally thought of as containing six per cent or less of fat. The indented classification, starting with halibut, lists aquatic foods with more than six per cent fat, which distinction is made not alone for nutritional reasons but in this book to remind the user that foods high in fat should be cooked or otherwise processed with that factor specifically in mind. Thus high fat fishes, like some of the flatfish and the herring and mackerel family, can be dry-cooked, particularly baked or broiled, without supplementary fat. Such fish can be fried (without supplemental fat) in some of our heavy aluminum pans with a tight-fitting lid; best at low temperatures and necessarily longer times.

The lowest flavor rating for halibut, as well as the other flatfish would be for commercially processed steaks. Halibut steaks, like the cross-cuts of other large fish, are subject to very sharp flavor modifications, mostly downward, in the scale of desirability, hinging on conditions of storage and sale and age. The desirability factors go down while the taste and smell factors go up, but not in goodness.

Flounder (45–75, av. 60)

This large family (*Pleuronectidae*) with around 55 genera and nearly 500 species is locally known by many names. It is a common food fish of all American coasts. Some species are strictly shore fishes, while others occupy water of moderate depths. The Pacific halibut like the Atlantic, with which it is considered identical, is one of those that dwell in rather deep water. The Starry Flounder (*Platichthys stellatus*) may be cited as a common shallow water shore form, ranging from Japan to Alaska and southward to Santa Barbara County, California.

The diminutive sand dab is probably the most delicately flavored flounder—around FN 40. Higher in the scale are the small halibuts, then the common halibuts, and above them the smaller, fatter, gross-feeding flounders and soles. Those varieties which are gross scavengers when taken from harbor waters may have flavor characters which are distinctly offensive.

Sole (62) (Family *Soleidae*)

This fish may have more different local appellations than any other. The sole of America is very different from that of England. The term *Dover Sole* was originally applied to a specific variety caught off Dover, England. Now it seems that every small flatfish, however remotely resembling sole, is marketed not only in England but in some sections of Europe as "Dover Sole." The offer of "Dover Sole" by the majority of regional restaurants, especially Continental, may be recognized as the outstanding example of a restaurant food fraud; commercial chicanery that can only be intentional deception directed toward naive and trusting tourists.

The member of the Righteyed Flounder family, *Pleuronectidae*, officially called Dover Sole, *Microstomus pacificus* (Lockington), is morphologically close to the Dover Sole of England but physiologically different, particularly in one factor. The Pacific Coast Dover Sole is characterized by a mucous exudation over the entire body of the fish (which is absent in English Dover Sole) which is responsible for its colloquial names of slippery or slime sole, despite which it is one of our best soles; but on a comparative basis it is inferior to its English relation.

Pompano (64)

Pompano (*Trachinatus corolinus,* Simon) is one of the best of fishes. Usually firmer than the true sole, and incidentally higher in fat, it keeps its form better in cookery. In areas where they are available fresh, they seem to be favored over all other fish.

Shad (40–80, av. 65)

Shad (*Alosa sapodissima*) is a member of the herring family (*Clupeidae*). The rating of 65 is based on the whole fish, with roe. The roe of shad, next to that of sturgeon, is an example of man's appreciation of the kinesthetic factors in his food. In our own fish markets, and particularly along foreign strands, the roe of many fishes bring the highest prices of all seafood. This is another prime example of taste and smell characters being secondary to other considerations of organoleptic preception. A liquid, experimentally produced from fish roe that has been cooked and cloth-strained, would be judged unattractive. The other factors of appreciation, particularly the crunch, are what we seek out and what we are willing to pay a premium for.

Salmon (68)

There are five varieties of true salmon:

(1) **Red Salmon,** *Oncorhyncus nerka* (Walbaum)—According to government standards Alaska Sockeye, called blueback in the Columbia River area, is the only salmon that can be labeled "red salmon."

(2) **Pink Salmon,** *O. gorbuscha* (Walbaum)—This fish is also called humpback salmon.

(3) **Silver Salmon,** *O. kisutch* (Walbaum)—It is also called Coho. This is a red meat salmon that is lower in fat than the Alaska sockeye.

(4) **Chinook,** *O. tshawytscha* (Walbaum)—It is also called king and spring salmon; flesh orange to white. When white meated it is sometimes called white king salmon.

(5) **Chum,** *O. keta*—It is also called the dog salmon. Light pink meat.

Turtle (40–100, av. 70)

See *Tortoise,* FN 50 for Green Turtle.

Narrowly defined, the word "turtle" is applied to land, fresh-water and marine reptiles of the sub-class *Chelonia.* In this book "turtle" means those that are most often taken on land, and "tortoise" those taken from water. "Terrapin" is included in the category of "turtle."

Terrapin meat, in the author's opinion, may be one of the most over-rated foods. It and other land turtles are dull in color and muddy in flavor. Unless very skillfully cooked the meat alone, just steamed, would probably be unacceptable to most people. Commercially it is never offered other than highly seasoned, virtually a flavor-masked dish. It is usually seasoned, and probably just as often green-dyed, to meet public ideas of what the delicacy should be. In other words, by itself considered, no epicure would judge it a delicacy. It may be likened to the popular clamor for *escargots,* land snails that nobody will eat plain.

The meat of some varieties of land turtles, and particularly young ones, the habitat of which is running fresh water, not brackish or salt, may flavor rate as low as 40. But the flavor rating of those land turtles whose habitat is adjacent to brackish or salt water may flavor rate well over 100.

Hawksbill Turtle (*Chelonia imbricata*).—One of the smallest of the marine tortoises; seldom longer than 30 inches. This reptile is the chief source of "tortoise shell." The flesh is not so highly regarded as that of the "green" turtle; tropical and semi-tropical.

Loggerhead Turtle (*Thalassochelys caretta*).—The most common marine tortoise of the Atlantic Coast south of New York. The eggs are commonly eaten but the meat is not highly rated.

Kemp's Gulf Turtle (*Thelassochelys colpochelys kempii*).—These are found along the southern Atlantic Coast and the Gulf of Mexico. The meat is superior to Loggerhead, but not as good as "green" turtle.

Luth or Leathery Turtle.—These are found along the coast of Florida and western South America; the meat is not highly regarded.

Diamondback Terrapin (Genus *Malaclemys*).—This is highly rated for its soup or stew values; usually taken from salt or brackish coastal marshes.

Snapping Turtles, Common Snapper (*Chelydra serpentina*) **and Hardshell or Alligator** (*Macrochelys lacertina*).—While terrapins have been popularized possibly because of their smaller size—they rarely exceed six inches—the two kinds of snapping turtles which grow up to 40 lbs. have food characters superior to those of the terrapins. It is something of a mystery why the terrapins are so much more popular than the snappers.

Soft-Shell Clam (70) (Family *Myacidae, Mya arenaria,* Linnaeus)

These are also called long clams.

The flavor rating is based on the brittle-shelled clam that is widely distributed in sandy and muddy shores. Other more or less soft shell clams are: Razor clam (Family *Solenidae, Siliqua patula*); the California jackknife clam (*Tagelus californianus,* Conrad 1837) is sometimes confused with the razor clam.

There are two varieties of large, relatively soft-shelled clams: Geoduck (*Panope generosa,* Gould), commonly called "gooey duck," it is frequently confused with the horse clam or Gaper (*Schizothaerus nuttallii,* Conrad 1837).

There are a fairly large number of rock-boring fragile-shelled clams, all of which are edible and most of them quite good but it takes mining tools to get most of them (Fitch 1953).

Winkles (45–90, av. 70)

See Sea Snails, FN 110.

Eel (73) (*Cyclostomi*)

This is one of the aquatic foods used and appreciated abroad far more than here. It may be the most neglected of our aquatic foods. Common ignorance is attributable to prejudice, because of snake form and because of some difficulty in pre-preparation, primarily beheading and skinning them, which is a little on the difficult side and calls for care and skill. In many of our inland waterways eels are so plentiful as to constitute a nuisance.

The two best known varieties of fresh water eels are the common eel (*Anguilla vulgaris*) and the lampreys (a genus called either *Petromyzon* or

Lampetra from their rock-clinging habits). There are some five or six genera and about 20 species, including the river lamprey (*Lampetra fulviatilis*). Among the best known marine eels are the conger (*Conger vulgaris*); the morays (*Muroena helena*); and the great sea lamprey (*Petromyzon marinus*).

The lamprey is the most despised variety in America because of his suction mouth and pugnacious habits when caught, but it may be one of the best sea foods. It is certainly one of the most sought-after in Europe and many other parts of the world. A puzzling facet of our food behavior is that we accept and pay fancy prices for eels in jelly and smoked eels, most of which are canned and processed abroad, while we disdain our native supply.

Eel cookery lends itself to more variations than the majority of other aquatic foods, mainly because the flesh remains firm under conditions where most other seafood falls apart.

Another strange angle to the eels picture is the fact that the sea eels, congers, some of the morays, and a large number of other species, when taken by coastal fishermen, are prized with or above the majority of other rock fish. They are rarely wasted. Try analyzing that kind of prejudice, where the sea eel is prized and the fresh water eel is disdained. Such are the vagaries of prejudice.

Hard Shell Clam (75)

The most generally marketed hard shell clam (Family *Veneridae*) of the Atlantic Coast is *Venus mercenaria* (Linnaeus 1758). Vernacular terms are: quahog, applied to large specimens; cherrystone clams, applied to medium-size specimens; and littleneck clams; applied to small specimens.

However, there are three other clams of the *Venus* family, called littleneck clams: common littleneck (*Protothaca staminea,* Conrad); rough-sided littleneck (*P. laciniata,* Carpenter); thin-shelled littleneck (*P. tenerrima,* Carpenter).

Colloquially some of the small clams of the *Venus* family are called cockles; officially, however, the term cockles is applied to members of the family *Cardiidae:* spiny cockle (*Trachycardium quadragenarium,* Conrad); smooth giant cockle (*Laevicardium elatum,* Sowerby); basket cockle (*Clinocardium nuttalli,* Conrad).

Some of the large varieties of the *Venus* clams are: Pismo clam (*Tivela stultorum,* Mawe); common Washington clam (*Saxidomus nuttalli,* Conrad); smooth Washington clam (*S. giganteus,* Deshayes). Both Washington clams are also called butter clams.

With the exception of scallops, of the family *Pectinidae,* most of the other clams are more or less soft shell clams (Fitch 1953).

Catfish (50–100, av. 75)

The catfish family (*Celuridae*) has more than 100 genera and perhaps 1000 species, mostly fresh water fishes and only a few are marine; possibly the fish of widest distribution in American waters from the river, stream, and channel catfish of the genus *Ictalurus rafinesque* to the many bullheads of the genus *Amieurus refinesque;* one of the few pink-meated fishes.

Like eels, they are almost invariably beheaded and skinned, in pre-preparation, because of the objectionable flavor and texture characteristics of those parts. Whole cooked, they would be slimy, not just gelatinous. Catfish fillets as well as chunks and steaks lend themselves to more variation in processing than most other fish. Consider their adaptability in cookery and in seasoning profiles with animal meats of the quadrupeds as well as poultry; one can do almost anything with them.

The common marine catfish is the "gafftopsail catfish" (*Felichthys felis*); another is *Ameriurus catus*.

Lobster (78)

The American lobsters (*Homarus americanus*), also known as Northern lobster, are found along the North American Coast from North Carolina to Labrador; and reach their largest size in Maine. They are macrurous crustaceans of the genus *Homarus*.

Sea crawfish, also known as spiny lobster, rock lobster, and southern lobster, is of the genus *Palinurus*. Other authorities name it *Panulirus interruptus*.

The true European lobster is *Homarus gammarus*. The langouste is *Palinurus vulgaris* (France and Spain); also known as the "spiny lobster," "thorny lobster" and "red crab."

The inherent qualities of lobsters vary with kind, variety, and sex, with point of origin and seasonal differences; then the specific condition of the individual specimen usually relative to time elapsed between its capture and preparation, and then the method of cooking.

This is one instance where the female is more succulent than the male (which is not always the case); but it is emphasized that the female is to be preferred only when it is in prime condition.

An important cookery note is that "cooked live" lobster meat is moist and almost elastic whereas the meat of a lobster that has been cooked after it is dead is flabby and soft.

There is probably more romantic writing and talking about the merits of lobsters steamed in seaweed or cauldron cooked than about any other seashore food experience. But the fact is that for fair appraisal lobsters should be steamed without extraneous seasoning or diluting influences. That doesn't mean we can't enjoy broiled or baked or fried lobsters, nor does it stop us from participation in a shore seawood-blanketed lobster- and clam-bake. They can be among our most delightful experiences, the stuff of which our fondest food memories are made; but they do not provide fair methods of technical lobster appraisal.

Shrimp (78) (*Penaeus setiberus*); **Prawn** (78) (*Leander serratus*)

San Francisco Bay shrimp is *Crago franciscorum,* sometimes spelled *Cragnon* or *Crangon* (Ricketts and Calvin 1952).

Consider this group of crustaceans, the prawns, as congeneric with shrimps. In general, they are much larger. As marketed in the United States the whole prawns measure from 2 to 6 inches, but there are some tropical varieties up to 2 feet. They are much more generally used than shrimps. The principal difference, beside size, is that the flesh of prawns is coarser.

The lowest flavor ratings would be applied to this group taken from inland waters during off seasons, and particularly when eaten raw, one of the popular Western Pacific ways of having them, usually with a spice dip. To skeptics it can be said that this combination has points of merit over some of our raw oyster combinations.

"Out of a number of species of shrimp in the South Atlantic and Gulf States only five are of commercial importance. . . . These are: the common shrimp (*Penaeus setiberus*), the three grooved shrimp (*P. aztecus*), (*P. duoarum* and *P. brasiliensis*) and the 'sea-bob' or 'seven beards' (*Xiphopenaeus*)" (Tressler and Lemon 1951).

In England, shrimp is *Crangon vulgaris.* "Prawn" is a name given to the genera *Palaemon, Pandulus,* or *Hippolyte.*

Abalone (83)

Green abalone (*Haliotis fulgens*) (Ricketts and Calvin 1952); red abalone (*H. rufescens*); black abalone (*H. cracherodii*) (Tressler and Lemon 1951).

Abalones are also called "sea ear" and "ear shell"; they belong to a family of marine snails, the *Haliotidae,* of which six species and one variety have been found on the Pacific Coast, but none on the Atlantic Coast.

The abalone is cut from the shell, the visceral mass and mantle fringe trimmed from the large central muscle, which is then cut transversely into slices. As thin steaks they may be fried, stewed, or minced for chowder. The juice makes good bouillon.

Dried and Smoked.—Oriental peoples dry and sometimes smoke abalones. Finely sliced and sometimes ground to a meal, it is used as a soup seasoning, which accords with some of their flavor preferences, but in general the flavor of dried or smoked abalone is not to western liking. Most persons would think it has a strong fishy flavor. The same comment applies to dried and otherwise cured sea-slugs and snails (*bêche de mer*).

Scallop (83) (Lamellibranchia)

A mollusk belonging to the Lamellibranchia. The family of *Pectenidae* includes about 40 species, four of which are found on the Atlantic Coast. Of these only two are of commercial importance. The common shallow-water scallop, found from Massachusetts to the Gulf of Mexico, is the most important commercial species. The scallop is ordinarily designated as *Pecten gibbus,* var. *borealis* (Say) although it is also called *Pecten irradians.* In England it is called "fan shells," "frills," "queens," and "squims." The giant deepwater scallop, found from New Jersey to Labrador, is *Placopecten grandis* (Solander).

Scallops are higher in protein than any of the other common edible shellfish. However, it must be remembered that only the adductor muscle of the scallop is eaten, whereas practically all the flesh of other shellfish is eaten.

"Less than 10 per cent of the whole scallop is eaten"; the remainder is used for fish bait, shells used in roadbuilding, etc. (Tressler and Lemon 1951).

Swordfish (85)

One of the fish with the densest meat, which accounts for its favor in the form of steak cookery. Swordfish can stand more abuse in cookery than any other fish; it seems to retain its character even when over-cooked.

Goose Barnacle (88)

Barnacles are listed because one of that family, the goose barnacle (*Mitella polymerus*) is not only edible, it is good. Common along most American shores, it is almost totally ignored!

Goose barnacles steamed like soft-shell clams closely resemble them in flavor. The only part eaten, the neck, can be likened to a clam neck, but is usually more delicate in texture and flavor.

Acorn Barnacles

No separate rating is given, because acorn barnacles (*Balanus glandulus*) are used almost entirely for flavoring broths. The edible part is very small.

Herring (88) (*Clupea harengus*)

The family *Clupeidae* embraces about 30 genera and 150 species. Most of them are salt-water; some species are anadromous, ascending fresh water streams to spawn. Some are fresh water species. In American waters there are 16 genera and about 38 species, of which the most common are the true herring and alewives of the Atlantic Coast, the pilchards of the Pacific Coast, the California sardine, the Spanish sardine (which ranges from Florida to Maine) American shad, and menhaden.

Anchovy (40–100, av. 88)

Family *Engraulidae* contains about 90 genera and 80 species. Closely related to the herrings, the "little anchovy" (*Anchovia mitchilli*) frequently called "whitebait" reaches a length of only two and one-half inches, whereas the "silvery anchovy" and the "striped anchovy' reach lengths of six inches, the California anchovy about seven inches.

Clam, Giant Sea (90) (*Tridacna gigas*)

Small specimens up to perhaps eight inches eaten raw, usually diced, would flavor rate alongside the largest quahogs and Pismo clams; the larger ones, chowdered, compare in flavor with conches.

There are several varieties of "giant clams" of the Indian and Pacific oceans, varying in size from baby specimens of 6 or 7 inches that weigh a pound or two, to huge ones between 20 and 30 inches in length and weighing 300 or 400 pounds. The principal differences are in the conformation of the shells which vary in ribbing and waving.

Sablefish (90) (*Anoploma fimbria*)

The true blackfish (black in color as well as name) which is a sub-variety of *Anoploma,* the skilfishes: commonly with the vernacular names of be-show, coal-fish, or skil, which lends itself to smoking processes because of its high fat content. In our classification its FN is 90! The true cods are bland and low-fat fish, which are flavor rated as low as 25!

The source of most sablefish marketed in the United States is Alaskan waters. It looks something like a small black ocean cod or hake. This is the fish that is most frequently marketed in the United States as "kippered cod," "smoked cod," "Alaskan smoked black cod," etc. The salmon color which tends to distinguish the smoked product in market presentation is *artificial,* produced by a dye-dipping process. The natural color of sablefish muscle meat is oyster-white, and it would not be possible to effect surface orange coloring by anything like ordinary smoking methods.

Sardine (90)

Sardines and anchovies, which are two different fish, have a number of characters in common. Both range from 3 or 4 to more than 15 inches in length, but sardines are rounder and firmer in texture, while anchovies tend to be longer, thinner, and with much finer flesh texture, to the point of softness. Sardines are commercially favored for canning, together with their close relations, the pilchards, whereas the anchovies are infrequently encountered as a canned, cooked product. Anchovies, on the other hand, are favored, particularly abroad, when oil- or salt-packed or marinated (see Herring, FN 89).

Limpet (30–130, av. 90) (*Acmaea digitalis*)

The small limpets would rate around 30; the large ones as high as 130, which ratings are based on their being steamed, not water-cooked. This is emphasized because the majority of limpet-gatherers prefer to eat them raw, out of the shell, in which state they would rate lighter than some of the more delicate clams in a raw condition.

There are many different varieties of limpets: volcano-shelled, ribbed (*A. scabra*), shield (*A. cassis*), and others.

Crab (50–150, av. 95)

There are far more varieties of crabs than there are of lobsters. Practically all of them are eaten by some peoples, from the tiny so-called "oyster crab" that seems to be a guest rather than a parasite of the oyster—and is relished by epicures—to the large king crabs. From the smaller shore crabs that vary from one to two inches in width, from soft-shell to hard-shell, from small-claw to large-claw and from delicately flavored to offensively seaweedy, rank flavored, they are all widely used.

Species of Greatest Economic Importance

Blue Crab (*Callinects sapidus*) is found along American Eastern shores and the Caribbean.

Dungeness (*Cancer magister*) is the common crab of the Pacific Coast.

Rock Crab (*Cancer irroratus*) is common to American eastern shores, and while abundant is not extensively commercially gathered.

Jonah Crab (*Cancer borealis*) of our northern shores, resembles the rock crab, but like the rock crab is relatively small in size, rarely exceeding six inches across the shell, and is not often commercially gathered.

Stone Crab (*Menippe mercenarius*) ranges from the Caribbean waters up our Atlantic shores, is larger than the blue crab but is relatively scarce, not often marketed.

SPECIES OF MINOR IMPORTANCE

Fiddler crab	(*Gelasimus pugnax, G. pugilator, G. minax*)
Green crab	(*Carcinus maenas*, Leach)
Hermit crab	(*Eupagurus bernhardus, E. pollicaris, E. longicarpus*)
Horseshoe crab	(*Limulus polyphemus*)
Kelp crab	(*Epialtus productus*)
Lady crab, sand crab, squeaker crab	(*Platyonichus ocellatus*, Latr.)
Mud crab	(*Panopeus herbstii*, Edwards)
Mussel crab	(*Pinnotheres maculatus*)
Oyster crab	(*Pinnotheres ostreum*)
Purple shore crab	(*Heterograpsus nudus*)
Red crab	(*Cancer productus*)
Sand bug	(*Hippatalpida*, Say)
Spider crab	(*Libinia emarginata*, Leach, *L. dubia*, Edwards)
Yellow shore crab	(*Heterograpsus oregonensis*)

It may be that the variations in the wide range of crab meat textures and crab flavors, and certainly the ways of using crabs may be realized only by a very few members of a hypothetical international society of beachcombers. Most of those wandering Americans who distinguish between "eastern blue" crabs and "western Dungeness," and occasionally are exposed to the different crabs of the Florida Keys, extol the virtues of two, three, or four varieties, usually prepared in just a few ways, but not until the food explorer is exposed to the homely preparation of local fishermen here and abroad does he begin to realize the epicurean possibilities inherent not only in the major crabs, but particularly in the non-commercial small crabs. Not until he goes abroad and mingles with the fisherfolk of the Occident and the Orient does it dawn upon him that there are more crabs and more ways of preparing crabs than most people have any idea of. Flitting by the case of some European tastes for raw crab "butter" fingered right out of the shell, to the serving of raw crab meat with an agreeable sauce by many Orientals, he encounters the common gathering of practically every kind of small crab by coastal peoples abroad, and their subsequent use in soups and chowders, or fried. The commonest usage of the small varieties involves only the center carapace. The center section is removed from the shell, stripped of the legs and claws; the body fluids, particularly the butter, as often as not are combined with the meaty section. The smallest varieties are eaten, membranous matter and all, or if too resistant, it is chewed and crunched and the shelly matter ejected, as we put a prune in the mouth and eject the pit. In most parts of the world youngsters and oldsters alike comb and sift the marshes in the spring for crabs of all kinds and varieties in their soft-shelled condition. This is one outdoor sport generally overlooked in America. With the exception of the kelp crabs and some of the ocean shore crabs that exist largely on a diet of kelp, all the small crabs rate from good to excellent. Some of the crabs which taste like seaweed are too strong for our acceptance. Note that the season and the locale are the major considerations of crab gathering and usage. In our American crab cookery we have one sin of omission: the common discarding of the crab butter. European cooks would shudder at this waste. The crab butter is a particularly good component of both hot and cold sauces. Its inclusion with "stuffed crab" dishes and crab salads is particularly good.

Tuna Family (95)

The class known as the tuna family (*Thunnidae*) includes the yellowfin tuna and bluefin tuna and the Pacific albacore.

The Skipjack family (*Katsuwonidae*) includes fishes closely related to the tuna family.

The meat of albacore is noted for its texture and flavor, and its color is somewhat like that of the white chicken meat. Because tuna has both dark and light meat and the fat component varies with specific sections of light or dark, it is amenable to many different ways of preparation. It is most generally known in its canned conditions. In the areas where it is marketed fresh, particularly abroad, it is used in more different ways than any other fish. It is favored in the Orient for dried and smoked products, in Japan for raw service (*sashimi*) where it is usually accompanied by a dip. The small tuna and subvarieties like yellowtail and skipjack lend themselves to cookery similar to that for mackerel weighing from 3 to 10 or 12 lbs.; foil enclosure and oven cookery are suggested (see Mackerel, FN 99).

Sturgeon (96)

Until recently it was most commonly encountered as a delicatessen item: "smoked sturgeon." In the last few years, fresh and frozen sturgeon steaks or chunk sections were available in markets. Fresh sturgeon is a favorite of discriminating cooks because it can provide steaks of such good flavor characters that they require little or no seasoning.

Mussels (30–150, av. 98)

The rating is based on mature sea mussels (*Mytilus californianus*). Surprising is the great variance of flavor rating between the small shoal mussels gathered in the spring that may rate as low as 30 to the very strong flavor of the large mussels gathered in the fall. The small mussels can be light in texture as well as flavor, as against the big ones being rubbery and just too strong in flavor. They vary in color from light salmon pink to a grayed orange. Another surprise is that mussel broth, from young, carefully selected mussels, is lighter in flavor than clam broth. It should be realized that most mussels have adherent guests, mostly small barnacles and limpets, and the steamed product, the mussel meat and the broth, results in a complex flavor of the mussel and its guests.

Mytilus edulis is the eastern mussel.

Mussels spoil quickly and therefore are ordinarily marketed alive in the shell from December to July. Most common preservation method is pickling. They are also available canned.

Warning: The paralytic poison of mussels which is attributed to a microscopic animal, the dinoflagellate *Gonyaulax* becomes very abundant in the ocean during the summer months and it is during these summer months that mussels feeding upon it become extremely toxic. The California State Department of Health follows the conditions of the bivalves carefully throughout the year and when they become dangerous, quarantine notices are posted in conspicuous places along the beaches of the State (Fitch 1953).

Mackerel (80–120, av. 99) (*Scomber scombrus*)

There are about 20 genera and more than 60 species ranging from the small common mackerel to the larger horse and Spanish mackerel. Vernacular names of the Pacific mackerel are blue, green, and striped mackerel.

The Pacific jack mackerel (*Trachurus symmetricus,* Ayres) is also called horse mackerel and Spanish mackerel.

A member of the Spanish mackerel family (Cybiidae) is the California bonito (*Sarda lineolata,* Girard) which closely resembles tuna.

Snails (Land) (30)

Snails, of which there are many varieties, both aquatic and terrestrial, are elementally aquatic animals. The different terrestrial snails may be the outstanding surviving examples of an aquatic animal having left its ancestral environment, becoming a seafood on land. Here a note of importance is that land snails are quite commonly accepted as food matter in Europe and elsewhere but disdained in the United States. The relished *escargots* of France are the garden pests of America; to be trodden under foot or poisoned! Here is a specific example of one man's meat being another man's poison—if we accept horticultural pests as "poison."

It is probable that the favored land snails of Europe are gathered from vineyards, possibly because a grape leaf diet (grape leaves are high in sugar) affects the flavor of the snails that feed on them. Americans with old-country backgrounds who gather garden and field snails in the United States usually feed the snails on ground corn or other cereals for a week or so before washing them in fresh or salted water and then cooking.

The intrinsic flavors of practically all land snails are low, other than their kinesthetic characters. If they were eaten after being simply steamed, they would probably be appraised as insipid. That this is generally acknowledged (by all who use snails) is evident by their preparation with or in quite high seasoning. The dominant flavors of *Escargots a la Bourgogne* are garlic, parsley, and salt butter. The implication is that most people wouldn't accept escargots if they aren't highly seasoned. In Italy and Spain the dominant seasoning usually includes tomatoes and, of course, garlic. Incidentally, along the Pacific and Indian Ocean shores of Asia there are large land snails weighing from a couple of ounces to a pound, that are everyday foods for some of those peoples.

Triton (110) (Sea Snails)

Periwinkles and whelks, commonly eaten in Europe, are varieties of the genus *Littorina.* There are many different varieties. *Littorina littorea,* L., are taken in large quantities in the British Isles.

The periwinkle is sometimes confused with the black turban snail (*Tegula funebralis*) which is the most common snail along Pacific tidal rocks in the western states of America.

The meats of some of the sea snails like those of the periwinkles, the turban snails, and the whelks, can usually be extracted by careful manipulation, without breaking the shell.

Whelks (Order *Pectinobranchia,* Suborder *Stenoglossa,* Tribe *Rachiglossa*)

These are commonly eaten in Europe. Atlantic species is *Buccinum undatum,* found from Cape Cod northward, and Alaska.

Different varieties of triton are among a large number of sea snails generally used. For purposes of classification and to emphasize their placement among the commonly known aquatic foods, several other comparable mollusks are scaled under Gastropods in the Aquatic Foods Chart. The land snails are terrestrial relations.

Winkle (70); **Whelk** (120); **Conch** (130).—The flavors of some of the small varieties of sea snails vary from mild to strong according to location and season. They are usually best when lightly steamed and lightly herb-seasoned.

Acceptance of any of the larger sea snails requires a taste for strong sea food.

Addendum to the subject of all snails and some of the larger gastropods: to obtain the raw body meat of any of the snails, small to large, without breaking the shell or cooking the animal in the shell, the snail is suspended for anything from a few hours to overnight (preferably in a cool place) by a hook through the foot. The animal gradually fatigues, and sooner or later the abdominal hold on the volute of the shell releases, leaving the body suspended free from the shell. The abdominal skirt can then be cleanly pared from the shell. Fish markets with walk-in freezers customarily do that, particularly with conches and whelks, for people who want the shell and don't want to go to the trouble of getting the snail out of its shell. A knowledge of this process is important if the cook wants to use only the muscle (just as he uses scallops and abalone) without getting what might be undesirable flavors from the stomach contents, which is just about necessary in the case of snails that may feed on seaweed. Naturally if such snails are cooked in the shell, the flavor can be quite rank.

Chiton (150) (Order *Polyplacophora*)

Chitons or sea cradles range in length from under one inch to seven or eight inches, or even longer.

Cryptochiton stelleri is the "gum boot," reaching a length of 13 inches. Chitons are used almost exclusively by Orientals with an acquired taste for extreme fishiness in soups.

Frog (32)

The common bullfrog (*Rana catesbeniana*) is the largest and most often used for food (Tressler and Lemon 1951).

In the natural habitat of frogs, ponds, streams, and swamps, their food consists of insects, small fish, and crayfish. Commercially they are pond raised and, as in trout ponds, they are fed with commercial mixes. Usually the back or jumping legs are the only part of the frog eaten. So far as is known, all common frogs, after skinning, careful evisceration and trimming, are edible. The meat of commercially raised frogs, as well as that of some of the running water frogs, is not perceptibly fishy. Properly prepared, it is practically indistinguishable from very young fryer chicken.

Aquatic Mammals

While it is general knowledge that the meats of such mammals as seals and whales are seafoods, two factors are usually overlooked: the first is that there are a fair number of aquatic animals that by some people are hunted for meat. These are represented in the Aquatic Chart by muskrat and polar bear. It is perhaps more important that the meats ot all aquatic mammals should be prepared with the knowledge that they are aquatic foods. Almost invariably, cookery formulation should include seasoning for correction of whatever fishiness the individual aquatic mammalian seafood may have.

The meat of polar bear is almost offensively fishy. For acceptability its cookery must be in line with that of extremely fishy fish.

Muskrats, like most salt marsh turtles, have a dominant flavor that can be thought of as "muddy." To make muskrat acceptable, its cookery formulation should include seasoning strong enough to overcome its muddiness—perhaps using what spice elaborators call "mock turtle seasoning." Acidic fruits such as citrus, pineapple, and mango, the ubiquitous tomato, and hot peppers are favorites. People alongside muddy rivers use a wide range of herbs and spices, many unknown to us, to make such aquatic foods tolerable.

Water Fowl

Ducks and geese are the only water fowl included in the column on Poultry in the Gustametric Chart, but probably few people realize that they are water fowl. Still fewer people prepare other water fowl—when they have the opportunity—and when they do, it is along the same lines as they would prepare ducks and geese.

Practically all commercially marketed ducks and geese are very young fowl. This fact is overlooked by the majority of hunters of not only ducks and geese but other water fowl. The contents of the game bag are alike prepared and cooked as though all the specimens were young, even very young. It takes only a little knowledge to distinguish between young and not-so-young aquatic fowl, but disregard or ignorance of the differences all too frequently results in poor food.

A broader discussion of this subject is under Game, Column 2. The young and very young of almost all water fowl are relished by many other peoples where they can be caught and more or less immediately used. Like other game, under proper conditions, primarily the proper time, practically all water fowl can be good, even epicurean, food. A mature seagull is not only fishily strong but one of the toughest of all meats; but a fledgling seagull can, properly prepared, make a fairly good dish. Some such food experiences would be voted by most people as acceptable, but once may be enough. All aged water fowl are to be avoided. They are strong and rank in flavor and offensive in odor—all of them.

Algae: Sea Plants

One of the impediments in the path of popularizing the use of marine vegetation is the common appellation "seaweeds." Like the term "toadstool" applied to fungi, the connotation of "seaweeds" is disdainful; both terms in the growth of language reflect regard of folklore and disregard of realities. The second obstacle to popular familiarization is the paucity of identifying nomenclature in our Western languages.

Terms of derision like "weeds" are particularly unfortunate because they have retarded consideration and, in the case of sea plants, use of one of the most abundant classes of food easily and usually freely available to so many, many people.

What will surprise most people is the statement of fact that (so far as the author is aware) with the exception of a single genus that seems to be found in a limited area along the coast of Chile, *all marine vegetation is edible*. However, the statement that all seaplants are edible should be qualified by saying that not all are *good* to eat. Studies in recent years indicate that as a people's standard of living rises, their consumption of sea plants goes down.

The reasons we wouldn't care for what may be the majority of marine algae are (1) that they are too tough or stringy, and (2) that they are too high in solids, both as vegetable matter, that is, fibrous matter, and most important, too high in mineral matter, not necessarily salts. Surprisingly enough, the majority of the agreeable, edible seaweeds don't taste salty at all when cooked, assuming that they are thoroughly washed before they are cooked. Further, the majority of the edible seaweeds do not tend to be deliquescent or slimy when cooked but can be described as varying from slightly gelatinous to gristly; that is, from firm and jelly-like to a crunchy consistency.

It may be pointed out that the taste for some of the seaweed combinations in desserts, that is in sweets, may be more or less an acquired taste. An example would be the use of the seaweed flavors in some of the Japanese gelatin desserts and cakes.

One of the similes of comparison of the seaweed textures to things with which we are familiar is gristle, which is a brother parallel, inasmuch as gristle is actually animal gelatin.

In the direction of the relative age of seaweed, from the standpoint of freshness from the moment of gathering to the time of use, it is important to bear in mind that the mineral salts and other factors in seaweed become much more evident as it ages. Some of the coral types of seaweed are used by the Asiatic peoples fresh and raw, somewhat as Occidentals use salads, with the qualification that such seaweed "salads" are generally used in advance of sea food meals. Some of the usage requires aging the seaweed anywhere from a few hours to a day or two so as to develop the flavor and perhaps the odor that is desired.

Still other varieties, the flat leaf, the very thin and light kinds, are used by the Japanese for "Sushi" rice rolls; for which purpose the seaweeds are sun-dried and then flat packaged, commercially available. So quite obviously, aging or seasoning the seaweed apparently develops a flavor that the people who use it definitely want.

Rejection of the idea of using seaweeds in our cookery reflects immaturity of consideration. If we are to consolidate the good ideas and the good usages of folk cookery we must consider individual usages on their merit, objectively, not subjectively, and certainly not tinged by individual prejudices. Some kinds of prejudice can be stated as attitudes of negation.

Nutritional Value

Principal components are carbohydrates (sugars or vegetable gums), small quantities of protein and fat, ash which is largely composed of salts of sodium and potassium and 80 to 90 per cent of water. Protein content and other components vary greatly in one species coming from different *localities.* Chapman (1950) indicates there is no agreement as to how much of the nutritive values are absorbable by the human body.

Agar-agar is made from certain kinds of sea plants. In the body it functions as a lubricant, but it is emphasized that it is *not* metabolized. Alginic acid derivatives such as alginates may replace tragacanth, etc. in jellies and ice cream, as stabilizers.

Summary

A large number of kinds and varieties of sea plants would be gathered if information about them were disseminated in such a way as to make the identification and use of such sea plants relatively easy, perhaps as easy as the gathering of terrestrial wild vegetable foods. The majority of the best sea plants are in the flavor range of most common terrestrial vegetables, from 25 to 75, if properly prepared soon after gathering.

The majority of sea plants are tasteless for the first four cardinal tastes. It is the fifth, the chemical taste, which is dominant in practically all fresh seaweed. That chemical taste is either subliminal or barely perceptible in the mildest plants when properly processed, but that chemical taste factor has the peculiarity in sea plants of rising with time or becoming accentuated when combined with some other foods.

When seaweed ages in its natural moist condition, it tends toward deliquescence under which conditions the inorganic chemical constituents as well as the products of bacterial action become offensive.

In a blindfold, pinched-nose panel trial, the presence of most seaweeds properly prepared would not be detectable. With the open nose test detection would vary with the kind of sea plant used and the method of preparation.

As a romantic aside, it is reiterated that when we are at or near the sea, we don't smell the salt sea air. We don't smell the salt. We can't. Salt is not volatile. What we do smell is the aquatic by-products, primarily algal matter, in a state of decomposition—particularly "seaweeds."

Marsh and tidal-flat smells may have predominant odors of decomposing animal matter—*but not salt.*

Pharmacology

All through history man has used sea plants for medicinal purposes. The literature of marine biology is peppered with allusions to folklore medicinal practices, but in view of contemporary medicine, caution is suggested in considering the use of "seaweed" pills and tablets and some other marine extractives, as probably classifiable as nostrums, medicaments that would not be approved by a physician.

Definition—Algae

Aquatic plants, "seaweeds" including fresh water and non-aquatic forms; from microscopic to giant varieties.

Botany.—A primary division of Thallophyta, coordinate with fungi, having leaflike and stemlike parts, but not a true vascular system (leaves and stems).

Names of Parts of Algae

Roots are called "holdfasts"; stems, "stipes"; leaves, "laminae"; plant body, "thallus." Plates of tissue are referred to in some not having laminae. Some small kinds are mainly filamentous (moss-like).

Classification

Sea plants are classified according to color:

(1) Green (*Chlorophyceae,* occurring in the sea, fresh water, soil, and on trees).

(2) Blue-green (*Myxophyceae,* occurring same as Chlorophyceae).

(3) Red (*Rhodophyceae,* occurring in the sea only). Pepper dulse (*Laurencia pinnatifida;* red). Pepper dulse (*Iridaea edulis* (bright red, and thicker than true dulse). The pepper dulses are extremely pungent, used in Scotland principally as condiments. One old method was to pinch these dulses between hot irons. (Some of their peppery constituents may be volatile.)

"Dulse" or "water-leaf" (its names in Scotland), "dillisk," "dillesk," or "crannogh" (in Ireland) is *Rhodymenia palmata;* which is dried and used for chewing, or sometimes chewed when fresh; sometimes cooked in milk. In Iceland it is called "sol," and is eaten along with dried fish, butter and potatoes; sometimes baked into bread. When dried and rolled, it is used like chewing tobacco. In the Mediterranean it is used as a flavoring for soups. "Sloke" (in Ireland) and "Laver" (in England) is *Porphyra;* used in salad or cooked in some breakfast dishes; sometimes fried in deep fat.

(4) Brown (Phaeophyceae, occurring in the sea only). "Sugar wrack," "dulse," "tangle" (in Scotland) is *Laminaria saccharina.* The young stipes or stalks are the parts used. Sweet to the taste, containing a polysaccharide sugar. Some varieties also have a nutty flavor, beside sweetness. "Murlins" or "badderlocks" (*Alaria*) also have this flavor in their leaflets or sporophylls. "Pain des algues" (seaweed bread, in France) is a composite jelly prepared from *L. saccharina* and *Chondrus crispus.*

The factors of selection are: (1) kind and variety; (2) point of origin; (3) season; and (4) part and age of plant used. Pre-preparation consists of clipping the holdfasts and tough stipes, then rinsing in cool fresh water. To prepare, simmer in one part water to one part sea plant.

Some of the kinds and varieties, especially the delicate mosses that are not highly gelatinous, may be heat-processed for only a few minutes. They are edible raw. The gelatinous kinds, like Sea Lettuce and the Irish Moss, are usually cooked to the condition where the mass is fairly gelatinous, at which point it may be strained through a fine cloth. Some blanc-manges are still prepared in the British Isles from an Irish Moss base, which results in a delicate green product; which really should be called a "vert-mange" ("Green food") instead of blanc-mange (white food).

The most common usage of sea plants is inclusion of the leaves or mosses in soups and stews, primarily because their gels add body to the dish and to a lesser extent for their kinesthetic and appearance characters. Many of the succulent filamentous and mossy sea plants are employed raw in European salad usage or dipped in sauces in the Orient.

In general the flavor of seaweeds, even the lightest, is not one that will appeal to most American tastes. The highest-flavor sea plants, such as the filament and the moss group succulents definitely require a taste cultivated to strong seaweed flavors. However, the knowing cook can, by the addition of a little seaweed, step up the flavor of a fish dish, especially some broths and chowders, bouillabaisse, and fish sauces. An example would be that if a clam chowder isn't "clammy" enough, add some seaweed. It might also add an agreeable color note.

Sea Tongue (115) (*Gigartina corymbifera*)

Sea tongue is one of the largest and best of the red sea plants. It can be very good when cooked, e.g.: fried in batter. It is agreeable in flavor and texture, not too salty; in fact, salt needs to be added.

Aquatic Vegetable Matter

The listings in this column are primarily for the purpose of classification; secondarily to indicate a few of the many vegetables that are amphibious. Most of the other such vegetables are little known and not widely used; most of them would be classifiable in listings of wild foods.

Irish Moss (30)

Carragheen or ***Carrageen.***—True Irish moss is *Chondrus crispus,* but the name is often incorrectly applied to *Gigartina stellata.* Other names for *C. crispus* are "pearl moss," "sea pearl moss," "lichen," "gristle moss," "curly gristle moss," "curly moss," "jelly moss," and "rock moss."

Carragheen is principally used for jelling as a stabilizer, etc.

AMPHIBIOUS VEGETABLES

Just as more than 30,000 different kinds of mushrooms are certainly unknown to most people, there are more than that number of amphibious vegetables, not only unknown but with a few exceptions unrecognized as food by most Americans. In the early days of America many of those vegetable foods were recognized and used, but today in many parts of the world they are not only extensively used, they provide much of the basic food of many peoples. For the bog and pond shore-comber who doesn't mind getting his feet wet, there can be some surprisingly good rewards. However, the study of amphibious vegetable foods requires the same kind of studious approach as that involved in mushrooms, without the hazards hanging over the latter. He who disdainfully refers to "toadstools" will probably likewise avoid skunk cabbage!

Cranberry, watercress, wild rice, rice, taro, and arrowroot are elsewhere covered in the listings of the Gustametric Chart. Taro leaves are one of the many pond and stream vegetables that abound in favorable environments, that are widely used, particularly in Asia, the Orient and the Pacific islands, but are here practically disregarded.

Water lily flowers are common food in many parts of the world. Incidentally, many of the young leaves of what are commonly called water lilies are edible.

Marshmallow leaves were much used in the days of early America, but their usage in cookery has been almost entirely forgotten.

The mature fruit of sea fig (*Mesembryanthemum aequilaterale*) when peeled is edible and just vaguely suggestive of tree figs. It is one of the most common vegetables of the Pacific sand dune areas.

Lotus root, one of the oldest aquatic root foods of man, is being popularized in both Chinese and Japanese cuisine of which it has long been a component. Lotus seed, about the size and faintly resembling the texture and flavor of the macadamia nut, is one of the delicacies of Asia and the Orient. It is available in American and European markets candied and canned. Marshmallow root is another of the many bog and swamp roots that were gathered by American colonists, the cookery of which has been almost forgotten.

PRESERVED FISH[1] (AQUATIC CHART)

The term "preserved fish" as used in this volume includes Salt Packed (Column N), Marinated (Column O), and Smoked Fish (Column P). Canned fish is discussed in Volume II along with other canned foods. In considering the meaning of the term "preserved" it is essential first to realize the following implications:

(1) By strict definition no food is preserved. The processes of preservation are physically and chemically limited. There are modifications from the primal conditions: first, microbiological; second, chemical. At the moment of death the body of an animal is inactivated, but some of its microbiological guests continue active, chemical changes result therefrom, under ordinary conditions occurring very rapidly.

(2) "Salting," or brining with sodium chloride or other salts and other chemicals slows physical and chemical decomposition, but does not arrest it completely.

(3) If for preserving fish only chemically pure salt were used, analyzing the products for flavors would be relatively simple, but in practically all commercial processes, even where commercially pure salt is used, there are other salts and minerals in the brining water or in the marinade or curing liquor.

(4) Preservational technology is moving toward addition of acids and chemi-

[1] See Preserved Fish, FN 200, Column 1 of Gustametric Chart and Fig 33.

cal inhibitors to minimize bacterial activity, and enzymatic digestion. Here contemporary technology catches up with age-old practices of wine marination of fish after it has been salt "cured." An example is "soused herring."

A glance at the Aquatic Chart will show that most of the aquatic foods flavor rated above FN 125 are preserved. As a general rule, food matter with flavor norms over 100 may be considered as *seasoning*. Reflection of man's food behavior will reveal almost universal limitation of such highly flavored foods to small quantities, for both metabolic and aesthetic reasons. A prominent example is man's seemingly natural limitation in the use of salted and smoked fish. When he uses them as basic dishes, he is inclined to dilute saltiness and smokiness in methods of preparation. The peoples of the west use salted and smoked fish more frequently as basic dishes than do Orientals and other peoples of the east who in contrast use bits and chunks either as seasoning for other kinds of food or as complements, but avoid making a meal of them. One of the representative foods of Korea is *kimche*, a kind of marinated vegetable, somewhat comparable to sauerkraut, which has traditional components of salted and smoked fish. Such Oriental use of preserved seafoods somewhat parallels our use of caviar. But whereas we tend to begin with a dab of caviar, they customarily use it as an accompaniment along with a basic dish of some other kind of food.

Consideration of the flavor rating of the different kinds of marinated, salted, and smoked fish should be based on usages which for chart purposes are centered in the Carrier classifications: Columns 11, 12, and 13. Accordingly, Marinated Fish (FN 150) parallels Marinades in Column 11, which in turn cues the flavor curves up or down according to marinade composition. All listings in Columns N, O, and P are flavor rated in line with average commercial practices. Variations of domestic products are discussed in Part III.

With few exceptions commercially preserved fish are marinated in a salt brine as a pre-preparational or preparational procedure for products within any of the three preserved fish columns.

SALT-PACKED FISH[2] (230)

Because the line between certain salt-packed products and marinated products is not definite, and because of the commercial practice of labeling as "salt packed" seafoods really marinated in more or less simple salt *brine*, this column is limited to fish and other aquatic foods that are *simply salted and dried*. Simply dried codfish marketed in "splits" or packed dry salt codfish is not *dry*, but relatively high in moisture. So long as there is any moisture present, chemical alteration will proceed. Practically all the larger fish like cod are eviscerated and at least superficially cleaned before brining and salting, or salting and drying; but many of the smaller fish, starting with some herring packs, are not eviscerated, and many of them not even beheaded. It must be obvious that the chemical alterations taking place in uneviscerated, uncleaned fish will result in flavors radically different from those of the fish in its primal condition. Not that anyone wants to eat the fish in its original raw state, but rather it must be granted that tastes for fish preserved by such crude methods certainly must be acquired. Regardless of nomenclature and by whom it is

[2] See Salt-Fish, FN 230, Column 1 of the Gustametric Chart.

used, in domestic or commercial usage, salt-packed or simply brined fish is pretty poor food. Flavorwise, it has only two factors: the dominant cardinal taste of salinity, and density or texture. Simply salted, different fish of the same family group taste alike. Salt is the common leveler of taste. The differences in flavor between the same kinds of fish processed in different areas or in the same area by different people will have extreme variations according to highly variable fishing and shipboard practices. Elements of such procedures include (1) the time between taking and marketing; (2) holding and pre-processing procedures; (3) packing house procedures; (4) the kind of salt and other additives to the brine or dry pack; (5) method of packing; (6) time, methods of transportation, and conditions of storage between packing and delivery to the consumer; and (7) the user's conditions of storage and the length of time in which the fish has been exposed to air before the product is used. All these factors enter into appraising the flavor of a salt-packed aquatic food.

Distinguishing between some simple salt packs of herring-like fish and the same fish simply salt-*brined* may present an indefinite division, but the difference is not superficial. Many of the simple salt packs involve crude techniques, and fish that have not been pre-processed for removal of viscera, scales, and particularly surface slime. In contrast, most of the simple brine packs are of fish trimmed and cleaned, most of the scale removed, and most of the skin slime removed in the pre-processing, brining step. Here the admonition is to survey, particularly for surface appearance, slime coating and above all smell for off-odors.

Usage

The usage of aquatic as well as terrestrial animal meats that have been either simply salt-packed or simply salt-marinated provides the class of foods that perhaps more than any other requires a knowledgeable application of the flavor balance of sweet, sour, saline, and bitter. Bear in mind that the only primary taste that should be present in a wholesome food within this column is *salinity*. Except for kinesthetic factors, *if there is any other taste present,* particularly sourness or pungency, *the food is probably not wholesome and should be rejected.* If acids in salted or brined meat have spontaneously developed to the point where one can taste them, it can be dangerous and should not be accepted as food. Here is a case where food may actually taste good but have adverse metabolic effects.

Caviar (125–400, av. 180)

The term caviar is applied to the processed roe of several varieties of fish but generally the term is thought of as applying to Russian processed sturgeon roe. Beluga (the Russian Caspian Sea sturgeon) is reputedly superior, possibly because the individual egg berries are large and of good texture. Mildly cured Beluga caviar is available in prime condition only close to points of origin in Russia, in Iran contiguous to the Caspian Sea and along the Danube where it would flavor rate lowest among the caviars at about 125. Other cures of sturgeon caviar packed in a number of different ways may have flavor ratings from 175 to 225. Connoisseurship is required to distinguish caviar from the smallest sturgeon-like Sevruga and the caviar-processed roe of other fish. Imitation caviar may be elaborations of the roe of herring and whitefish beside others.

Russian caviar from the different sturgeons varies in color from gray to black.

The roe of other fish processed to imitate caviar is usually seasoned and grayed to simulate the flavor and color of the Russian prototype.

The different sturgeon caviars as well as caviars prepared from many other fish provide, beside their peculiar flavor characters, one of the most agreeable kinds of kinesthetic experience by their crackling, crunchy chewiness and usually pleasing and—if of good grade—not too fishy after-taste.

Several kinds of *partially dried* caviar-processed roe are produced in different parts of the world; an outstanding example of the highest grade would be that produced in Turkey where the product resembles a buff-gray, flattened sausage of elongated tear-drop form, and generally sold in pairs. It is usually served in thin slices not more than $^1/_{16}$ inch thick, as an appetizer or in elaborate salad makeups. Its flavor rating would vary from 200 to 300 according to grade.

Other roe products are sometimes combined with seasoning, and even smoked, particularly in the Orient; the results are modified caviars, to which flavor ratings between 300 and 400 would be assigned. A critical appraisal of some of those caviars might rate them too strong to be acceptable.

People in other countries use such caviars as seasoning components rather than eating them straight. The imaginative cook, by rejecting some of the low grade caviars for straight usage will consider them as seasonings, not alone with other fish dishes but, like some kinds of pickled herring, in salad compositions. Caviar used as seasoning offers some interesting variations: start with its saltiness as the dominant taste character for balance with the other cardinal tastes, and then plot on the Gustametric Chart for agreeable flavor composition. Take advantage of the outstanding kinesthetic values of the different caviars. Example: combine the commonly available and inexpensive American whitefish caviar with chopped black olives. The result is two different textures with the average cure of black olives resulting in a combination that comes close to being an extender of not only the caviar flavor but its color. It is usually voted agreeable in a canape composition.

Onions, finely ground and minced, are the traditional accompaniment of caviar. Use the combination with sliced cold potatoes as a taste blotter and kinesthetic cushion of salad makeups. Caution will prescribe watery dressings, very mild, preferably winey and with very lightly sour characters rather than oily or mayonnaise-viscous carriers. One of the most rewarding sports of the do-it-yourself school lies in variations of the caviar type of processing of many different roes.

MARINATED FISH[3] (50–500, AV 150)

Historically, aquatic food preserved by some kinds of marination is one of man's oldest and most widely practiced processes. The way he uses the resulting marinated fish today would fill a very large book, even if reduced to an outline.

If salt is the great leveler of food flavor, the same is true of marination, but here the flavor coverage goes much further. Different kinds of fish (or other food, animal or vegetable) marinated together long enough will taste alike, with the exception of kinesthetic differences.

It is useful to consider the relation of a marinade to a brine. A *simple brine* consists of water and salt only, in either saturated or unsaturated solution. A

[3] See Marinated Fish, FN 150, Column 1 of the Gustametric Chart.

compound brine has water and seasonings such as sugar and other additives, and *may not include salt.* Many shellfish and other aquatic foods are commercially packed in either simple or compound brines. A *marinade* (from the Latin word *mare,* meaning "sea") is *water* with salt or other minerals or seasonings in which food is immersed. Another name for marinade is *pickle.*

Marinated fish may be separated into two kinds: raw and processed. The first includes fish subjected raw to any kind of marination. In general, commercial preservation of fish by marinating starts with raw fish, usually but not always eviscerated and trimmed.

Raw Fish Marinated.—The simplest marinated fish is by definition raw fish held in tap water. By common interpretation, however, it means holding raw fish in a salt solution, but here the subject from the standpoint of flavor appraisal becomes intricate. The final flavor of the marinated fish will vary with the following:

(1) What is in the water beside sodium chloride; except in the case of rain water, there will be mineral and sometimes vegetable matter in the makeup water.

(2) The temperature of the brine and whether it is a saturated salt solution or the salt content is below saturation.

(3) The time element.

(4) Many processors change the brining liquor several times during the brining period, and these brining steps precede processing the fish in the marinade in which the product is offered to the public.

Commercially pure table salt is the only kind commonly available in American and most European markets, but elsewhere the picture is in reverse. Crude sea salt and rock salt are found in many markets. Our industrial marination processes are according to standards, not alone of the kind and condition of fish to be brined, but also the grades and quantities of seasonings as well. Abroad, there is little or no supervision or control of those factors.

One observation which the food explorer abroad finds strange and hard to explain is the fondness of many peoples for crude sea salt marinations. His first taste of seafood cured in salt water from ponds that skirt the sea is likely, particularly if served hot, to bring a reminiscence of gas warfare; indeed he will conclude that a taste for some of the seafood cooked in sea water in the Philippines will have to be acquired—by someone else.

Cooked Fish Marinated.—The second kind of marinated fish applies to fish that has been pre-cooked or otherwise pre-processed before marinating. Examples are herring fried and then marinated in a crock, in a more or less mildly seasoned brine for short-term usage. This process is common throughout Europe, particularly in Italy, where red wine vinegar, bay leaf, oregano, and other herbs beside salt and pepper provide one of the traditional foods of the Italian coasts. "Soused" fish, particularly herring, in a wide variety of pre-preparational marination processes with a seasoning component of wine is a Teutonic process of broad coverage.

The flavor range of marination may start with some of the very lightly flavored liquors and rise to 500 or higher with both use and concentration of vegetable and animal seasonings. Highest ratings would be assignable to what must be considered components of decomposition of fish, of which an example is Philippine *bagoong* (paralleling Roman *liquamen*) the viscera of fish fermented to liquefaction, strained and salted, which is far above the taste and smell tolerances of most of us.

The range of marination flavors is covered in more detail under Column 11 in Part III of Volume II.

The lowest flavor rating of pickled herring may be assigned to some of the mild packs of Germany, particularly the milchners (whole herring in the milt stage); intermediate flavor rating to some of the Holland and Scandinavian packs; and the highest rating would be assigned to *gaffel bittar* ("fork bits" in Sweden) and other highly seasoned herring fillets.

Canned and commercially processed and packed foods are not considered in this discussion; however it may be pointed out that canned shellfish, particularly from the Orient, with a label reading "packed in brine," crab, crawfish, shrimp, abalone, and many kinds of sea snails are given complex preparational brining processes. Oriental aquatic foods such as mussels in the shell, soft and hard shell clams are usually packed in broth instead of brine; eels in highly seasoned marinades or a jellied pack. *Gaffel bittar* and *matjes* (Scandinavian "fish fillets") are usually in tin or glass or small casks. Other Baltic herring fillet products may be lightly brined and seasoned and marinated in white wine and sliced onions or some of the sour cream compositions. Anchovy paste is a comparatively modest modern transposition of the Roman and earlier production of *liquamen* (a liquid concentrate of fermented whole fish) which was used in every good Roman household as soy is used in modern kitchens. Such products are discussed in Volume II, mostly in Columns 11 and 21.

Since marination techniques vary from simple salt brining to seasoned marinades, and since appearances and smells of marinated products can be extremely deceptive, there should be a general rule: survey carefully, including appearance, firmness, smell and above all, taste a fragment of the fish before preparation or usage. And be prepared to expel the sample if it proves undesirable! The number of batches rejected in such a test, particularly from over-age wooden cask packs, will surprise all but the cognoscenti.

SMOKED FISH[4] (75–350, AV. 250) (COLUMN Q)

Only a few kinds of fish are listed in this chart, but it should be known that practically every fish that swims, and a lot of other aquatic animals, are smoked by one or another of the world's peoples. Fresh water fish processed by knowledgeable amateurs as well as by professionals are almost universally very lightly smoked. Such fresh water fish must be much more carefully trimmed and cleaned than salt-water fish, usually very lightly brined and then lightly smoked. Perhaps the most popular are trout and whitefish. As marketed, most smoked trout and whitefish are frozen, and being lightly processed, their shelf life is relatively short. Only at points of origin are such fish at their best, used within the first day after smoking, and of course not frozen.

Some of the fresh water fish, like whitefish, shad, and sturgeon, that are medium-smoked for longer shelf life, are usually also subjected to longer pre-preparational brining. The result of all this is pretty strong smoked fish. Note that mildly smoked sturgeon and salmon, the delicatessen offerings, have extremely short shelf life at ordinary room temperature.

Smoking techniques vary from simple chimney or smokehouse cells, using any available combustible wood, with a banked fire, to industrial smokehouse establishments. The factors of smoking are the following:

[4] See Smoked Fish, FN 250, Column 1 of the Gustametric Chart.

(1) *The smoking structure or chamber,* consisting of firebox, accessories or heat-control equipment, including instrumentation.

(2) *The wood chips* or the composition of the combustible material: wood is used in most cases, peat in some areas.

(3) *The maintenance of relatively low atmosphere smoke and the draft control.* Some of the mild-smoking is done under 100°F., but most commercial smoking is done between 110° and 120°F.

(4) *The factors of time and temperature.* The time in which aquatic food is subjected to smoking usually varies with the temperature; anything from a few hours to overnight at either low, medium, or high temperature. It is most important to hold the fish at the temperature at which the smoldering wood or peat will *cook* the fish. A suggestion of smokiness in raw fish may involve smoking it for an hour or two at low temperature. Overnight at that same temperature, the fish may be partly or wholly cooked, according to the kind and condition of the fish. The higher temperatures of smoking are only employed when extended shelf life is required.

(5) *Color.* Regardless of the kind of combustible material used for smoking, the color of the fish so processed will vary from light gray to a smoky umber. Any other color appearing on the fish, ranging from yellowish to brown is whatever the fish itself contributes. The common example is kipper or bloater where the skin of the fish and to some extent the exposed meat are colored by the heat of the smoking process, but all smoke *per se* deposits a grayish coating. All of this is emphasized to point out the fact that much commercial pre-processed "smoked" fish is artificially colored. Some of it is even artificially "smoked" by being chemically flavored and colored. Most commercial "Alaska Smoked Cod" is sablefish, finished with a vegetable smoky salmon coloring that *suggests* smokehouse curing. Sablefish is flat white to grayish blue in skin color, and there is no way of getting that beautiful color, that smoky orange, on sablefish unless it is dyed.

Usage

Mild smoked fish is relatively easy to prepare and is very popular among people who develop a taste for it, but it does require educating individual tastes for smoked fishiness. Medium or hard-smoked fish, and particularly some of the unusual smoked aquatic foods require knowledge and experience to prepare for consumption by anyone other than people who have been exposed to long experience with such foods. Here note that the peoples who customarily use hard-smoked fish, as in the case of salt-packed and marinated fish use only small quantities of such foods, either as accompaniments or complements, but possibly most frequently as components of other food compositions. Anyone who voluntarily eats simply smoked mackerel *likes fish.* Even liking hard-smoked finnan haddie requires the taste of a crusty old fisherman.

Flavor Rating

A minimum increment of 50 flavor intensity units for *mild* smoke-curing should be assumed. Differences between varieties of trout and seasons, condition, kinds of processing should be taken into consideration; see chapters on *Preservation* and on *Marinades* in Volume II.

The effect of smoking on the flavor rating of fish is indicated in the examples presented below:

Trout (25)

Trout, Mild-Smoked Rainbow (75)

Proportionally 50 points higher than the flavor norm of the same trout when steamed.

Trout, Smoked Steelhead (100–300, av. 175)

Smoke and other preservational processes of steelhead trout may be considered as resulting in flavor norms paralleling some other kinds of salmon, similarly processed.

Finnan Haddie (Smoked Haddock) (150)

The flavor norm of finnan haddie will probably center around 150, but virtually all of the common cookery procedures involve carriers and processes that effect dilution of its inherent smoked fishiness.

CHAPTER 7

Animal Meats and Meat Products

COLUMN 2

Introduction

The title of the classification in Column 2 might be *Meats,* because that is what most people have in mind when they think or talk about the individual foods listed in this column, but with very little consideration it will be realized that the word "meat" must be qualified.

Animal. Definition: "A living creature, or anything that once breathed."

Meat. In this column it is intended to apply to the edible parts of warm-blooded, terrestrial, four-footed animals.

While the heading of this classification is *Animal Meats,* it really should have the broader title of *Animal Meats and Meat Products.*

The fleshy tissue primarily referred to in discussing meats consists of fibers. The secondary meat tissues are fats in different forms. The third are yellow or white connective fibers. The fourth are fibrous capsules and sheaths, and the fifth are bones and their cartilaginous parts. Beside these five basic forms, there are other considerations concerned with organ meats, the blood and lymph circulatory systems, and above all, a constant awareness of the potentialities involved in animal pathology should keep one on the lookout for visual evidence of animal diseases.

By "spoilage" is meant a condition produced by the excessive growth of bacteria and/or molds. Even though the food may thus be considered inedible, it is not usually dangerous to health. By "food poisoning" is meant the condition produced by the growth of specific micro-organisms or organisms which produce toxins or which will induce disease when consumed. Trichinosis is an example of the latter.

Factors of selection of meats include the kind and variety of animal, its age, sex, feed, season of slaughter, conditions after slaughter, and of course the part or section of the animal being considered. For example, a prime roast of beef may be a rib section of one-year-old Black Angus steer, corn fed, slaughtered in the fall of the year and hung for 8 to 10 days at 32 to 40°F. and 60 to 70 per cent humidity.

Federal grading is not necessarily a clue to *flavor quality.* Federal marketable grades indicate only variations in age and conformation; there is no consideration of flavor factors such as breed and feed.

Age at time of slaughter is important from the standpoint of tenderness as well as nutrition. Using beef as an example, color is a fair index of flesh age, ranging from light pink in young calves to dark red in old cows and range bulls. The muscle texture of young animals is much finer than that of old ones. Each muscle fiber is sheathed in an envelope which is delicate and whitish in infancy, but as the animal grows older, yellows and toughens. The consistencies of fat and fatty tissues in different parts of the body range from white, soft, and moderately firm in the very young animals to yellowish and quite hard in the older animals. The connective tissues, the sheath terminations, and the tendons are quite light, almost white, when very young, acquire a characteristic color in age. The joint envelopes or capsules and the sheaths that envelop every bone, and the characteristic periosteum are thin, pliable, and light in color when young; and ivory in hue, thick and tough when old. A transverse section of an average bone reveals the cancellous honeycomb-like structure that in the heads and bases provide incontrovertible evidence of animal age. In very young animals the cancellous bone varies in pinkishness, and it is between soft and moderately firm; fingernail pressure results in easy to just-possible penetration. With increasing age the color of the cancellous cross section darkens, and the osseus (bony) tissues calcify to the degree where fingernail penetration is not possible. In uncut bones or where the cancellous tissue is not easily observable, the articular cartilage of the neck, head, and base can provide fairly good evidence of animal age. Cartilage varies from gelatinous in infancy to hard and rubbery in age.

Immediately after slaughtering, animal tissues have some characteristic appearances. Most of the surface and some of the deep tissues reflect characteristic shininess, which in time by storage or other processing becomes dull. Immediately after slaughtering the animal passes into a state of *rigor mortis*, a state of stiffness which is gradually lost in subsequent relaxation. The degree of relaxation can easily confuse a judgment of relative firmness of animal tissues, particularly muscle meats, which is one of the indices of animal age. Pressure trials provide kinesthetic and visual clues. There is only a little yield and much bounce in young meat; the surface of the meat quickly returns when thumb pressure is removed, but the resilience decreases with advancing age to the point where the "get up and go" of youth is *gone*.

"Aging" of Meat

The intrinsic condition, the textures, and flavors of all animal meats are progressively altered from the moment of slaughtering and vary according to time and the conditions in which they are processed, particularly storage. Under today's meat packing industry practices all animal carcasses are held in cold rooms for varying lengths of time; first, to dissipate the animal's body heat; second, to age or mature the carcass to an extent that varies with the individual packer's methods, which in turn vary with his marketing requirements. This implies that practically no animal meats are marketed immediately after slaughter. Further, most retail butchers (and practically all good hotels and restaurants) hold some meats according to their trade or customer requirements or preferences.

Under the usual conditions of aging meat in this country, the only appreciable change is in tenderness. This change has been shown to be associated with the relaxation of *rigor mortis.* It has been shown that no more than 8 to 10 days at 34 to 40°F. are required for maximum tenderness. A few beef specialty houses still age their meat from 30 to 60 days. When this is done, the accompanying mold growth causes a distinctive change in flavor, even though the mold may be trimmed away. according to Dr. G. F. Stewart of the University of California.

Under *ordinary refrigeration temperatures (38° to 42°F.)* meats rapidly "age." Their intrinsic physical characters change; they soften and their flavors change from slightly to radically.

In today's development and expansion of the packing house industry into conveniently packaged frozen meats, most small sections and cuts of different animal meats are available to the user in good condition, both texturewise and flavorwise. It can safely be assumed that hard frozen chops, steaks, and roasts are aged according to the standards of individual packers. Further, it will be apparent that such frozen meats are uniformly aged, which is an effect not possible under ordinary refrigeration (38° to 42° F.).

Under old customs, meats were aged in cool places or cold rooms for ten days or longer, then subsequently trimmed free of surface mold and spoiled sections. Even when hung in refrigerator compartments nowadays, meat held for even a few days usually has to be trimmed. Flavor comparisons of the same cuts or sections of hard frozen meat may demonstrate organoleptic differences with time. No difference is detectable in a few months after packing, but after three years or longer, the flavor changes will be apparent to some people.

Cutting

Returning to the first example of the prime roast of beef, the "eye" or fillet part of a rib roast is the most tender part of the rib section, which frequently is the only part eaten. The more fibrous muscle meats are frequently rejected. The "eye" may comprise from a quarter to a third of the weight of a rib roast. This means that a ten pound rib roast may average less than one-third of eye or fillet meat. The much more highly flavored muscle tissue between the ribs and alongside the crown bones is wasted on people who will not gnaw a bone or eat with their fingers. The skirt meat of a rib roast is of higher flavor than the eye, but is frequently voted tough by people who may gradually be losing their ability to chew.

In general it can be said that there are no beef "bargains." Assuming that for a premium cut such as a ten pound rib roast that a butcher must get ten dollars (a dollar a pound), if he trims a pound or more from the section, he must still get ten dollars for it. If he trims *two* pounds off a ten pound roast, he will thereupon charge $1.25 per pound for an eight pound roast, still getting ten dollars for what started as a ten pound roast. Further, if he produces a six pound boneless, relatively lean *rolled* rib roast from that ten pound original section, he will have to charge in excess of $1.67 per pound to pay for the labor required to produce the rolled roast.

Veal (10–30, av. 20)

Flavor level of 10 indicates very young veal.

Dry cookery procedures markedly raise veal flavor rating above 30. Seasoning is usually recommended for wet or dry cookery for veal acceptability.

Pig (15–50, av. 25)

Pig.—The young of swine (*Sus scrofa*).

Suckling Pig.—Pigs before weaning.

Shoats, Piglets, Pigs.—Specifically, the young of swine that are weaned but less than one year old.

As a generality, pork is thought of as the meat of swine of any age, while the term "pig" should be more or less specifically limited to young swine or pork less than one year old. In turn, the term swine is commonly applied to domesticated animals of the genus *Sus*, or family *Suidae*. The common species is *Sus scrofa*.

Rabbit (15–45, av. 30)

The flavor norm is based on an average of domestic rabbits (*Royctolagus cuniculus*). Young rabbits will flavor rate as low as chickens. It would only be mature wild rabbits that may, according to age and feed, flavor rate as high as 45.

Rabbit should not be confused with hare (*Lepus leporidae*). Rabbits when cooked have whitish meat that is relatively light in flavor, whereas the meat of hares is dark and flavor rates higher. Raw rabbit meat is light pink and light in odor while that of hares is reddish and gamey in odor. (See Hare, FN 70, this Column.)

In the United States only two breeds are commonly marketed: New Zealand White, all white fur; and California, white body, with brownish black ears, nose and feet brown-black.

Domestic rabbits are commercially marketed in three grades: "fryers," weighing between 3 and 4 lbs. and up to six weeks old; "roasters," weighing between 4 and 6 lbs., between 6 and 10 weeks old; "stewing rabbits," weighing between 6 and 10 lbs., no age limitations.

Kid (20–65, av. 34)

Even very young kid has caprilic (goaty) flavor overtones. The older kids, according to their environment, require elaborate processing to make them acceptable.

Pork (30–50, av. 35)

The carcass of swine *Sus scrofa* more than one year old as distinguished from *pig*, which is less than one year old.

Substantial differences exist between carcasses from more or less natural or wild-fed animals which eat acorns and other nuts, wild roots and herbage—and grub and root among harvested peanut fields of the eastern United States—as contrasted with the cornfed porkers of the middle west. Alfalfa fed hogs acquire a characteristic flavor.

In pathology, trichinosis (a disease caused by a nematode) is predominant, especially in garbage fed swine, but other pathogenic organisms like amoebae and tapeworms may be included.

Beef (35–65, av. 45)

The term "beef" should apply to bovine carcasses (Genus *Bos*) over one year old. If the carcass is under one year it is veal. The bulk of domestic marketed beef is that of steers. Bulls and young cows are also marketed but usually downgraded. Mature bovines are rarely on the domestic markets. They are federally classified as "canners," and the majority of them go into packing-house products. The oldest of them go into dog food and inedible animal by-products. Textures of the sections, as well as color of the fat and meat of the older animals should be easily distinguishable. The odors of beef markedly differ according to maturation and aging.

Lamb (35–70, av. 50)

Mutton (55)

The flavor rating of lamb is based on marketed lambs, which in California range in weight from 37 to 53 lbs. (for spring lambs) and up to 58 lbs. at other times. In other areas according to season and feeding conditions, the lowest average weight may be around 32 lbs. for spring lamb carcasses in Florida.

The cookbooks of the world will show far more usages of lamb, mutton (and goat) than beef, for the simple reason that far more sheep and goats are raised for meat (and by-products) than beef animals. Further, there are many more methods applicable to sheep cookery than to the meats in sections of larger animals. Small to large lamb, half and whole carcasses can be baked or roasted; lamb legs, racks, and shoulders cooked or roasted.

A pertinent observation is that foreign cookery of sheep, particularly in the Near Eastern areas, is toward rareness, what we in the United States would think of as underdone. This implies that abroad, most sheep meat is cooked so that it remains juicy; roasts are finished lightly rare to medium "well done." A tenable criticism of American lamb cookery is that we overcook it. A rejoinder is that taste for rare to medium-cooked lamb is an acquired taste. Rare or undercooked lamb or mutton is at a much higher flavor level than the same meat finish-cooked. Incidentally, study of foreign cookbooks will reveal much use of layer- and sprinkle-seasoning of lamb roasts, showing a wide application of the principles of flavor balancing in and on such meats as well as with the accompanying foods.

American taste favors "spring lamb," particularly small legs, shoulders, racks, and chops, but most of the lamb and mutton is marketed for stews and in the form of boneless rolled roasts. Observe that there is comparatively little lamb or mutton steak (cross-cuts of legs or shoulders) for sale, which is odd. In this form lamb or mutton is in one of its best conditions for cookery.

The meats of utility grades of lamb and the older ewes, wethers, and rams, are almost entirely turned over to the meat packing industry for elaborated canned and packaged foods, and particularly sausages.

Game (15–300, av. 60)

Animals . . . "killed in the chase," are supposed to be the hunter's objective. Many of the animals we think of as the game of sportsmen are the everyday foods of many people—when they can get them: caribou, reindeer, and venison are examples. Water buffalo is a game animal in some parts of Africa but is propagated as are beef cattle in many other countries.

Venison (40–150, av. 60) (Family *Cervidae*)

The highest flavor rated meats are in the field of game. Here it should be noted that in the march of civilization man has domesticated only to a very limited extent for food purposes game animals the meats of which would flavor rate high in our scale. Contrary to common impressions of reindeer and water buffalo, which are domesticated in great numbers, their meats are of relatively low flavor norms—they are only a little higher than beef and mutton.

Roe deer, commercially produced and the meats professionally processed in Europe, provide examples of median-flavor rated, very good meats.

(See Pheasant, FN 48 in Column 3, Poultry; and Hare, FN 70, this Column.)

Organ Meats (12–200, av. 65)

The term *organ meats* is used in this category only as applying to marketed animal substructures.

Organ meats really include heads and tails and the odd parts between.

Tripe (5–100, av. 12)

The term "tripe" is, by U. S. marketing customs, applied to the first or second stomach of a ruminant that is chemically leached in pre-preparation for food. In obsolete English, "tripes" referred to all of the animal viscera, not just the stomachs. Chitterlings or "chitlings" are the small entrails of tripes. By extreme processes, the resulting tripe may, with the exception of kinesthetic factors, be flavorless. To be acceptable as food, such tripe must be seasoned and cooked with much care. Considered by itself, it is poor food. Even skillfully prepared, the best that can be said for it is that it has an agreeable texture. The contempt that is heaped on spinach can, with more justification, be piled on tripe.

Tripe is assigned higher flavor ratings as it is used in forms approaching its natural condition. The animal paunch, particularly the sheep's stomach that cased the traditional haggis, was not leached—just washed.

The use of superficially washed first or second animal stomachs is one of the examples of low food, any way it is rated.

Pathology of Tripe.—The term "tripe" and cognate terms are technically assigned to animal entrails, not just the stomachs. The presence of some pathogens is visually detectable in tripes, particularly chicken gizzards. Ulcers in such areas are generally caused by foreign matter, which dissection will reveal.

The most common pathological factor in tripes is the presence of metallic foreign matter. In cows' tripes, which is by far the most common, the barbs of barbed wire are occasionally subcutaneous—out of sight, but not out of crunch.

Brain (10–25, av. 18)

Wet cooked brain is almost flavorless and kinesthetically uninteresting. Dry cookery is customary.

Puréed and lightly seasoned brains are becoming a preferred baby food.

Heads (25–75, av. 48)

Calf or sheep heads, wholes or halves, are almost exclusively sold to "our foreign population." Actually they are used by more and more people who know or have gotten to know foreign preparation and services of some animal heads.

Oddly enough, people who disdain roast head of veal relish calf's head *vinaigrette*.

The romanticized boar's head of "merrie olde England" has fallen into social neglect, which startles the tourist when a roast pig's head is served to him in Germany. So, what was once one of the "rights of the lord" the most liked part of the animal—the head of the boar or the swine—is now largely disdained.

Properly roasted pig's head is one of the best foods. The constituent parts, which long ago were chosen by the masters for the simple reason that they were the best animal meats, are now only available on special order—an outstanding example of our neglect of what is good.

In order, the snout, brain, lips, ears, tongue and cheek muscles were prized. The other edible parts of the head were also valued.

While the heads of *young* boars and pigs, baby veal, and baby lambs were and still are roasted in the whole after laborious scraping and leaching to remove bristles and hair, the heads of young animals are usually skinned.

The cheek muscles of ovine and bovine heads are frequently marketed as specialities. The cheek muscles of young beeves are one of the best stew electives for all-round flavor—particularly texture. Incidentally, they are the animal muscles lowest in fat components. In young animals they are a bit on the rubbery side but not tough.

Most animal organs are not generally marketed. Some of the more delicate head skins, wet-cooked or crisped, can be fair.

Marketed Glands (10–100, av. 19)

A technical definition of glands includes livers, kidneys, etc. Marketed glands are primarily sweetbreads, and secondarily testicles—marketed in the southwest as "Rocky Mountain Oysters." In the sheep countries these glands are sought delicacies.

Sweetbreads (12–30, av. 20)

These are the thymus glands, which are in the throats; and the pancreas glands, which are near the stomach.

Tails (35–65, av. 42)

What is marketed as "oxtails" are immature beef-tails. It is presumed that the tail of an ox, which is a mature draft animal, would be too tough to eat. Flavorwise "ox-tails" are among the best animal meats, but they do require laborious pre-preparation and rather careful cookery procedures.

Tongue (av. 62)

There is as much difference between the tongues of young lambs and mature mutton as there is between calf and beef tongues. All of them should be eviscerated and trimmed. They are usually skinned *after* cooking.

Liver (50–80, av. 63)

Piglet liver may be lowest on the flavor scale. Porcine livers may have the most agreeable kinesthetic and other flavor factors, and they may be the most overlooked. Why they are so widely disdained in the U. S. markets is a puzzle.

Calf livers may be more popular because they are lighter in color than young steer livers; but only in the mature beef livers is the texture noticeably coarser than that of younger animals. The other flavor differences, like the colors, are noticeably higher in the livers of older animals.

Cracklings (av. 70)

The crisp skin or rind of pork, roasted or rendered. Also the crisp residue of hog's fat after it has been dry-rendered.

Chitterlings or "Chitlings"

Chitterlings or "chitlings," derived from *chatter*, suggesting that which quivers. The word "chitlings" and its cognates apply to entrails, most frequently the small intestines of porcine animals. Historic references disdainfully refer to chitlings as part of tripes, which were fried, roasted, and sometimes used as stuffings, as "foods of the very poor."

Heart (45–95, av. 75)

Hearts should be graded and rated according to kind and age of animals.

Kidneys (45–95, av. 78)

The kidneys of young porcine animals may rate the lowest with the most agreeable texture when compared with the kidneys of other animals. Young pork kidneys may be the most delicate, flavorwise. Lamb and steer kidneys are intermediate, and those of the game animals are the highest on the flavor scale.

Kidneys should not be flavor rated *unless they are defecated.*

Feet (39)

Feet of lambs, commercially called "trotters," and those of calves are widely used abroad but rarely encountered in American markets. See European cookbooks, especially those of Italy for usages.

Hare (50–100, av. 70)

Definition: "a rodent quadruped of the genus *Lepus* having long ears and hind legs, a short tail and a divided upper lip" (Oxford Dictionary).

A distinction must be made between hares, which properly are wild animals (game) and wild and domestic rabbits (including "Belgian hares" which are neither Belgian nor hares), their much milder relations.

The qualities of young hares vary more with their feeds than their varieties. Mature hares, by locality and body condition can be representative of animal gaminess. One would have to be pretty hungry or not at all particular to accept a stew of old hare. Roasted or otherwise dry-cooked, they are usually too stringy and rubbery to be considered normally edible.

Pathology.—Hares, particularly jackrabbits, in the western United States, have two endemic diseases that make one approach their preparation with caution. Tularemia, caused by *Pasteurella tularensis,* is the more dangerous, showing focal infections in the liver. The other disease, whose symptoms are watery cysts under the skin, having cores of living, worm-like animals, is probably caused by the *Enchinococcus granulosus. Rubber gloves should be worn at all times when eviscerating or trimming either hares or rabbits.*. (See Rabbit, FN 30, this column.)

Belgian hares are not Belgian. The breed seems to be an English domestic rabbit.

Salted Meats (50–300, av. 80)

(A) Such meats must be flavor rated as they are received from the brine or pack, without further seasoning or processing other than draining and steaming.

(B) *Salt,* sodium chloride (*NaCl*), commonly *table salt,* is frequently not the only salt, chemical additive or other substance flavorwise or physically influencing the flavor of *salted meats.* Some are intentionally added; others are unintentionally contributed—particularly contaminants; chemical components of the salts; or chemical contributions which migrate from packages!

(C) Few meats are only salted; most are brined.

Products like *corned beef* are usually marketed in a super water-saturated state—the meat tissues are water-logged. Accordingly their net usable mass should be appraised.

(D) Salt-packing, brining, or otherwise marinating meats for *preservation* is usually followed by modification in cookery. Such meats are usually trimmed and otherwise prepared by the removal of tag ends and undesirable salt or brine components.

Pathology.—The animal bacteria and vegetable molds that develop in salt pack and marinated meats may have results that vary from undesirable or disagreeable to lethal. Commercial processing is usually under the supervision of chemists and rarely if ever results in dangerous meats as marketed.

Purified salt is commercially used here but crude salt, even sea salt with traces of iodine, chlorine, and bromine, is much used abroad. Metallic oxides (from packages) may be present in imports.

Salted packages should be surveyed for evidence of waterlogging; amount and kind of salting, presence of other seasonings, chemical additives; especially bacterial decomposition, but should not be tasted if in doubt. Fungal development is rare, but should be looked for after protracted shelf or refrigerator storage.

Salt Pork (65–95, av. 80)

Simple salt packing and curing of porcine meats is customary in many European and some Far Eastern countries, but in the United States commercial salt packing of pork sections usually goes through thorough pre-preparational steps and then supervised marination processes. Foreign carcasses are not always thoroughly bled, and the arteries of the legs and shoulders are rarely brine-inflated before curing. Our own commercial processes, most of them under federal supervision, go through thorough precleaning, in-process cleaning, arterial defecation, and brine-pumping through arteries and some veins in the curing steps.

Flavor Rating.—There is surprisingly little difference between simply wet-salt-packed or brined pork, hams and shoulders of animals of different ages, small to large. What amounts to oversalting seems to kill all flavor factors except salinity and the kinesthetic factors. The curing processes modify the tissue textures and usually result in meats that texturewise are more agreeable than such meats not salt-packed. The salt packing of meats tends to firm the animal tissues, which are then more agreeable than the untreated meats. More pork is marketed as pickled (bacon, hams, and shoulders) than the same sections as fresh pork.

Pathology.—Salted pork products, more than any other kind of animal meats, are subject to mold contamination and bacterial decomposition. Only a small part of such a contamination is attributable to packing processes. Most of it develops in the processes of marketing and storage. While the molds on salted pork are usually harmless and careful scrubbing for their removal may be satisfactory, allow for the rare appearances of colonies of pathogenic bacteria, the evidence of which is not visually apparent. The bacterial colony may be developing in the deep tissues.

The presence of pathogenic bacteria, to which pork is particularly susceptible, is a common hazard in foreign productions of pork sections, principally attributable to primitive butchery and neglect of contemporary meat curing technology.

Corned Beef (80–200, av. 88)

Corned is an Americanism which originally denoted *grains* of salt. Most other peoples apply the word "salt" or "salted" to meats so packed or processed. The English use the term "bully beef" as a cognate to our American "corned beef." Commercial production of corned beef rarely consists of simply salt processing. Small and large producers of corned beef, like packers of hams and bacons, have individual processes and brands developed on individual seasoning ideas starting with the addition of sugars to salt. Some more or less prominent brand-name producers of corned beef produce elaborately seasoned products. Some contemporary portion marketing of corned beef sections includes packets of pickling spices for optional usage.

While flavor rating starts with mild-cured meat from young animals (recommended for usage within a few days), allow for seasoning additives, desirable and undesirable, and particularly variations in kinesthetic factors of different sections, according to age of the basic animal and the section of meat.

Sausage (25–800, av. 100)

Definition as originally applied: a quantity of finely chopped pork, beef or other meat, spiced and flavored, enclosed in a short length of the intestine of some animal, so as to form a cylindrical roll. In a generalized sense, the word is applied to *meat* thus prepared. The word may stem from *salsicius* (meaning "prepared by salting"); animal or vegetable food finely cut or chopped and packed in a casing or delivered in bulk.

The term was originally applied to stuffery.
French: *saucisson.* Italian: *salcissa* (or *salame*). Spanish: *salchisa.* German: *Wurst.*

The encasement of seasoned meat products in an animal intestine as a means of transportation or preservation is one of man's oldest and most important food inventions, but it is not until comparatively recently, possibly starting with the medieval French, that the end results were called "sausages." What we now call "stuffings" for poultry and other animal foods as well as what we think of as sausage mixtures of the wet or relatively fresh types were called "puddings" or known by comparable names throughout history.

In the *Cookery* section (Volume II) sausage composition also is covered, under the head of *Puddings.* This means that sausages may well be considered as variations of pudding production. This reference should explain why some compositions of fresh or wet sausage, like the mildest puddings, may flavor rate as low as 25 in contrast to highly spiced, cured, and dry sausages which may not only flavor rate as high as 800 but exceptionally may be so strong as to be inedible. Aged *chorizo* may be peppery and smokey and highly rated, just as *pemmican* may be so ripe as to exceed 800 and to most of us be untouchable.

The placement of sausage at 100 is arbitrarily indicated as the approximate center of the flavor range allowing for the bulk of the members of the group being under 100, perhaps in the range of from 75 to 100, but some of the very strongly flavored sausages to be far up in the scale, some of them possibly between 400 and 500. The extreme limits of the sausage range might be represented by very mildly seasoned pork sausage, that is, fresh pork sausage, which might rate as low as 25, to some of the Mid-European pressed sausages like Landjegger. The salame group would probably vary from around 90 to perhaps as high as 300, depending upon makeup and age. Some people extol the quality of salami of considerable age, that is, over two years, but this author cautions against the high free fatty acid content in the samples he has tested, some of which ran to 50 per cent. It should not be over 1.75 per cent!

Some sausage compositions are marketed in pan, cake, slab, or leaf forms varying from gelatinous puddings to meat or vegetable compositions under 25 per cent moisture, which is very dry for such foods.

Three classes of sausages are marketed in the United States:

1. Raw (not heat-treated) compositions of more or less finely ground meat or vegetables. Country sausage may vary in composition from only ground pork to pork and other meats with cereals and seasonings. It is commonly understood that sausage makeups in this class must be cooked.

2. Compositions with some foods partially heat-treated or otherwise processed. Italian breakfast sausage, primarily lightly processed salame-type pork makeups, is an example.

3. Fully processed sausage compositions that are intended to be "ready to eat" from a Landjegger (Swiss hunter's flattened and dried sausage) with around 15 per cent moisture; "dry salami" with about 25 per cent moisture; to head cheese, with about about 80 per cent moisture.

Pathology of Sausage.—The "ready to eat" sausage may be the one with the most frequent potential dangers to health. It is assumed that all people know enough to cook the first two classes of sausage (raw, and partially heat-treated), but it is ignorance of the potential pathogenic hazards that leads so many people to use sausage "as is," ready to eat when they shouldn't. It may be ready to eat, but it isn't good to eat.

Symptomatology.—The term is generally understood as being applied to human beings. By extension it may well be applied to the detection of living organisms in food.

If in general, foods are thought of as being hosts to living organisms, good, harmless or bad, and that visual or other sensory application of what may be involved in symptomatology is applied, it would in many, many cases avoid discomfort and even disaster.

Mold on a shriveled and hard salame provides two visual and one kinesthetic symptoms overlying a syndrome of gastric diseases in a sausage that is "ready to eat" but shouldn't be eaten "as is" if at all. This observation applies particularly to what may be spoiled home-made sausage.

Trichinosis.—A disease produced by the ingestion of pork containing *trichinella spiralis.* What is not generally realized is that there are many different kinds of pathogenic bacteria and viruses present in sausage compositions *plus bacterial spores.* Ten minutes' under-boiling or boiling will kill almost all pathogenic bacteria, but it may take more than an hour at 50 lbs. per sq. in. pressure to kill the spores. While storage under refrigeration, particularly at very low temperatures, inhibits bacterial growth, such depressed temperatures do not kill the bacteria. However, freezing and storage at 10°F. or lower does kill trichinae. It should always be realized that storage of sausage at ordinary room temperatures encourages growth of bacteria.

The thermal death rate of bacteria, and particularly their spores, varies with temperature and time. The shortest recommendation commonly made is ten minutes' boiling; but that is so rough as to be meaningless, when one realizes that any strict, controlled procedure must be based on the internal temperature of the sausage.

Knowledge of the origins of sausage as a class of food and its current kinds of production is desirable for the usage of some sausage stuffs that must be cooked or pre-prepared.

Most sausage production is aimed at preservation. Its origin started with bagging macerated animal and vegetable (usually cereal) matter. Hide or intestinal sacks or bags evolved into "casings." Pemmican and primitive puddings are examples. Simple drying or smoking were frequent practices.

Today animal meats, especially organs, that are not specifically liked are accepted when they are components of sausages. The outstanding example is frankfurters, wieners, hot dogs, the lower grades of which contain meats not commercially eaten as such. He who says he never eats organ meats should *read the label* of commercially packed frankfurters; he should know the makeup of most concessionaires' "juicy hot dogs . . .!" The label would also specify the chemical preservative additives!

Some knowledge of origin and composition of sausages is positively necessary where potential pathological hazards are involved. Not only raw but partially smoked or otherwise preserved pork sausages must be properly cooked.

Aged sausages of most kinds should be cooked.

Smoked Sausage (125)

The flavor range of smoked sausages varies according to (1) composition, the lightest of them being pork and veal to those made up of components of utility meats or game; (2) fat and moisture content; and (3) the kind and degree of smoke processing. The maximal is in some of the salamis, and partially dehydrated forms such as the Swiss *Landjegger.*

Smoked Meats (65–400, av. 200)

Smoked here denotes more or less heat-dehydrated meats subjected to atmospheric and sun effects and the action of combustion gases commonly called "smoking."

Sun-dried meats are here disregarded, because primitive disregard of spoilage factors invariably results in some chemical deterioration of tissues, which radically and frequently unpleasantly alters flavors.

To determine the flavor level of a dried meat it should be rehydrated with proportionate water, pierced to facilitate rehydration, and simmered in a closed pressure cooker.

Commercially "dried" meats are usually marinated before simple or smoke curing.

While there is some commercial chemical-smoke curing, most commercially smoked meats are processed in an atmosphere of damp wood smoke. This should be understood to be a physiochemical process by which slow combustion of wood liberates its pyroligneous components and by distillation partially impregnates and always to some extent coats the meat being smoked. So, wood-smoked meat always contains some volatile phenols. Some of those phenols are agreeable and harmless, and others may be disagreeable and harmful. Some of the commercial liquid smokes are refined to minimize the results of meat oxidation.

While the volatile chemical components of smoldering wood under favorable conditions permeate meats very little, such permeation goes a long way toward altering the inherent flavors of the meats. Apple and hickory wood cures are examples.

Distinguish between slow and fast, low and high smoke cures. The "low" cures are usually produced at low smoking temperatures and lightly flavored, and almost invariably have a very short shelf life. They must be used soon after curing.

Technology.—The outstanding problem is dehydration of internal tissues without radically altering inherent flavors. Electronic or light-ray processes may be the solution. Sterility of product is essential. Pre-preparation by marination or through cooking (wet or dry) physically and chemically modifies tissues and alters flavors. *All meats* are dried and smoked by some peoples, but only very few, those that are commonly marketed in the United States, are here listed and discussed.

Note that smoked meats with bone inclusions have more flavor than boneless sections from the same animal. The high flavor level of smoked meats is attributable to a combination of the inherent flavor of the meat, the salting and other seasoning and the smoking.

Bacon (55–150, av. 85)

Commercial bacon is marketed in at least six sections and many grades, ranging from sowbelly, the fattest, at the bottom of the skirt, to back bacon, the leanest. The shoulder section of the back bacon may be the choice.

Smoked jowls may be thought of as cheek bacon, sold as "bacon squares." Many consider it the best bacon for cookery.

Smoked Ham (65–400, av. 90)

The range of flavor rating between commercial hams is not large. With an FN of 90, they will vary between about 70 to 125. That is about the flavor range of hams that have been commercially cured according to United States industrial standards, followed by ordinary wet cookery. Wet cooked hams with seasoning added for cookery or the same hams baked will accordingly flavor rate higher.

Until the differences between the elements of curing hams are understood it will be difficult to explain the extreme range of flavors, particularly of the country-style hams. While the flavor range of the average commercial hams, when cooked, will be between 70 and 125, the flavor range of country-style hams, when similarly cooked, will range from 90 to more than 300. In the upper range, say between 200 and 300, it may not be possible to identify such country ham as pork if, on a blindfold test, other smoked animal meats are concurrently appraised.

The terms "country cured" and "country style" refer to hams (and other meats) that are dry or wet salt packed before smoking. The principal difference between the old country style and contemporary industrial hams is that most commercial hams go through a brine needling process whereas the country hams are simply salted or soaked in a brine bath. Comparison of cross sections of the two types of ham will visually demonstrate the commercial practice of forcing a brine solution through the arteries of the ham as the first step in the brining process, which usually results in a uniform curing effect of each part of the cross section; whereas the country ham that has been brined *only from the outside* will not only have physical but color differences visible in different parts of the cross section.

Many, many country cured hams are lost because they start spoiling alongside the bone. By insertion of knives and making something like a "dagger thrust and wiggle" careful country packers can thus partially needle brine into hams or other meats while occasionally turning them during the salting process. Even with the utmost care and much skill packers, both domestic and commercial, of country style hams produce many hams which they usually discard.

Here in the United States there is a relatively small commercial production of country style hams, which production is almost always under Federal supervision so that it may be safe to assume that hams of country style like Smithfield and "Smithfield type" are good, wholesome hams.

Country hams not produced according to industrial standards may not only be partially spoiled, they may be dangerous. Above all, beware of hams or other cured meats from unsupervised producers. Here is one instance where every specimen of a class of foods should be smell tested; first, before buying; second, before using.

The feed of the porker noticeably accounts for greater variation of flavor of hams taken from the animals than is the case for any other animal meat. Acorn, peanut and corn-fed pork meats have different flavors. After that comes the kind of smoke cure. Then, whether it is cooked or "raw"; the mild cured hams of young porkers are flavorwise more delicate; but here a qualification enters; the size of the ham is not a good index of animal age. The young and mild-cured are at the bottom of the flavor scale, and the desiccated, dry hams like Smithfields and what the trade calls "prosciutto" are at the top of the flavor scale. Scrawny hams are not bargains. No amount of soaking and blanching will rehydrate an excessively dehydrated Smithfield ham. Flavorful, plump, and moderately moist "country cured" hams can be acceptably moisture-restored. The others will remain leathery, no matter what is done.

Smoked Pork Shoulders, Shoulder Hams, "Picnics" (70–400, av. 98)

Smoked pork shoulders on the average flavor rate higher than the hams. In general shoulder meats flavor rate higher than most muscle meats of the same animals; the closer texture of the muscles is probably the cause. Marketwise, shoulders are lower priced than hams probably because they are not so easily sliced. The epicure may prefer shoulders and disregard the handwork and the price.

Ribs (80–400, av. 100)

The term "smoked pork ribs" might properly be limited to the chop sections. For some reason that doesn't make much sense, smoked pork chops are not nearly so popular as in Europe. Mild-cured, they are one of the best pork meats. Smoked shortribs, the distal section of the rib cage, formerly discarded by packing houses, have been popularized as smoked or barbecued spareribs.

Smoked Beef (100–400, av. 200)

Dried beef, "chipped beef," and jerked beef are commercially marinated before curing.

Smoked Lamb (105–400, av. 150)

Smoked legs and shoulders are rarely marketed in the United States but common in most sheep-producing areas of the world. Smoked lamb chops and smoked lamb's tongues, usually mild-cured are rare in the American markets; but they should be more popular.

Like smoked kid meats, lamb tends to become caprilic (goaty) if the curing process goes on too long.

Smoked Game (100–400, av. 250)

Jerked venison and the meat strips of other game animals processed by jerking usually flavor rate higher than the meats of domesticated animals similarly processed—primarily because of feed. Commercial smoking of game meats usually aims at mild cures as contrasted with the haphazard work and effects of amateurs.

Smoked beef and smoked mutton are very high on the flavor scale because so far as the author knows such meats are always brined or marinated as a preliminary curing ahead of smoking, so the combination of the salt and spice and smoking plus dehydration brings the flavor components up very high. Some of the country cures of such meats are very, very strong, quite unpalatable to all but the locally "educated" tastes.

Starting with the low flavor norm of 80 for salt pork and a high of 200 for smoked beef, here are some of the extreme examples of assignment of a flavor norm rating to a food that in its mildest form may be very low and in its strongest form may be so high as to be unacceptable by the majority of people. Each of the listed foods is sometimes so lightly processed that it is not only very low on the scale, but its keeping qualities are so poor that it must be used within a very short time after production.

An observation which generally applies to animal foods is that some of the best smoked fish, red meats, and poultry, are so very lightly seasoned and smoked that they must, to be at their best, be either refrigerated or cooked and used the same day they are produced, or at most one or two days later. Contrast this knowledge with the fact that the same kinds of foods, thoroughly processed, might be edible for a number of years. This is a rather good example of a food that, though edible, is not necessarily good. An applicable adage might be: "a wholesome food may not be a *good* food."

CHAPTER 8

Poultry

COLUMN 3

Definition

Poultry in this column includes domestic fowl, some domesticated game fowl, some wild fowl and some poultry products including eggs and organ meats. For definitions of some varieties of fowl refer to the specific kinds: chicken, 30; pheasant, 48, etc.

Introduction

It is emphasized that most of the ratings of foods in this column are based on *fresh* poultry, meaning freshly slaughtered and immediately cooked. Refrigerated poultry and poultry parts would have different flavor levels. In the commercial production of frozen poultry the birds go through icing and some chilling steps that may substantially alter intrinsic flavors. Methods of packing and storing and the length of storage times influence flavors.

Relative to specific items in this classification are factors which may be considered applicable to other poultry. This will be obvious in considering the notes on processing for cookery under the headings of Turkey, Wild Duck, and Smoked Poultry.

Game Fowl.—Some kinds of wild fowl that are thought of as "game" are listed as poultry because they are being commercially propagated in the United States. Parallel practices in other classifications of food are the commercial raising of deer in Europe, buffaloes, and especially trout in the United States.

Commercial practices applied to the raising of pheasant and quail as well as other domesticated game birds in the United States closely follow the patterns of advanced poultry husbandry. Game breeders are highly selective in their choice of varieties and strains, because most game birds are difficult breeders, and the chicks much more delicate and subject to infant frailties than is true of chickens. In adolescence the feed and feeding of domesticated game birds are fraught with problems and hazards.

If a young wild duck and a young domesticated duck, assuming both weigh the same, are roasted at the same time and for the period judged proper for the young domestic duck, the flavor level of the wild duck will not be more than about 25 points above that of the domestic duck! If the domestic duck is basted with pineapple and sherry, its flavor level will be as high or higher than that of the simply roasted wild duck.

Hanging of Game Fowl.—Storage of game in the open involves the phenomena of degradation; physical and chemical changes according to time and method of storage. Immediately after slaughter all animal meats are relatively tough, which is probably attributable to death shock. Thereafter the different tissues pass into a process of degradation, which is rather commonly thought of as maturation or aging. The meat or the carcass is processed to *maturity* according to the ideas of different people. Meat so matured or aged physically softens; it is said to become more tender, but chemical changes cause the flavor profiles to rise. Thus mature game will soften as it is aged but its "gaminess" will increase. Here enters a phenomenon of wild game preparation and participation that is particularly applicable to the use of wild ducks but rarely encountered in the United States as applied to other game: the taste for rare or half-cooked wild ducks. That phenomenon may parallel the fairly general taste for long-hung game, particularly in England.

Accompaniments for Game Fowl.—It may be well for the knowing cook to contemplate game dish accompaniments from the viewpoint of a campfire cook who more or less follows camp customs and works according to restrictions both as to methods and as to choice of foods, particularly in the direction of accompaniments. There may be few available where he is. But if the game is to be prepared in a contemporary, well-equipped kitchen there is usually a free choice of optional food accompaniments. In the camp fire example it should be realized that the game has been roasted, broiled, or fried and usually over-cooked. Further, primitive and much contemporary camp cookery involves basting roasting game with berries or other fruit crushed or juiced. All of those camp fire processes end in productions of quite high flavor levels and, again by custom or tradition, the accompanying foods are at comparatively high flavor levels. Here note the age-old tendency of man to try to balance flavor levels.

Contemporary cuisine should start with objective appraisal of game according to kind, and particularly according to its intrinsic flavor profile. By gustametric scale measurements there is comparatively little difference between young venison and mature beef, or between young wild fowl and mature domestic fowl. The flavor differences appear only when the two different classifications are cooked by different methods, particularly because by custom game is more highly seasoned. One of the big differences between campfire (and barbecue) and domestic kitchen cookery is that meats are partially smoked and substantially dehydrated in campfire cookery. Further, in the process of combustion, campfire wood by distillation imparts flavor components to roasting meats, varying with the kind of wood being burned.

Through age-old customs, man has accompanied game dishes with fruit preserves, like currant jam with roast grouse in Scotland or bramble-berries (blackberries) accompanying roast wild duck in England. What may be the earliest comparable combination in the United States is cranberries with wild turkey. Study of old cookbooks and folk literature will reveal that fruit preserves of high sweet-sour and sometimes bitter profiles were and still are quite common accompaniments of game dishes. Many processes of game cookery involved components of sour-sweet fruits. Both of these factors should be considered as examples of people striving for two things: one is the inclination toward the sweet-sour-bitter balance, and the other is to cloak or mask the intrinsic flavors of game dishes.

Conventional combinations indicate specific requirements like cranberry sauce with roast turkey, but consideration of the niceties of flavor adjustments will point to the desirability of combinations that will vary with the flavor profile of the basic dish. Here is an example of flavor level appraisal that may provide a pattern for application of the basic thesis underlying the Gustametric Chart, in that the primary invariables appear on the Chart but the variables that have been set forth as qualifications applicable to those invariables can be anticipated. Consider both turkey and cranberry sauce as invariables. Think of such variables as the part of the turkey, method of its cookery, what modification of cranberry sauce is used, and temperature of the food at time of eating. In other words the temperature at which to serve "turkey" and "cranberry sauce" in combination should be determined after considering *what* is used (e.g., what part of the turkey, what things are in the cranberry sauce); and *how* it is cooked (e.g., roasted as against steamed turkey). To illustrate the importance of this: highly concentrated and sweetened cranberry sauce is so high in both sweetness and sourness that it strongly overpowers even mature roast leg meat of turkey if both are served hot. If that same strong cranberry sauce is served hot as an accompaniment to cold roast turkey leg meat, the contrast is even more marked. But if that cranberry sauce is served as a cold accompaniment to hot roast turkey leg the flavor levels of both approach balance. Therefore, the consideration of these factors will incline one toward the service of cranberries in either a diluted composition (to lower both sourness and sweetness) or as a cool sauce or a cold jelly with a calculated flavor relationship to the part of the turkey, how it is cooked and the temperature at which it is to be eaten.

Smoking of Poultry

The flavor level of smoked poultry varies with the following factors:

1. The kind of poultry: variety or subvariety (called the "breed" when applied to commercial raising of poultry); its production conditions and how and what it has been fed.

2. How it is pre-prepared for the smoking process: (a) method of butchering and evisceration; (b) marination or other pre-processing.

3. The smoking process: (a) mechanical facilities for smoking; (b) method of suspending the bird in the smoking area; and whether it is periodically basted or simply smoked; (c) process of smoking: kind of fuel, the temperature and time within the smoking area.

Consideration of the flavor values of smoked poultry begins with the differences between western and Oriental, particularly Chinese, procedures. Most western procedures may be thought of as simple extensions of primitive methods of smoking: the bird is eviscerated, hung head down and smoked more or less simply. In contrast, the Chinese basic method is elaborate, involving even more pre-preparation and more in-process elaboration than is required for most other Chinese dishes. Chinese smoked poultry is always *sweet*-smoked. The process starts with butchery specifically performed for the smoking procedure.

The head is not severed, so the neck skin can be tightly bound to make it liquid-tight. The viscera are carefully removed through a clean-sliced vent. Then the bird is hung in the smoking chamber, suspended by the feet. Ahead of smoking, each bird is basted with honey and sometimes seasoned syrups in one or more successive coatings, allowing each partially to dry, then the body cavity is filled almost full with a seasoned liquor after which the vent aperture is closed with skewers. Some procedures involve basting with the syrupy compound during smoking. The liquor used for the cavity may vary from a broth to a highly seasoned mixture, sometimes including rice wine or one of the Chinese alcoholic liquors. Both the bastes and the cavity liquors are usually fairly high in sweetness, with some soy sauce being almost invariably present in the cavity liquor. For relatively low temperature and long-period smoking, the cavity liquor is usually introduced at room temperature, but for short period smoking the cavity liquor is introduced hot.

The point of marked contrast between western and Chinese smoking processes is that the Chinese methods aim at two accomplishments: first, the smoking should result in flesh which is moist throughout; second, preparational procedures always include supplemental seasoning of a kind that is more or less conventional for the specific kind of poultry. Our western smokery procedures, being simple for chicken and turkey alike, result in simple smoke modifications of the intrinsic flavors of chickens and turkeys, but the Chinese season and smoke each kind of poultry differently. The flavor of Chinese smoked squab is entirely different from that of smoked chicken; their smoked duck is entirely different from either the squab or the chicken.

Cookery Notes.—More and more barbecues are being built along the lines of Chinese smoke ovens, to make them function for either purpose. Some commercial adaptations of Chinese smoke ovens are available both as mobile units and for permanent mounting, usually for a brick firebox. Utilizing the combination barbecue and Chinese smoke oven concurrently poses several problems, primarily concerned with temperature and time. If the temperature of the firebox is high enough for barbecue service it is too high for conventional smoking, and the time factor of smoking is too short. The meat will be primarily roasted with only a little background of smoking. On the other hand, if the temperature is low enough for good results in smoking, it is too low for barbecuing, but it should be realized and perhaps appreciated that meats (not only poultry but chops and steaks and fish) have a smoke-roast finish with flavor components peculiar to the Chinese smoke oven performance.

The Chinese methods of processing poultry for smoking may well be emulated in conventional baking and roasting, particularly in the direction of cooking the bird with the cavity at least partially filled with broth or a seasoned liquor. Roast chicken or turkey so processed will be moist-meated and if desired, seasoned at will, *from the inside.* To accomplish this result, beside properly preparing the bird, requires either cradling it breast down and tilted so that the vent is high (with the neck tightly bound) or providing the oven with a hook or a gallows so that the bird can be suspended vent side up for the roasting period.

Here it may be noted that many peoples, not only the Orientals, section and salt pack poultry for storage, usually for preservational purposes but many smoking procedures are preceded by more or less short term brining, particularly of older or lower grade poultry sections. They blanch some poultry ahead of smoking, either because a customary formula calls for it in some young birds, or more frequently because the formula requires fast processing, or the birds are more or less mature. Chinese pressed duck usually involves some brining processes ahead of partial dehydration and pressing. Subsequently such foods, like pressed duck, are wet cooked, either alone or as components of other dishes.

Eggs (25)

The flavor level of eggs is based on coddled, fresh average flavor of *chicken eggs.* If a specialized scale of eggs were to be set up to determine flavor levels of different kinds of eggs, it would start with a list of some bird eggs, which rate lower than chicken eggs, and progress upward to the eggs of some sea birds at the upper extreme. Plover eggs, which are relished and quite common in northern Europe in the short spring season, are relatively mild but still much higher than goose and duck eggs which would probably rate around 45. In turn the eggs of some of the Peking ducks would rate lower than those of Indian runner ducks.

Chicken (15–60, av. 30)

The word "chicken" is Anglo-Saxon, but oddly enough some of the early English dictionaries do not list it. In Great Britain and the Commonwealth what we call "chicken" is called "fowl." Peacocks are called "pea-cocks" or "pea-hens." "Guinea-fowl," etc. are other terms different from American usage. Varietal differences are most important as a basic consideration in the selection of poultry. The difference between a scrawny Leghorn fryer and a Rhode Island or Plymouth Rock is substantial; but contrasted with the Cornish Game it is radical. Consider the relative values of all factors: appearance, which generally implies conformation, and the elements of mass, including color; then the quantity of meat relative to bone and other unused parts; finally, the flavor and texture characteristics. In the past there has been some selectivity between the so-called "dark" and "light" chickens, particularly when offered as fryers and roasters. But it must be considered that only a very small segment of the public exercises any substantial discrimination even in this direction.

In the field of poultry production, while a fair percentage of chicken raisers may understand a little about varietal differences relative to food values, the tendency of the industry is to follow the line of least resistance and produce marketable birds in the shortest possible period at the lowest possible cost. Incidentally, Federal and State and particularly agricultural college experiment stations are consistently progressing in the development of not only chicken but other poultry to produce high quality strains. The results starting to appear in the markets are not only less bony and more meaty but more flavorsome poultry. The intrinsic flavor of all poultry is attributable to feed and feeding practices more than to varieties or strains. However, with chickens as with cattle, the American public is assumed to "demand" tenderness of meat rather than consider flavor value to any substantial degree, a "demand" which may have been developed by advertising. Pronounced flavor in any food is coincident with the maturity of the food. Maturity of flavor in chicken is inconsistent with tenderness of youth. A chicken dish based on a six- or eight-week-old fryer is limited in flavor value by the inherent blandness and underdevelopment of that fryer. Skillful seasoning can step up the flavor level in cookery, but the bones cannot be padded. Body fat, readily perceptible on dressed chickens, provides some indication of maturity and, by its relative firmness, of condition and age. Since most market birds are eviscerated, the odor, particularly of the cavity, can be an index of the time interval between slaughter and selection.

The poultry industry deserves a great deal of credit for what has been accomplished in the last 20 years. Our commercial strains and crosses of meat birds are among the finest in the world. A 3 to 4 pound bird can be produced in 7 to 9 weeks. After slaughter, a short period of aging and proper cookery, it is a delectable product. So far as flavor goes, the main controlling factors are age of bird and nutrition. In the case of chicken and turkey, maximum tenderness occurs in 24 to 48 hours after slaughter.

Quail (33)

The flavor norm of quail is based on young pan grade commercially produced birds. White meated and at its best, quail can be likened to a tiny plump chicken but with its own peculiar light game flavor characters. The flavor characters of mature, especially wild quail is higher and in kinesthetics substantially variable, particularly as concerns feed and growing conditions rather than variety.

Grouse (37)

Refer to Game Fowl, p. 157, this Chapter.

Duck (30–55, av. 40)

There is as much difference between flavors of different varieties of ducks[1] as there is between different varieties of chickens. "White Pekin" is the name of the duck most commonly propagated for table use. For eggs, some varieties of ducks are better layers than Pekin. Indian Runners are among the best small-bodied table ducks and the Rouen (domesticated Mallard) is one of the largest-bodied and best table ducks.

Partridge (45)

Refer to Game Fowl, p. 157, this Chapter.

Pheasant (48)

The variety commonly marketed in the United States is the Chinese Ringneck, but whether domesticated or wild, one of the characteristics of this bird is its tendency to dryness. The bird being a runner in either domestic or wild life, it is muscular and lean, relatively high in solids and low in both moisture and fat. Accordingly in catering services the breasts are usually the only parts prepared. For baking or roasting, pheasant should be blanched or lightly parboiled ahead of any form of dry cookery, which is best performed by a wrapper technique and fast open-pan finishing for browning. Abroad, pheasants and other such relatively dry game birds are most frequently wet-cooked for stews, pies, etc. Unless the bird is quite young, the legs and wings will be rubbery or tough unless carefully (and usually long) wet-cooked. Those parts are frequently used as components for the accompanying sauces.

Turkey (35–70, av. 50)

All commercially produced turkeys are descendents of the North American wild turkey[1] (*Meleagris gallopavo*). There were five recognized subspecies: (1) the eastern wild turkey, which ranged over the eastern half of the United States from Maine to Florida, westward to eastern Texas; and northward to Canada; (2) the Florida wild turkey which ranged over the southern two-thirds of Florida; (3) the Rio Grande wild turkey, which ranged over southern Texas and northeastern Mexico; (4) Merriam's turkey, which inhabited Arizona, New Mexico, southern Colorado, western Texas, and northwestern Mexico; and (5) the Mexican wild turkey, which ranged over central Mexico. Six standard varieties, popularly called breeds, of domesticated turkeys are recognized by the American Poultry Association: Bronze, White Holland, Bourbon Red, Narragansett, Black and Slate. The nonstandard varieties are Broad Breasted Bronze,

[1] See Game Fowl, p. 157 this Chapter.

Beltsville Small White, Royal Palm, Wild Jersey Buff and the Charlevoix, a small-type Bronze turkey originating in Canada. Of all these varieties the Broad Breasted Bronze, standardbred Bronze and crosses between them are by far the most popular, probably together comprising 90 per cent of the turkeys raised in this country (Mardsen 1953). The Turkey with the smallest body and the best conformation is the relatively new Beltsville variety developed by the United States Department of Agriculture at Beltsville, Maryland. Flavorwise, it may be the mildest. Commercially, there are two types of turkeys: (1) large (bronze or white in color) and (2) small or "Beltsville" (white or bronze). When mature, the large males run from 20 to 40 lbs. and the females 16 to 25 lbs. The corresponding figures for the small type are 10 to 16 lbs. and 6 to 10 lbs. Until recently turkeys in the United States were considered a luxury food and only available at festive times. What seems like an overnight phenomenon is the production and availability at comparatively low cost of turkeys and particularly turkey parts. Time was when only a rather large bird could be purchased and processing had to be along more or less formal lines: baking or roasting. Now that turkeys are available as fryers, boilers, broilers, or roasters, and in various sections, a range of turkey cookery is opened to parallel any procedure applicable to chickens. Turkey cookery should be approached with several qualifications: (1) primary condition, whether freshly slaughtered or stored; (2) maturity; (3) whether in the round or parts. Processing should take cognizance of the fact that turkey fat has its peculiarities that in maturity or in storage have or acquire flavor characters that vary from high to disagreeable. For cold services of turkey, particularly slicing, like most other poultry, it should be simmered in water to cover and allowed to cool before dismembering and slicing. Any kind of dry cookery results in flesh shrinkage and, according to the method, loss of moisture or juiciness. The giblets of turkeys, with their high flavor characters, may well be separately processed for sauce or stuffing, to make them acceptable.

Goose (55)

The male goose is the gander and the female is the goose, but in popular parlance the word "goose" is applied to both. Most common tame geese are descended from the wild gray goose. Some of the uncommon, both smaller and larger, varieties are strains of European and Asiatic geese. Some of those small varieties are more than proportionately low in body fat. Usually marketed when around six months of age, in some other languages they are termed "goslings" or "green" geese. In the gosling stage, geese thighs are characteristically down-covered. Anatomically, geese somewhat parallel ducks, but most varieties are larger, the meat coarser, and considerably higher in flavor components, and under domestic feeding conditions they are usually much fatter. In Europe goose fat is popular as a bread spread and a component of *pâtés; pâté de foie gras* is *usually* made of goose livers.

Guinea Fowl (68)

The male is "guinea cock" and the female is "guinea hen" (*Numida meleagris*). Only one breed is favored for commercial propagation, with two different basic colorations: the one has pale blue, white-spotted plumage, and the other is all white. Anatomically and flavorwise, they should be identical. They are usually marketed at broiler age because they rapidly toughen with maturity.

Being very low in fat, the recommended process of European cookery involves *barding* (wrapping in fatty tissue, such as bacon) or larding. The deep, pheasant-like breast can compensate for laborious cookery, but the wings and legs, which are scrawny, fibrous, and rather tough even in infancy, are usually used in game stock or sauce make-ups.

Squab (73)

Wild pigeons are called "doves." Squabs, the young of pigeons (*Columba livia*), are usually marketed around four weeks old. After that they rapidly toughen, which explains why more mature pigeons are rarely marketed. Because of their fattiness, squabs are preferably broiled or roasted. The cookery of mature pigeons requires game cookery techniques, (see Wild Duck, below).

Organ Meats (75)

In common parlance, the organ meats of poultry are called "giblets." The livers of chickens, domesticated ducks, and geese are usually mild in flavor characters but bearing in mind that all other poultry is quite closely related to their wild ancestors, their livers are quite gamey. The same observation holds true for the kidneys and stomachs. Most European chefs either restrainedly use organ meats for game sauces or stocks, or they discard them.

Wild Duck (80)

While there are many varieties of wild ducks, there is comparatively little difference in flavor level between different varieties that have been raised under the same feeding conditions and processed the same way at the same stage of maturity. There are some anatomical differences, the principal one being skin, some having skins that are thin and tender and others that are thick and tough. Other than differences in size and conformation, the legs and wings of all wild ducks tend to be stringy and tough. The main flavor difference between ducks of the same or different varieties is attributable to feed. Prime ducklings that have developed more or less undisturbed on marsh, pond, or lake vegetation, are the first choice almost regardless of variety. With rare exceptions they are low in fat, which they may accumulate by supplemental grain feeding on their first migratory flight. From the standpoint of cookery, such grain-finished ducklings may be considered the best. In the duckling stage, the majority of wild ducks are mainly vegetarians. It is as they mature and as their feed varies in migration that their gamey flavors rise. From a beginning of almost all vegetable feed they by necessity resort to more and more aquatic animal feed such as tiny fish, shellfish, and small crawling things. They all dote on land snails. The big difficulty with wild ducks is that as they age they toughen. With ducks aplenty the fastidious hunter will for himself choose only very young prime ducks for roasting. If he uses the older ones, he will probably stew the skinned breasts and either process the carcass for sauce or stock, or discard it.

Preparation of Wild Ducks and Wild Geese.—The selection and preparation of wild ducks and wild geese requires knowledge, discrimination, and application of reasonable practices. For example a hypothetical instance: random selection in a chicken yard, then discriminating in processing between a tough old rooster, or an old hen, a pullet, and a fryer. A game bag of ducks should be dealt with the same way: the tough old birds would be used only for the soup pot, a decent gustatorial burial. A young hen could go into stew or pie or what Europeans call "game puddings." Preparation of a young bird is limited only by the cook's knowledge and ability. The order of pre-preparation is:

(1) Behead. Hang by the feet to bleed freely. If body has been shot-peppered, slit down the back, starting from the neck; eviscerate and remove the tail section; there are rather strong glands there.

(2) Eviscerate in the field. The viscera of most game birds are more or less strong, and should be removed as soon as practicable. If body is to be left intact eviscerate through vent. If it is older bird, slit it down the back and clean carefully. Do not wash the cavity until it is to be kitchen-prepared. If the giblets are undamaged and are wanted for specialty preparation, clean and care for them separately.

(3) Some that have either very tough skin or some, like coots and gallinules with skins that tear easily, can be easily skinned with the feathers, if the operation is performed immediately after kill. Start at the neck and rip down. Poultry or kitchen shears can be used to clip off the second wing joints with their feathers, and two snips will remove the feet at the knee so that the skin, feathers, and feet come away in one mass.

Wild Goose (81)

With the qualification that most wild geese are larger and different in conformation from wild ducks, the discussion under the heading of *Wild Duck* is applicable to wild goose. A marked physical difference between wild and domesticated geese is that wild geese are quite low in fat and unless they are taken very young or have been more or less undisturbed on a grain feed they tend to be dry, in some cases drier than some wild ducks. Their flavor norm is just a little higher than that of wild duck.

Smoked Poultry (95)

The "flavor norm" is based on fryer grade turkey, commercially mild-smoked. The flavor level of smoked poultry varies with many factors. (See Smoking Poultry, p. 160.) Because of their high flavor levels, the placement of smoked poultry in a meal should be toward the end of a meal service, not the beginning. Even the cold service of a small quantity of smoked poultry at the beginning of a meal is high enough and persistent enough in flavor carry-over to dominate the much lower flavors of most other foods subsequently served. Here again conventional Chinese cuisine calls for a small portion of cold, finely cut smoked poultry with exactly the right kind of sauce, which makes it a complement, not contrast, with other milder flavored foods. If smoked poultry is to be served as a snack, then it is always with a tempered sauce. It may be served with simply steamed unsalted rice, but note that this is a radical contrast of flavors. In western commercial processes where only the young poultry is used and the smoking is without other seasoning, where the Chinese sweet-sour highly seasoned sauces are not present, such smoked poultry can be served in large portions and even in the middle of a meal. However it would require an educated taste for smoked food to accept smoked poultry as the main, large quantity dish.

CHAPTER 9

Dairy Products

COLUMN 4

Milk

Milk is in one sense the most nearly ubiquitous of human foods, for since we are mammals, milk is consumed by all peoples in infancy. In all but a few cultures, however, and among these primarily only in fairly recent times, consumption of fresh milk after weaning is uncommon. It is significant that among the dairy products raw milk is the only food that is not processed. Fresh milk is a highly perishable commodity; until the advent of rapid transport methods and refrigeration, its use as such was necessarily restricted to the immediate vicinity of its production. In contrast, many of the cheeses produced from milk can be kept for long periods and transported with ease; in addition, cheese is a highly nutritious food, for if milk with a water content of 87 per cent is reduced to a cheese having a water content as low, in some cases, as 30 per cent it is clear that the cheese must have a much higher caloric value per unit of weight.

CHEESE

Due largely to the different fermentative organisms which mature cheese, and in part to differences in processing methods, cheese is on a par with wine with respect to the variety and range of flavors, textures, and colors available. It is therefore a food of high acceptability. It may be that the majority of Western peoples like cheese; and, as in every classification of food, there is a small percentage of so-called "cheese lovers" who favor some of its members more than they do most other foods. However, surprisingly few cheese connoisseurs have more than a smattering knowledge of the subject. Here again connoisseurship is usually limited to a few kinds and varieties. More than any other single class of food, discrimination among the many, many different cheeses requires substantial technical background.

Most cheese is "natural" cheese, that is, it is made directly from milk (or whey, in a few instances) as opposed to "process" cheese, which is made from a blend or combination of one or more kinds of natural cheese (Food 1952). Natural cheese is made by coagulating or curdling milk, stirring and heating the curd, draining off the whey, and setting or pressing the curd. Desirable flavor and texture are obtained in many cheeses by curing the cheese, that is, holding it for a specified time at a specific temperature and humidity.

There seem to be as many methods of making cheese as there are varieties. But as cheese is, by definition, the ripened curd of milk, there are three steps basic to the production of practically every sort of cheese:

(1) **Formation of the Curd.**—Cheese curds may be divided into two classifications:

(a) ***Acid curd,*** which is the starting point of most farmhouse or natural cheeses. Under almost all natural conditions the lactic acid component in all milk will sooner or later coagulate the casein, producing curds and whey. Any acid, however, will curdle milk, so that many natural cheeses are acidulated by acids other than lactic.

(b) ***Rennet-acid curd.*** Rennet (containing rennin, an enzyme found in the gastric juice of animals and some plants) reacts with the lactic acid in milk. Rennet curd is the basis for most process and ripened cheeses. The classic method was addition of rennet from the stomach lining of a suckling animal (usually a calf) to coagulate the milk into curds. Industrially processed rennet is used as the coagulant in the production of all standard cheeses.

As a rule the milk is heated to between 80° and 95°F., before the rennet is added. In the case of very hard cheeses such as Parmesan, it may be heated as high as 125° to 135°F. The enzyme coagulates and precipitates the casein of the milk as an elastic curd which encases the fat globules of the milk.

(2) **Separation of the Whey.**—When coagulation has progressed to a suitable stage, the curd is reduced to particles ranging in size from a wheat grain to a walnut, to aid in separation of the relatively clear, aqueous whey. It may be heated for a further period, drained, and sometimes milled; after which it is put into forms and pressed, which further drains off the whey.

(3) **Ripening or Curing.**—Firm and hard cheeses are stored from a month to two or three years in cool (35° to 60°F.), moderately humid rooms, and are turned frequently to keep the fat evenly distributed. If salt was not added to the curd, the cheese may be dry-salted (rubbed on the surface), or it may be soaked in a brine solution. During the ripening process the cheese is subjected to the action of other proteolytic enzymes (principally pepsin) in the rennet, causing conversion of some of the hard, insoluble protein of the curd into soluble compounds and thereby giving a soft, smooth product. Also, through the action of various bacteria and molds, some of which may actually be added to the curd as an inoculum, the cheese develops its characteristic flavor. To some extent texture and

color also are dependent on the action of these micro-organisms. (See Table 2, Additional Flavoring of Cheeses, p. 174.)

In the United States more than 99 per cent of all cheese is produced from cow milk. A large part of our production goes into processed cheese. Abroad much cheese is made from the milk of sheep or of goats, or from animals other than cows. The milk of virtually every domesticated mammal is used for cheese in some countries: mares, camels, and water buffalo, in addition to cows, sheep, and goats, are the principal common contributors. With the exception of a few countries of Europe the bulk of cheese produced in other countries is what we designate as *natural* cheese as opposed to *processed* cheese, which is produced by blending shredded natural cheese with water and an emulsifying agent at temperatures around 145° to 165°F.

Distinguishing between the different kinds of American-produced cheeses is relatively simple, since we produce comparatively few types and we use only one kind of milk. All the standard varieties, with the possible exception of "Brick" are reproductions of European types—including "American" cheese, which is basically English Cheddar. Industrial cheese producers cater to the tastes for the different cheeses according to season, aging, and other conditions. Cheddars produced according to industrial quality control may have many factors in common with the products of "old fashioned" cheese makers, given the same type of cheese, same age, and same basic conditions of production. The notable differences will stem from the probabilities of technological control as against accidents in rugged individualist production. The nature of the milk (cow, ewe, goat, mare, etc. or mixed) and the chemical process of conversion from milk to cheese are the two main sources of variability. The farmer within limits knows what milk he has to start with, but his knowledge is vague concerning the acids or enzymes that curdle the milk or the bacteria that develop its flavors, desirable or undesirable. Indeed, so myriad are the variations imposable by slight differences in source and quality of the milk, method of processing, strain of micro-organism used, temperature, and time, and location of curing, etc., that each farmhouse cheese has individual characteristics.

All Cheddars (and other types of cheese) are produced in the United States to conform with established standards of identity applicable to each factor, physical, organoleptic, and aesthetic. Accordingly such American Cheddars will look alike, cut or bite alike, taste alike, and smell alike. Broad connoisseurship of European cheeses alone, on the other hand, could be a lifetime study. Qualifying oneself for judgments between different productions of the same variety of one kind of cheese by districts and countries of origin would in itself present a formidable project. One marketer in Paris, Androuet, lists more than 400 *French* cheeses he has available according to seasons. The average daily choice will vary from 60 to 100. His luncheon and dinner selections will be between 50 and 60 (all of which may be sampled!). Another tabulation (Jarratt 1956) indicates "not fewer than 2350" *manufacturers* of Parmesan (Parmigiano-Reggiano) in the Parma district of Italy. Further, there are many other manufacturers of Parmesan-type cheese, not only in Italy, but elsewhere in Europe, in the Argentine, and in the United States, and there are *distinguishable differences between the products of any two producers.* Entering the field of other types of cheese may induce bewilderment when it is seen that Phil Alpert, for instance, markets in New York between 500 and 600 different varieties of cheese from 48 nations, beside those of the United States (Alpert 1958).

Italy produces more different kinds and types and variations of cheese than any other country. The coverage of nomenclature of cheese in Italy is numerically impressive, beyond designating kinds and types. More than any other people they pickle and smoke cheeses and finish them in an amazing variety of forms and packages. Several of the advantages of the Italian language are realized by noting the variations in cheese nomenclature covered in this section; because much of the Italian nomenclature of cheeses refers to form and size. For example: *Provola* is a pear-shaped cheese of a specific kind. *Provolone* is a large Provola (*P. Giganti* is from 50 to 200 lbs. and *P. Affetale* from 9 to 14 lbs.). The same cheeses produced in a sphere about 5, 6, or 7 lbs. are *Provoletti, Provolatini,* and *Provoloncini.* The same cheeses when produced in sausage shapes are *Provolone Salame* (10 to 12 lbs.), *Provolone Salamini* (under 10 lbs.), and *Provolone Salame Giganti* (12 to 200 lbs.).

As has been pointed out, discrimination in selecting a cheese requires technical knowledge. On the other hand, there is a paucity of technical writing on the subject. Some classes of food are well covered from the technical as well as from the romantic side; wine is one such class. So far as the author knows, however, there is no definitive work on cheese: it is the class of food with the least coverage, with the possible exception of spices. For the serious investigator the bibliography referring to this chapter may be useful. More information, however, may be obtained from the commercial departments of the representatives in this country from the various cheese producing countries, and from the trade associations within those countries; for example, the Milk Marketing Board of England, will answer questions on English cheeses.

It may be that technical writing on cheese is wanting because the subject matter is so difficult to classify. A taxonomy of cheese is needed.

Classification of Cheeses.—Most of the divisions of botany, zoology, and other natural sciences lend themselves to orderly classification, but when the attempt is made to apply the basic thesis of taxonomy to unnatural subjects, statistical presentations become subject to variation. Cheese may be arranged into limited groups, but they will still be highly variable, because production methods are not at all uniform.

Cheeses have been classified according to method of production, country of origin, texture, flavor type, or method of ripening. Among the several U. S. Government classifications of cheeses are *physical condition,* varying from soft to hard or grating cheeses; *relative moisture;* and *milk fat content;* sometimes by *country.* It is emphasized that several of those classifications are arbitrary, based on empirical standards of identity applied to a given cheese. Under physical condition, for example, the cheeses that are classified as *soft,* according to storage conditions and time will progressively become *hard.* Many *hard* or *grating* cheeses are used as soft or medium firm cheeses when it suits their producers to do so. Other variables of which there are many will be mentioned in discussing specific cheeses in this column.

A breakdown of a classification according to physical characteristics of a cheese would require a description of its *body,* by using various customary terms indicating conformation or shape (reminiscent of the Italian terminology) of which there would be many categories. A classification by textures or consistencies (still within the description of *body*) would give a better clue to *flavor,* which is the chief objective of a person when selecting a cheese as opposed to merely enriching his knowledge. Listed by terms such as "soft" to "hard" meaning slightly *viscous* to *firm,* such a description should be applied to each type of cheese. The conflict in meanings between "cream cheese" in the Teutonic and the English languages may present difficulty here. (See Cream Cheese, FN 43, this Column.)

Classification according to physical description would also include *type of rind,* varying from no skin or rind as in cottage cheeses to different kinds of skin, including those that are mold ripened (using terms such as "mold," "fuzzy," "velvety"); and those of the "soft" group and the "firm" group which will go from indentable, firm to hard, shell hard, etc. There might even be terms involving shear test for penetration.

It can now be seen that attempts at classification lead into the maze of nomenclature of cheese. To cover nomenclature completely would take more space than is available in this book. The glossaries in the books listed in the bibliography are suggested as sources of information.

The meaning of "hand cheese" varies according to country. In the Teutonic countries it has no restricted meaning, other than according to local idiom, except the tendency to apply it to very small cheeses, perhaps under three inches in diameter and less than one inch thick.

Other classifications according to kind of milk, method of production, maturation or transportation could also be elaborated. Because of the evident inadequacy of other classification methods, however, in this column all the standard cheeses have been grouped within ten classes according to *flavor level.* These groupings are arbitrary but are consistent with other groupings of foods in the Gustametric Chart. They may be said to be arrangements of convenience for segregating cheeses into a semblance of order most nearly natural according to flavor level, at what may be considered the optimum condition and quality of any given type of cheese or in some cases individual varieties of cheeses. An attempt is also made to give descriptions of the main differences in *kind of flavor,* among the commonly accepted cheese types. However, a study of the individuality of some fermentative processes which account for the differences in flavor factors will show that some cheeses with relatively high flavor ratings are almost odorless, while others are highly odoriferous; and some as they age develop fungal odors suggesting mushrooms and damp cellars, while others as they ripen develop odors that are offensive to the majority of people. The flavor norms of many types well known by name are not given, because they are too variable. (See Feta, FN 30 in this column.)

The Gustametric Chart coverage of cheeses assembles the ten classifications and arranges them according to flavor levels ascending from Ricotta with an assigned flavor norm of 30.

Uses of Cheese

One of the objects of the Gustametric Chart is to provide the meal planner with alternative choices both as to inclusions for preparation, in the foods, and as accompaniments to the foods. These ideas are clearly demonstrable in projecting the curves from meat to vegetable columns or other seasoning columns and running the curves through the dairy products column, for the purpose of providing variety in cheese options.

Until comparatively recently most Americans used the different cheeses in their natural conditions only, either in sandwiches or separately. We used them as accompaniments with, rather than in our foods, and used them as is rather than as inclusions in sauces or otherwise converted in cookery. Aside from the many different modifications in the way of spreads and sauces or sauce-covers, consideration should be given to the inclusion of different kinds of cheese as part of *liquid carriers,* bearing in mind that all dairy products by proper processing, while they do not dissolve, do go into suspension. So it is emphasized here that some kinds of cheese, particularly the many different kinds of Cheddars, add not only flavor but solids, providing body for meat and vegetable concoctions. Instead of limiting the use of cheese to grated finishing touches as with the hard Italian types like Parmesan, some of the Cheddars can be used in basic stock make-ups or as secondary ingredients of vegetable or meat sauces or soups. However, here the tip of caution is to use only enough to provide a background without intrusion of a dominant cheese flavor or consistency. Incidentally, cheese is one of the royal roads of masking the objectionable grassy flavors of some vegetables. It also acts as an absorber for fishiness in some cases.

Mechanical blenders make possible reduction of lumpy, firm, or hard cheeses into liquid dispersions. For blender dispersion, the fresh cheeses, cream cheeses, and club cheddars liquefy most readily at ordinary temperatures; the firm to hard cheeses are more rapidly liquefied if the liquid carrier is warm or hot.

Because *fondues* probably originated in the Alpine area of Central Europe, Swiss-type cheeses are customarily and almost exclusively used, and writers of cookbooks perpetuate this prejudice, as well as that of using only Cheddars for Welsh rabbit. The Gustametric Chart provides suggestions for uses of all cheeses, not only in frying, baking, and broiling techniques (and the *fondue* type of cookery) but all other combinations where cheese can be either a component of a base of any possible food combination. Even limited trial of cheeses of types other than Swiss will provide agreeable *fondue* compositions, the flavors of which can ascend or descend from customary Swiss *fondues*.

Here again it is stressed that not all discussions of a specific class of food are restricted to a single column. For example, the use of dairy products in cookery is referred to at some length in several columns, where their different functions are discussed. Thus cottage cheese is also considered as a constituent of Stocks in Column 12 and Sauces in Column 19, both considered in Volume II of this work. Sour dairy products (yogurt, sour cream, buttermilk, etc.) are similarly dealt with.

Ricotta (Whey Cheeses) (30)

The prototype of the bland or whey cheeses is *Ricotta* as produced in Italy. Whereas most Italian Ricotta is made from whey with less than one-half per cent of milk fat, American "Ricotta" contains 4 to 10 per cent milk fat. The compositions of whey cheeses are more variable than the names by which they are called (if that is possible) in the different areas and countries where they are made. Fresh cheese of this kind may contain less than one per cent of milk fat, from 10 to 20 per cent protein, up to five per cent carbohydrate (primarily milk sugar, lactose), one and one-half per cent or more salt, and moisture as high as 75 per cent. All of the cheeses in this category are low in fat. The moisture of American cured dry Ricotta (according to U. S. Standards of

TABLE 2

ADDITIONAL FLAVORING OF CHEESES

Cheeses Supplementally Flavored During or After Production

(This category includes process cheeses, cheese foods, cheese spreads, and cheese sauces)

I. Cheeses supplementally flavored during production
  A. During setting or curding (initial acidification or fermentation) by
    (a) Different acids
    (b) Different salts
    (c) Animal or vegetable additives
      (Examples: (1) Cottage and natural cream cheeses with vegetable or animal admixtures
      (2) Thuringia potato cheese, containing ground raw potatoes)
  B. Collateral with the cheddaring process, by
    (a) Different acids and/or enzymes
    (b) Simple salts or salt compounds
    (c) Animal or vegetable additives, including infusions and emulsions, herbs, and spices
      (Example: Caraway and other spice cheeses)
    (d) Coloring matter
      (Example: Annato added to most American Cheddars)
  C. Flavors added or acquired during maturation; bacterial or vegetative, intrinsic or extrinsic flavor producers, by
    (a) Intentional, planned inoculation by or exposure to molds
      (Example of mold inoculation, Stilton type; example of mold exposure, Camembert type)
    (b) Unintentional contamination in ripening, storage, or transportation conditions, by
      (1) Manual or mechanical contact with molds or bacteria, or animal infestation
        (Examples: Wild yeasts and cheese mites)
      (2) Undesirable gases or vapors which either produce off-flavors *per se* or introduce undesirable molds or bacteria

II. Cheeses supplementally flavored during maturation[1]
  A. Primary process influencing flavor of finished cheeses
    (a) Storing the maturing cheese in vegetable or animal matter to influence its flavor
      (Examples: Continental cheeses ripened in dry clover or hay; *Grapillon*, a French cream cheese ripened in grape pomace)
    (b) Brining or marinating for storage or transportation
      (Examples: Pickled cheeses such as Feta and Greek Teleme)
    (c) Treatment of surface, by
      (1) Additives used to flavor skin of fresh cheeses
        (Examples: Paprika, salt, or pepper added to surface of matured farmhouse cheeses)
      (2) Rind finishing or processing hard crust cheeses by supplemental coat of wax (Example: Edam, coated with red wax to seal surface and prevent contamination)
  B. Secondary processes where flavoring components are combined by blending one cheese with another or with other foods
    (Here cheese should be considered a type of *solid carrier*, in contrast to a liquid carrier; wherein the solids on a wet basis exceed 50 per cent by volume of the food)
    (a) Process cheeses: Almost all process cheeses are not only blends of the same type of cheese but have admixtures of other milk solids
    (b) Club cheeses: A term used in the United States for mulled single or blends of plain or seasoned cheeses. Abroad they are sometimes called "pastes"
    (c) Cheese foods: Largely process cheeses with inclusions of vegetables or meats (Examples: pimiento, bacon, etc.)

(d) Potted cheese
  (1) In non-alcoholic liquors
    (Example: European farm cheeses packed in or mulled with cider)
  (2) In alcoholic liquors
    (Example: English Cheddars and Stiltons in port)
(e) Spreads, pastes, and dips
(f) Sauces and other specialized fabrications
(g) Dehydrated cheese products varying from combinations of
  (1) Dried cheese powders. In the process of production the flavor of the final product is substantially different from the base cheese or cheeses
  (2) Compounds of granulated cheese and other foods

[1] There can be no sharp division between a cheese that is still in process of production and one that is in process of curing or maturation; hence this division is arbitary.

Identity) is around 60 per cent. Abroad the moisture may be much lower, perhaps 35 per cent, fat 5.2 per cent; protein 18.7 per cent; carbohydrate 4 per cent; ash 3.6 per cent and salt (in the ash) 1.5 per cent.

The body of prototype Ricotta is a soft, plastic curd that may be finished so that it is paste-like or crumbly. The physical character peculiar to all of the whey cheeses is that none of them has any butter or fat-like characters. When fresh or very young, they may be lime-plaster white, wet plaster-like to wet-firm when young and from flat white through yellow to light brown and moist to a consistency like drying plaster in body when old.

The flavor of most of the cheeses in this class is really bland, lightly sour, in contrast to the next class of cheeses: the Cottage group which are in the medial range of sourness. (Note: Whey cheeses are low acid as compared with the Cottage group, which are medial, and the Sour Cream group which is high in acid).

Cheeses in this category are *usually* uncured, but there are many examples of such cheeses being more or less cured and marketed under the original names. In other words the term "Ricotta" is applied not only to whey cheeses with almost no fat, to some that have up to ten per cent fat, from high to quite low moisture. Most confusing is that while it is supposed to be a fresh, newly-made cheese, it is frequently marketed in advanced conditions of curing and aging.

Mozzarella is somewhat similar to Ricotta and was originally produced in southern Italy.

Feta is a Greek cheese resembling Ricotta and marketed sweet, salted, or packed in brine. A flavor norm is not established for Feta and most other individual cheese varieties because in most instances their composition is so variable as to make impracticable the most arbitrary measurement of flavor intensity. Feta is an example of the impossibility of assigning a flavor norm; When freshly made from cow milk, unsalted, and much of its moisture is expressed, it may be as tasteless as wet chalk. When freshly made from ewe or goat milk and not substantially pressed, it may be lightly cheesy in flavor and slightly acid, depending upon the kind and the acidity of the milk from which it was made. If Feta is salted, it may have a complex and high flavor profile.

Other bland cheese resembling Feta are: *Kareish* (Egypt), *Queso anejo* (Mexico), *Queso blanco* or *Queso fresco* (South America), *Surati* (India), an example of cheese that is produced for domestic consumption and is only available locally, *Primost* ("first or early cheese" produced in Norway), *Mysost* ("whey cheese," Norway), and *Ziger* and *Schottenziger* from Germany.

All of the bland cheeses are normally low in flavor. They rate lowest in aroma; the odor peculiar to almost all of them is the smell of lactic acid which characterizes the atmosphere of all initial cheese production. This comment applies alike to cottage cheeses in their basic types and early stages. As cottage cheeses mature the odors of specific characters develop, most of which may be thought of as resembling the odor of a clean farmhouse cellar.

Monterey (35)

The prototype is Portuguese *Serra* or *Cabreiro;* what is now called "Monterey" is one of the bland or whey group first produced by Portuguese settlers in Northern California. Its consistency is pliant and plastic through states of firmness to hard. According to United States standards of identity, this cheese may be made from pasteurized whole, partly skimmed, or skim milk. Whole milk Monterey is semi-soft; Monterey made from partly skimmed or skim milk (called "grating type Monterey" or "Dry Jack") is hard and is used for grating. (See Grana, FN 100, this column.)

Flavorwise, the cheeses in this class are between the bland and the medial sour cheeses which are the cottage cheeses.

Teleme (Greek) is a so-called "pickled" cheese (i.e., packed in salt brine). As marketed in the United States, Teleme is *not pickled.* It is a full milk cheese, softer and more plastic than Monterey.

Queso esteia ("matted cheese") *Queso de prensa* ("pressed cheese") and *Queso de la tierra* ("cheese of the country") are all Mexican equivalents.

Queso huloso ("rubber cheese") is the Costa Rican version.

Cottage Cheese (38)

The ancestor may have been the first cheese made by man. According to United States standards of identity it is a soft, uncured cheese made from skim milk or non-fat dry milk solids. According to different methods of production it is said to be soft or plastic through low firmness with small to large curd or grain. The flavor level is between low and medial, consistent with its low acidity. Not only in Europe, but in the United States, as the term implies, cottage cheese is the product of farmers, and naturally the term cottage cheese in the original basic meaning applied (and still does) to *natural* cheeses. One of the simplest classifications of cheese divides all cheeses into two groups: natural cheeses and industrial cheeses. All of the prototype unripened cheeses, together with all of the quick-ripening or short-term-ripening cheeses that were or can be produced by farmers or dairymen without industrial equipment and technology, are classified as natural cheeses. By far the majority of the different kinds and varieties of the world's cheeses are in this group. The opposite group comprises cheeses industrially produced under more or less technical or technological control. According to our standards of identity cottage cheese is an unripened cheese, but according to other interpretations, the term applies to a number of ripened cheeses.

Baker's cottage cheese is a grade that is softer and finer grained than standard cottage cheese.

Cooked cheese according to United States standards of identity differs from cottage cheese in that the cheese curds are heated in a process which is on the threshold of Cheddar cheese manufacture. This grade is named and based on German *Kochkäse* ("pot cheese"). Not only in Germany but in all the Continental countries there are many compositions of cooked cheese varying from low to high fat and consistencies from soft, like *Camembert,* to the firmness of some of the *hand cheeses.* Such hand cheeses are low fat, low to medium acid, simple or elaborated cheeses manipulated from cottage cheese and known by many different names throughout the world: *Handkäse, Altekuhkäse* ("Old cow cheese" so named because it is so lean) or *Harzkäse,* from the Harz Mountains, *Thuringia Caraway* are all hand cheeses of Germany. Austrian hand cheeses include *Olmützer Bierkäse, Quargel,* and *Sauermilchkäse. Queso de mano* is the South American version (U. S. Dept. Agr., 1953).

The broad differences in flavors between the American and the European prototype cottage cheeses and the elaborated hand cheeses are attributable not only to the different kinds of milk and the conditions under which they are processed, but to the planned and unplanned factors involved in the production of milk curds and the ripening of the resulting cheeses.

Cream Cheese (43)

The prototype is Austrian or German *Rahmkäse.* The term "cream cheese" is a semantic label indiscriminately applied by Americans, and by some other peoples in their own languages, to a cheese or "cheese food" either because it is high in cream or because its color or the viscous or plastic consistency of its body texture suggests cream or creaminess. But to Teutonic peoples "cream cheese" is a cheese high in cream. Other words indicate the slithering quality of cream, and those cheeses are called *Schmierkäse* (which may or may not be high in cream). On the other hand, application of the term "pot" to cheese is bewildering because while most English speaking peoples understand "pot cheese" to be skim milk or other low-milk-fat cheese; many of the provincial continental cream cheeses are locally called "pot cheeses." (See Cottage Cheese, FN 38, this column.)

According to United States standards of identity cream cheeses are soft, *uncured* cheeses high in milk fat. However, colloquial terminology loosely applies the term to *creamed* (mulled with or without the addition of cream, butter or other fatty matter) cottage cheese or other low fat, usually soft, cheeses. What is most confusing is that many Continental cream cheeses are more or less *cured* cheeses. European cream cheeses may include both underripe and decidedly overripe specimens. The cheese called "Neufchatel" as made in the United States, and some cheeses like Philadelphia (made by Kraft) are specified as *uncured cheeses.* The European equivalents vary from uncured to cured. For example: the prototype *Neufchatel* in France is marketed fresh (within a few days after pressing) or after weeks or months of curing. The young cheese is called "*Neufchatel fleuri,*" but after aging, it is called "*Neufchatel affine*" when it is marketed more or less ripe, more or less pungent. One country (Austria) qualifies the labeling of cheeses by the term "cream" by specifying the milk fat content of such cheeses (Simon 1956):

Austrian Cheeses.—The percentages of milk fat to total dry matter in cheese, according to Austrian laws (Simon 1956), are: Doppelfett (double cream), 65 per cent butter-fat content; Ueberfett (extra cream), 55 per cent butter-fat content; Vollfett (full cream), 45 per cent butter-fat content; Dreiviertelfett ($^3/_4$ cream), 35 per cent butter-fat content; Halbfett (half cream), 25 per cent butter-fat content; Viertelfett ($^1/_4$ cream), 15 per cent butter-fat content; Mager (thin), under 15 per cent butter-fat content.

Swiss (45)

Emmenthaler is the prototype in Switzerland. Imported into the United States, Emmenthaler is labeled "Switzerland Cheese." Vernacular names for Emmenthaler type cheese made in the United States are "Swiss," "Schweitzer," "American Swiss," "Wisconsin Swiss," etc. Process Swiss cheese is discussed under *Cheese Foods.*

Emmenthaler.—The term "Swiss" has become generic as applying to *one type* of Switzerland's cheese. Like the terms "Cheddar" and "Parmesan" that are derived from the place names of origin, it typifies a specific cheese wherever produced. Austrian *Emmenthaler* is the only one bearing a name similar to the original. On the French side of Switzerland the cheeses tend toward the Gruyere type and have such names as *Comte, Vacherin,* or *Gruyere francais.* On the Italian side they are called *Battelmatt,* or *Fontina,* etc.; and on the German side, *Allgauer.* They may be made from whole milk, or have extra cream added. The one thing common to all of the cheeses called "Swiss" is the large "eyes" or gas holes. Emmenthaler, in addition, has a specific flavor note which distinguishes it on a blindfold test from Gruyere. Another note of confusion is that many Emmenthaler types of cheese made outside of Switzerland are labeled "Gruyere."

Gruyere.—The prototype is named after a valley in the Canton of Fribourg, Switzerland (Simon 1956). From a purist's standpoint, the only genuine Gruyere is the cheese so labeled which is produced in that valley. All other "Gruyeres" are Gruyere type cheeses. The same observation applies to the Emmenthaler type. The differences between Emmenthaler and Gruyere cheeses are roughly perceptible. Gruyere cheeses range between 16 and 25 inches in diameter and from 3 to 5 inches in height, whereas Emmenthaler cheeses vary between 27 and 31 inches in diameter and between 5 and 10 inches in height. Emmenthaler cheese has numerous large gas holes while Gruyere cheese has comparatively few and small ones. Gruyere body is slightly more dense, its flavor slightly more intense and saltier than Emmenthaler. The texture is similar, other than the size and number of holes, although in the older specimens Gruyere tends to be firmer.

The other cheeses classed with Swiss in the Gustametric Chart are flavor rated higher than the norm assigned to Emmenthaler.

Caciocavallo is the relatively mild, dense, plastic cheese originally produced in Southern Italy.

Provolone is somewhat similar to Caciocavallo, usually (in American markets) higher in milk fat.

Edam (53) and **Gouda** (56)

Considered as sub-types of *Swiss.*

In the cooperative dairies of Holland all cheese, etc. is produced under and according to rigid technical standards, aimed at quality control. The bulk of Edam cheeses are round and most Goudas are flat. The minimum age at which Goudas are marketed is five weeks, the maximum age is two months. Within the past few years there have been several developments in processed cheeses of both types, varying from cream spreads to bricks and loaves of different consistency.

The substantial differences in flavor among Edam and Gouda cheeses are attributable to three factors:

(1) ***Difference in milk fat content.***—A higher fat content means richer flavor and Edam contains 40 per cent milk fat and Gouda 48 per cent. This eight per cent makes a great difference in richness of flavor.

(2) ***The age of the cheese.***—A two-month-old cheese will have a higher flavor rating than a five weeks' cheese. Taste rests on comparative maturity.

(3) ***The size of the cheese.***—A five-pound cheese, made under identical conditions and sampled at the same point of maturity as a one-pound cheese from the same batch will have better flavor characteristics.

There is comparatively little farm house production of cheese in Holland today, and what there is is sold by the cooperatives and *subject to the same regulations.* The restrictions here are in marked contrast to conditions existing in other lands where the farmer is permitted to sell his cheese and other dairy products to an unwary traveler.

The author's on-the-spot appraisal of farm house cheeses ranged from inferior to superior. Some of the farm house products would be rejected because of appearance. Because of various faults, many farm cheeses (in the cooperative factories) are usually mulled or further processed. One of the objectives of processed cheese production is maintenance of what the producer establishes as his standard, not alone of flavor *per se,* but appearance, consistency, food values, etc. There was a substantial difference in flavor of farm house cheese over that of the cooperatives which was narrowed to two factors:

(1) Some of the farm house cheeses were from six months to eighteen months old, and some of them were over 50 per cent milk fat.

(2) The more important factor was the lower moisture of more mature cheeses. Here it is emphasized that the kinesthetic factors of relative firmness, or what we think of as hardness in cheese strongly influences our process of flavor appraisal, which in turn is undoubtedly attributable to the time-factor in ingestion. We certainly take longer to munch a given quantity of hard cheese than to down a bit of soft cheese. The time of ingestion of firm cheese is in between that of soft and hard. Judging three cheeses of the same kind from the same producer, one soft, one firm, and one hard, will give the reader his own conclusion as to placement on the flavor scale, up, down, or sideways. The best Goudas in this particular appraisal session were among the half dozen around 18 months old, from local farmers who were supervised by cooperative technologists, but somehow managed to produce a cheese superior to those of the cooperative.

While *Edam* prototype is produced in the area of Edam, Holland, the *Edam type* of cheese produced in other countries may be labeled according to the shape, like *Queso de Bola* in Latin America.

Gouda prototype is produced in the area contiguous to Gouda, Holland. Examples of *Gouda type* cheeses produced in other countries are *Bitto* (Italy), *Prato* (Brazil), and *Patagras* (Cuba).

The majority of both Edam and Gouda type cheeses imported into the United States from countries other than Holland are labeled (without apologies) "Gouda" and "Edam."

Cheddar (60)

The prototype is *Cheddar* from Somersetshire, England, where the town of Cheddar is located. The Cheddars of England differ from the *Cheddar-type* cheeses produced in all other countries (under the name of "Cheddar") in that they are uncolored as marketed; and the textures when young in some varieties are almost buttery, but when mature are soft and crumbly, something like the texture of average blue cheeses. In England the different Cheddars are marketed by community or district names, such as "Derby," "Gloucester," "Warwickshire," "Wiltshire," "Cheshire," "Lancashire," and "Leicester." All of those Cheddars vary in color from flat white through different hues of cream. In flavor, Cheshire may be the lightest and Lancashire the strongest.

Caerphilly (from Wales) is flat white, crumbly, soft in texture, and may be the most lightly flavored cheese in England. *Dunlop* (in Scotland) is creamy white in color and the body texture approaches that of soft American Cheddars.

Cheddars in the United States with few exceptions are colored (in the process of cheddaring) and their textures are more dense than those of the English prototypes. Further, few of them are as mild in flavor and have such definite territorial flavor characters as the English Cheddars. American Cheddars tend to vary in texture and flavor from west to east: most of the softest and most lightly flavored Cheddars are produced on the West Coast, mainly in Oregon; medium firm and mild Cheddars predominate in the central States and the firm to hard and strong Cheddars are produced in the eastern States, principally New York. Most American Cheddars are marketed under brand names and, conforming to one of the fundamentals of American food technology, all of those brand name Cheddars are produced according to both individual and industry-wide regulations of *quality control.* All Cheddars (and other types of cheeses) are produced to conform to established standards of identity applicable to each factor: physical, organoleptic, and aesthetic. Accordingly such American Cheddars are made to look alike, eat alike (bite alike), taste alike, and smell alike.

Cheddar-type cheeses are produced in almost every dairy country. It is the most widely commercialized type of cheese, but here is an odd facet to the production of Cheddar type cheeses throughout the world: with very few exceptions, Cheddars produced in the different countries both for home markets and for foreign trade, do not follow the prototype English Cheddars but imitate American Cheddars. Practically all of them are artificially colored, their body textures are firm and smooth and their flavors relatively high. Individual cheese makers may produce Cheddars similar to those of the *quality-controlled* products of large manufacturers. The greatest difference between small scale (what may be termed "natural") and large scale technological Cheddar production is in the field of Cheddar fabrication. This field may be separated into three classes, each one of which fabricates Cheddars in different ways. In the order of quantitative production they are:

(1) ***Process Cheddar Cheeses.***—These are blended, milled, and pressed Cheddars, sometimes with other dairy supplements.

(2) ***Club Cheeses.***—These are single or blended Cheddars, milled by themselves or with other food additives. There are more smoked (or smoke flavored) club type Cheddars than any other kind of American cheese.

Simple Club Cheddars being only Cheddars that have been clubbed or milled and shaped for convenience packaging, have three remarkable qualities:

(a) While most Cheddars used for club cheeses are very young (from 5 or 6 weeks to 6 months old) the flavor of the finished club cheese approximates that of Cheddar from 12 to 18 months old. It has the flavor of a medial ripeness.

(b) At room temperature, Club Cheddars should spread like coarse butter at the same temperature.

(c) Club Cheddars, because of their particulate structure lend themselves to more cookery procedures than any other kind of firm cheese; the body crumbles without grating and readily spreads with a knife or spatula.

(3) ***Cheese Foods.***—Mostly made with Cheddars, simple or blended, to which other foods are added.

(4) ***Dips, Spreads, and Sauces.***—Many of which use Cheddar cheese as the principal component. (See also Table 2, *Cheeses Supplementally Flavored During or After Production,* p. 174.)

Sour Cream (70)

This flavor level is based on commercial sour cream, the production of which parallels the primary stages of cheese manufacture. Sour cream should not be thought of as cream that has gone sour. Commercially, sour cream is developed along the same strict concepts of quality control as those applied to cottage cheese.

Yogurt (66) is whole milk with a culture of *Bacillus bulgaricus.*

Koumiss which is fairly close to yogurt in consistency but somewhat higher in flavor, was originally produced in Asia Minor from mare or camel milk.

Buttermilk (68) is the by-product of butter production. The average commercial buttermilk is heavier or more cream-like in consistency and less acid than the natural dairy product. Here again is an example of food technology applying predetermined standards of quality control.

All of the dairy products listed here (most of which can be technically considered as cheeses) are in all cases in the group of so-called "natural" or "unripened" cheeses. Unless elaborately packed and stored under unusual conditions, all of them must be used within a few days of their production, and none of them should be allowed to ripen.

Usage.—In cookery, sour cream ranges third as a favored component, the first being milk and the second sweet cream. Yogurt is frequently favored over sour cream in combination with fruits, desserts, and pastries. Commercial buttermilk lacks some of the flavor characters of sour cream, but in most cookery it functions equally well. To distinguish between heavy buttermilk and sour cream as components of a sauce (if fairly done) would be most difficult. On a blindfold test it may be impossible.

Grana (100)

The prototype is Parmesan *Reggiano* from Parma, Italy. This classification is headed "Grana" because that is the generic term in Italy, and because it designates all of the different so-called "grating cheeses." In the English speaking countries, the call is apt to be for "Parmesan" or a "Parmesan type" cheese. In other words, an Italian would probably ask for a "*grana* cheese" and then select a specific variety, of which there are literally thousands of variations. Some of the best known of the *grana* cheeses of Italy are:

Parmesan (90) is called *Parmigiano* in Italy.

Asiago when fresh (from 5 or 6 weeks to 4 or 5 months old) is called *Asiago di taglio,* meaning that it is for table use. Note that this same phraseology applies to all the other *grana* cheeses when they are young enough to be sliced at the table or eaten out of hand.

Romano, and *Romanello* (little Romano) is the *grana* cheese originally produced around Rome.

Sardo Romano is the Romano type produced in Sardinia.

Pecorino Romano (95) is made from ewe's milk.

Vacchino Romano is made from cow's milk.

Caprino Romano is made from goat's milk.

The above cheeses are not named in any order of flavor intensity because it is impractical to attempt to assign an arithmetic value to a flavor level for any given *grana* cheese for the reason that their intrinsic flavors vary radically within each type according to highly variable producing conditions, both regional and individual. On a blindfold trial some Romanos will be confused with some Parmesans and Pecorinos; whether made from ewe's, cow's, or goat's milk. They shouldn't be but sometimes are indistinguishable. This is an instance where a discriminating panelist is sometimes assumed to be able to smell the difference, but the probability is he can't.

In the United States a number of *grana* type cheeses are produced, the qualities of which parallel some of the best products of Italy. This observation particularly applies to American Parmesans. *Dry Jack* or *Dry Monterey Jack,* a cheese of American origin, is usually an aged-to-hardness cheese that has become one of the most popular grating cheeses, not only because it is milder in flavor than most other *grana* type cheeses, but because it grates or crumbles more easily.

While we apply the term "grating cheese" to hard, actually over-mature cheeses, it should be realized that all cheeses, from young to mature, are gratable so long as they can be sieved or rasped into small particles. This fact is part of the education of every chef worthy of the name, and helps him to appreciate the great possibilities of the usages of the many softer cheeses in cookery.

Blue Cheeses (125)

The prototype is unknown, probably prehistoric, but may be primitive *Kajmak* (Turkey) which, when young is interspersed with gray-green mold. Up to maturity the body consistencies of all the cheeses in this category may be described as like soft wax but crumbling like chalk. This body texture is attributable to a combination of the mechanical processes of production followed by the development of (usually) a specific mycelium: *Penicillium glaucum,* var. *Roqueforti.* While the cheeses in this group are listed as "blue," factually there are more varieties of other colors. Most of them are light gray-blue, then there are degrees of grayed yellow-green, grayed blue-green, and grayed green. Every blue cheese has a different mycelium. The so-called "Danish Bleu" is another variation. The Roquefort is distinctly on the blue side and the other is distinctly on the green side. Literally, the blue mycelia are the cave dwellers of the cheese world, and there are thousands of them.

The classification of blue cheeses covers the cheeses that are ordinarily mold-ripened by external contact with mechanical innoculation, the end products *usually* carrying the color of the mold peculiar to the variety. It should be realized that almost all cheeses in the blue category are sometimes available at their points of origin *not* mold colored, but could be called "albino." They may be white to light salmon color. In both texture and flavor the white "blue cheeses" differ from their family relations; their textures tend to be more dense and homogeneous and their flavor characteristics lower. However, some albinos veer toward light bitterness. Such white "blue cheeses" are intentionally produced largely for local consumption. However, much of such cheese is accidentally produced; either the mechanical or the natural mold induction process fails. White Stilton and *Gorgonzola Bianco* are commercially produced on a small scale but rarely if ever exported. A generality of all blue cheeses is that their mycelia tend to revert to earthy colors as the cheese ages and loses the brightness of the blue and become a muddy gray-green. At the same time the cheese is becoming offensive, with "decomposing" odors; strongest of all are in the sheep and goat blue cheeses. Parenthetically it should be noted that the common understanding of the term "green" as applied to cheese (stemming from early English accounts) refers to *young* cheese. The flavors of the cheeses in this blue category vary from light (like a rather dry and chalky composition of cottage cheese and buttermilk) the flavor level range of which might start around 60, to the creamy, firm body and strong earthy flavor of mature Gorgonzola, which would flavor rate around 250.

Both the intrinsic flavor and coloring of each of the blue cheeses, with few exceptions, sharply vary from the inside out; the core of each cheese is almost always the mildest part of it, the flavor level progressively rising rindward. Although the body of a mature blue cheese may be acceptable, the rind and sometimes a substantial section under the rind may be so strong as to be rejected for table use. Continental cooks after carefully paring a blue cheese rind will use the rejected trimmings as components of dips, sauces, and spreads. The principal blue cheeses are:

Stilton (105). Prototype: Leicester, England. Other English blue cheeses are *Cheshire, Wensleydale, Blue Vinny, Dorset.* Prime *Stiltons* are the most delicately flavored of all the blue cheeses. They are rarely available at their best outside of England. There is no large commercial production of Stilton type cheese outside of England.

Roquefort (120). The prototype is a product of the village of Roquefort, France, made from ewe milk. The other blue cheeses of France are made from cow milk: *Cantal, Fourme d'Ambert, Bleu d'Auvergne, Gex* or *Bleu de Haut-Jura, Bleu de Sassenage, Epoisses* (Simon 1956).

Gorgonzola (140). The prototype is a product of Gorgonzola, a village in Italy. Other Gorgonzola type cheeses of Italy are marketed under their place names (e.g., *Castemagno*) or according to color or other qualitative designations. The white or yellow Gorgonzola type cheeses (with little or no characteristic mold perceptible) are called *Dolce* or white (*Gorgonzola Bianco*) and *Pannerone.* The color of young Gorgonzola tends to be from light cream and grayed green blue veining; as it matures the cream color darkens to almost buff and the veining becomes more gray green than blue. The crust of mature or overmature Gorgonzola type cheese is the strongest of all the cow's milk blue cheeses.

Blue Cheeses of Other Countries. There are a number of other cheeses that have the body and color characters *at their points of origin* of other blue cheeses. Examples in the Scandinavian countries are *Gjetost* ("goat cheese") and *Gammelost* (implying old method), both light brown cheeses with shades of blue-green in the veins. In Spain, *Cabrales* is a green mold goat cheese of highly variable color and flavor qualities. *Edelpilzekäse* is the Austrian and *Kopanisti* the Greek equivalent.

United States.—Production of the different types of blue cheeses in the United States is practically all of cow's milk. The same observation applies to the blue cheeses of commerce, for example, Danish *Bleu*. The production of blue cheeses in the United States is largely based on Roquefort. A relatively small quantity of Gorgonzola type is produced. It should be interesting to try American reproductions of goat cheeses, like Gjetost, and compare them with the imported article. The author's classroom experience indicates that the majority preference is for the milder, more uniform, and qualitatively stable American products.

Limburger (325)

The prototype is a product of Limbourg, a province in Belgium. The cheeses in this category originally were made from sweet whole cow's milk or whole milk and cream. Contemporarily there are many variations of composition both as to kinds of milk (different animals) and inclusions of skim or dry milk. All of these cheeses are in some categories called "natural cheeses" (which technically is not correct) but ordinarily all of them are medium to high ripened cheeses. Some of these cheeses ripen from the inside and others ripen both ways; they are said to be "outside-ripening." However, with few exceptions ripening starts and progresses rather rapidly from the inside, while the outside mold-ripening almost always (fortunately) gets off to a slow start, because once the outside mold growth develops, it will under favorable conditions accelerate and take over the cheese. The combination of processes of production and maturation, particularly the forces of surface molds, result in all of the cheeses in this category being designated as "quick ripening." Some of the industrial cheeses in this category, particularly those weighing more than two pounds have firm and relatively thick surfaces, most of which cheeses are not surface-ripening.

All of the farmhouse cheeses in this category weigh under two pounds and comparatively few of such cheeses industrially produced weigh over five pounds. The body when young is like compressed cream cheese. In maturity it alters to a buttery and then an outright cream-like consistency. Some of the larger industrial types at maturity pass through a soft cheddar-like condition to a moist granular state. None of these cheeses, properly matured and subsequently properly cared for, becomes really firm.

Most *but not all* of the cheeses in this classification are commonly called the "smelly" cheeses. They are high in volatile flavors, low to medial in the physical tastes and very low in the chemical tastes. Without exception most of the strong flavors in Limburger are in its coat. Some of the farm cheeses in this category have thin, crinkly and more or less velvet-soft coats. If the coats are moist-viscid, it is usually due to packaging. The farmhouse prototypes in their cellar or cave curing racks are barely moist to the touch, unless they have been ripened in a crock. The farmhouse curing areas for such cheeses give off a milky-earthy smell, not the odors that are commonly associated with smelly cheeses, which are usually no more than vaguely perceptible until the cheese is cut. It will be found that if the surface, and (hinging on the kind and condition of the cheese) a part of the subsurface is removed the core will be found surprisingly mild and low in flavor.

Most of the farmhouse cheeses in this category are locally marketed when very young; called "breakfast cheese," "fresh cheese," "white cheese," "natural cheese," etc. Aged from a few days to a few weeks they are mild, almost flat in flavor, and from odorless to just barely odoriferous. Such cheeses are the favored start-the-day spreads of the European farm producers (and many gastronomes).

Royal Brabant is another Limburger type cheese of Belgium.

Romadur, Steinbuscher, Weisslacker, Bierkäse, Backsteiner and *Stangenkäse* are Limburger types from Germany.

Schutzenkäse, Schloss (which can be described as between Limburger and Brie) come from Austria.

Port du Salut is the Limburger type in France.

Cheeses that can be described as placing between Limburger and Camembert are *Münster* (Germany), *Tilsiter* (Prussia), *Brick* (United States). Sometimes marketed under name of state or trade name: e.g., "Oregon Brick," "New York Brick," or "Beer Cheese," some Brick cheeses are quite mild, very low in Limburger characteristics; others almost parallel prototype Limburger. *Chantelle* (Kraft, United States), *Liederkranz,* FN 250 (Borden, United States), *Oka* and *Trappist* (Canada) are others between Limburger and Camembert.

Brie (150)

The prototype of this cheese is a product of the Department of Seine-et-Marne (U. S. Dept. Agr., 1953). While Camembert technically is a mold-inoculated processed cheese, Brie is a more nearly natural cheese, being produced from renneted whole milk. The crust of Brie may be soft and velvet-like and vary in color from light cream to reddish brown, whereas Camembert tends to have a comparatively firm crust that is creamy pink in color. The body of Brie is normally softer than that of Camembert, many times to the point of being fluid when the cheese is cut. Bries are made up to 16 inches in diameter, but generally under one inch in thickness. Brie could be considered a larger and more refined cheese of Camembert type. All of the flavor characteristics of Brie are lower than those of Camembert (50 points lower on the gustametric scale). Not only French Bries but most of the Brie type cheeses elsewhere produced may be considered the lightest in physical and organoleptic factors of all the cheeses in this group.

There are a number of other Brie type cheeses produced in France and marketed under place names. In the Teutonic countries, Brie type cheeses are called *Fromage de Brie.* Some of the German *Schloss* ("castle") cheeses are shaped like small bricks, weigh from two to four ounces, and may vary in form and process of maturation from Brie to Camembert. When marketed fresh or very young this same type of cheese may in Germany be called "Breakfast Cheese." Actually, the same cheese may be "Breakfast Cheese" in the morning and "Beer Cheese" at night.

Camembert (200)

The prototype, named after a very small village in Normandy, France, is a soft bodied, high fat cheese, usually round, under six inches in diameter and under $1^{1}/_{2}$ inches thick. The characteristic flavor is the development of *Penicillium candidum* (Simon 1956). However, American Camembert type cheeses are produced with one or more other strains of *Penicillium,* the products of which develop little or nothing of the ammonia note that characterizes senescent French Camembert. Another Camenbert type cheese produced in France is *Pont l'Eveque.* In Germany and Austria some breakfast and so-called "hand cheeses" are in this category. French Neufchatel may be considered a mild version of Camembert. Parenthetically, the cheese produced under the name of "Neufchatel" in the United States is in the classification of the cream, rather than the "smelly" cheeses. The true Neufchatel is mildly odoriferous.

OTHER DAIRY PRODUCTS

Three dairy products included in one Column 4 group, buttermilk, sour cream, and yogurt, should technically be considered one kind of dairy food. It may well be thought of as the yogurt group, because most commercial buttermilk and sour cream are dairy foods produced by culturing processes chemically paralleling the production of yogurt. The progenitor of buttermilk was simply the milky whey by-products of butter production, and sour cream meant cream that had gone sour. Today, simple buttermilk and soured cream are rarely, if ever marketed. Further, according to contemporary production, buttermilk, sour cream, and yogurt should be considered forms of cheese, because their production actually parallels that of cheese, particularly cottage cheese; the principal consideration being that the yogurts constitute a group of liquid cheeses.

Dehydrated Dairy Products.—Milk and milk product concentrates (including the powdered cheeses) are important technological contributions to cookery. As fillers, binders, and thickeners, dehydrated milk products substitute for flours and other starches, contributing flavor as well as nutriment. *For surface coating in place of flour or bread crumbs* dehydrated dairy products add flavor. The use of dry milk products is more fully treated in Volume II on cookery.

Skim Milk (13).—The sole difference between skim milk and whole milk is that skim milk has been processed so that it is almost free from milk fat. However, skim milk has all the nutritional components of whole milk, other than the milk fat. By itself, skim milk is commonly rated as tasteless, but like different varieties and conditions of milk it is used as a *carrier* in Column 11, a *Stock* in Column 12, and a *Basic taste substance* in Column 19, and a *sauce ingredient* in Column 20 (in Volume II of this work) besides being a component in the formulation of different kinds of food matter such as marinades and preserves. While not strictly fat free, it has the lowest flavor norm in the classification of *Fats,* Column 13; likewise in *Beverages,* Column 14.

Milk (20).—The flavor norm is based on an assumed commercial pasteurized milk. The comparatively small volume of raw milk marketed in the United States is with rare exceptions subjected to Public Health certification. The bulk of marketed milk comes from cow breeds the milk production of which is high in volume but low in milk fat. Holsteins produce large volumes of low-fat, and Jerseys a small volume of high-fat milk. The milk fat content is a substantial flavor factor. A more important influence is the nature of the feed and the season. The flavor rating of raw milk from a Jersey feeding on spring's first wild clover would be substantially higher than that from a Holstein stall fed on last year's hay.

The flavor levels of dehydrated milks may be assumed to parallel those of the corresponding whole milks. When rehydrated in water, the constituencies of different dried milks radically vary from skim milk practically free from fat to the equivalent of rehydrated cream. Skim milk powders are used both in dietetics and cookery; whole milk powders in ordinary cookery.

Pathology: Brucellosis (undulant fever).—Milk commercially marketed in the United States is processed according to Federal, State, or local regulations and is either pasteurized or certified, the primary object of such public health measures being avoidance of inclusion or exposure to brucellosis, caused by *Brucella,* a genus of bacteria responsible for undulant fever. While *cheese* production is stringently regulated in the principal foreign cheese producing countries, there is little or no supervision or control of source or production of farmhouse or other non-commercial *milk* or other dairy products. This observation applies not only to the principal cheese-producing countries but more especially in the lesser cheese countries. All of this means that raw milk may be more hazardous in some foreign areas than raw water. Beside undulant fever, raw milk can be the carrier for not only hoof and mouth disease (which may rate second to undulant fever among milk-transmitted diseases) but all the other pathogenic bacteria or virus diseases that man is heir to. The long and short of this is that raw milk at room temperature serves as an ideal culture for every known germ, whereas by contrast normal water is more selective in encouraging bacterial life.

Cream (37).—The flavor rating of cream is based on commercial table cream with a milk fat content of 20 per cent; whipping cream with a milk fat content of 35 per cent would flavor rate one or two points higher. Commercial creams like commercial milks are blends, primarily directed toward obtaining the specified milk fat content. Commercial milk processors and market distributors, beside grading dairy deliveries of milk according to milk fat, check deliveries from each producer, particularly for detection of off-flavor components such as wild onion and wild garlic, and more rarely, an excess of fish meal as an animal feed supplement. If there are off-flavors in the milk they will be concentrated in table cream and proportionately more so in whipping cream. Here note that the quantitative factor of flavor conveyance is somewhat proportionate to the fat component of a given food: whipping cream would carry milk flavors higher and longer than table cream. Flavor influences vary according to season, breed, and feed.

Butter (40).—The flavor norm is based on commercial *unsalted* butter. The solid product resulting from churning of cream is somewhat darker in color than cream, contains about 15 per cent moisture, and is bland in flavor. Most commercial butters (both salted and unsalted) are made from blends of creams and are colored with an additive of yellow coloring. One of the surprises in European markets is the display of different varieties of unsalted butter, usually tagged according to kind of cow, ewe, goat, or other animal etc. which gave it, and graded according to source or point of origin, as well as other physical conditions. Comparatively little salted butter is marketed in many foreign areas. Flavor levels will vary according to breed, feed, and season, as in milk and cream.

Ghee is clarified butter fat. The Asiatic prototype is unsalted butter, from many different cattle; largely from Brahman cows, water buffalo, and yak. Any butter can be processed for *ghee* by heating it to the point where the casein will precipitate and then pouring the *ghee* off the precipitate. There are three principal advantages to *ghee* over butter: (a) the smoking point of *ghee* is much higher than that of butter, perhaps by a hundred degrees (depending on the kind and condition of the basic butter); (b) being free from casein, *ghee* provides a sauce carrier of better clarity; and (c) *ghee* keeps longer under normal conditions without refrigeration than ordinary butter. There are two prominent disadvantages to *ghee:* (a) it doesn't have the nutritional value of butter, and (b) its mouth stimuli are largely fattiness and stickiness. So, *ghee* may be primarily considered as a cooking fat.

Buttermilk (68).—The prototype of buttermilk is the simple, unfermented liquid remaining after butter is churned from cream that has been skimmed off whole sweet milk. Commercial buttermilk is the product of skimmed milk (the cream of which has been removed by centrifugation), dry milk and a laboratory-produced culturing starter. Such starters usually consist of mixtures of lactic streptococci (*Streptococcus lactis* or *S. cremoris*) with aroma bacteria (*Leuconostoc citrovorum* or *L. dextranicum*).

Other than about 0.1 per cent milk fat, commercial buttermilk has most of the other solids of milk in solution or suspension. Natural buttermilk being lower in total solids, higher in acidity, is more watery and more sour than commercial buttermilk. Its sweet-sour factors are not as balanced as those of commercial buttermilk; it is too sour for many people.

Commercial buttermilk closely approximates yogurt in flavor and body, other than the gelatinous texture of yogurt.

CHAPTER 10

Vegetable Matter

COLUMNS[1] 5 THROUGH 10

INTRODUCTION

The grains and legumes are normally alive, but in a dormant condition. If they are so old that the germ is dead, they are in a state of decomposition. A familiar example is wheat-germ, which develops a characteristic rancid odor within a few weeks after the package is first exposed to atmosphere. This will be recognized as a degradation of the fats, secondarily the proteins; thus accounting for the off-flavors noticeable when over-age dry beans are cooked. There is overemphasis on the starch content of solid vegetables, particularly beans, to the neglect not alone of their protein content, but also the oils and cellulose (the fibrous matter) they contain.

Selection and preparation of vegetable matter is contingent upon kind, variety, and condition (alive, dormant, not-alive, or processed). One of the oldest fallacies of man is vegetarianism under the misconception that vegetables are not live foods.

Fresh Vegetables

In the historical literature of food there are many references to foods once common but now strange. Leaf and root vegetables that were used within large areas of Europe are now gathered or cultivated by the discriminating few, usually the hobbyists. Flowers and herbs of the field and forest and many wild vegetables that were once among the common foods of many peoples are now restricted in gathering and use to limited areas. The rural people of Europe still know and use many vegetable foods, flowers, herbs, and vegetables, that are theirs for the gathering and

[1] Columns 5 through 10 of the Gustametric Chart, while titled "Vegetable Matter," are intended to classify cereals, root, stalk, and leaf vegetables and raw fruits.

Observe that vegetable matter commonly used for seasonings and as condiments is in Columns from 14 to 24. One of the objects of the Chart's differentiation of vegetable matter is classification according to common categories.

The majority of the classifications in the Gustametric Chart starting with Column 5 are concerned with vegetable foods.

The parallels that exist between vegetable and animal food substances, carbohydrates, and proteins, should be noted. Most animal and some aquatic meats are the end-products of vegetable conversions. Vegetable and animal fats are chemical relations. So are the vegetable and animal proteins.

to some extent processing, the names of which sound queer to us and their utilization almost altogether strange. Here a social phenomenon enters—the gathering by children and families of wild food, a kind of excursional project that was carried over into American Colonial customs and almost abandoned by us today. It is part of the story of rural economics.

In both the Gustametric Chart and some of the supplementary charts there are vegetable foods, some of which will be strange to most Americans, but are known and commonly used by other peoples, with the purpose of stimulating a revival of interest in their utilization. Some of those things that sound odd and queer to us have been traditionally used by others. They are neither odd nor queer to many other people. Among the vegetables that, without doubt, will be new to many are the roots of some varieties of parsley, as well as other members of the umbelliferous family: rampion (the bellflower of Central Europe) of which the roots are used like onions and leaves used raw in salads or cooked like spinach; red sage that we know only as a flowering plant is elsewhere used for the tender green tips; angelica that we know only in the candied form or as a flavoring is used raw in Europe like celery or cooked; lemon verbena and rose geranium which we think of only as flowering shrubs are much used in Europe for flavoring.

In the Dry Botanicals Chart covering *vegetable flavoring substances* there are listed most of the common and some of the uncommon herbs and spices, and in the notes supplementing that chart are briefly discussed some of the listings where it was felt that expansion of the subject might lead to interest in wider usage.

Maturation of vegetable matter differs according to classes. How each different class of vegetable matures and to some extent how we use each class is briefly discussed in the introductions to the columnar arrangements. That there are radical differences between various species in what we think of as ripening or maturity is discussed under the classifications. For example, fruits ripen from the inside, whereas green leafy vegetables are selected according to maturity of their outer leaves.

Most root vegetables, with some exceptions like potatoes and yams, are used in an immature state. With rare exceptions, cereals, legumes, and nuts ripen from the inside and are used when mature.

All of this preamble leads us to one of the cardinal differences between vegetable and animal foods—no vegetable matures absolutely uniformly, but there are only slight chemical differences between different parts of mature cereals, dehydrated legumes, and some tubers—like potatoes. In those cases there is no sensory difference. What differences there are would have to be laboratory-determined.

CEREALS AND CEREAL BY-PRODUCTS[2]

COLUMN 5

Rice Flour (11)

The product is usually milled from polished rice of the "soft" varieties.

Arrowroot Flour (12)

This is the true Arrowroot (*Maranta arundinacaea*), originally coming from St. Vincent's Island in the West Indies.

Lindley (1866) quoted in the Oxford English Dictionary (1933) lists several other genera, as follows: "Other descriptions of Arrowroot are *Canna, Curcuma, Patropha, Tacca.* 'English Arrowroot,' is the starch obtained from the tubers of the potato."

Arrowroot contains about 23 per cent starch. It is a light, white powder, odorless when dry, but emitting a faint odor like that of corn starch, but lighter; when boiling water is added, and swelling to make a smooth paste, translucent and jelly-like. It is used for giving body to sauces without cloudiness. Most substitutes lack its jelly-like quality.

Corn Starch (15)

The commercial end product of corn (*Zea mays*) that has been decorticated, degerminated, and refined. For thickening, its usage is second only to wheat flours.

White Flour (17)

Commercial white flour is usually the refined product of different lots of wheat. Exceptionally the flours of some other cereals, particularly oats and barley, may be included. Both the physical cooking as well as the flavor qualities of white flours differ with the nature of different cereals: for example, soft, semi-soft, or hard wheat; and the quality and quantity of their protein components.

All-purpose flour may be assumed to be milled with what may be an average composition of the different cereal components.

Cake flour should be of low protein content. Exceptional cake flours are labeled for specialized kinds of cake.

Hominy (19)

The kernels of corn (*Zea mays*), decorticated but not degerminated. Variously processed, usually leached, to a bland, soft, and almost white condition. Corn kernels so processed and then ground are called *hominy grits,* which distinguishes it from *corn meal* (which is not leached before grinding). Kinesthetic characters of hominy and hominy grits in combination with other foods should be more appreciated.

White Bread (20)

Flavor norm is based on commercial white bread. For taste test munch crust and core together. Separately tasted, the crust, because of the phenomenon of

[2] The flavor ratings of the cereals in the left and the cereal flours and meals in the right section are based on the averages of natural grains or average milling processes. In other words the ratings are based on raw, uncooked cereals, cereal flours and meals, with some obvious exceptions.

more intense heat treatment, will have a more pronounced flavor than the core. The foreign types of white bread vary from our common American breads: (1) in composition and (2) in form. Some of the Austrian bread compositions are almost but not quite as bland as ours; principally because foreign wheat flours are neither so finely milled nor refined as the American flours. The Italian types of bread composition tend toward sour doughs. Some of the Central European white breads have potato flour inclusions, and almost all European breads, particularly the Italian, use more salt. In conformation and crust finish, most European breads, and our American types of them, are processed for both eye and organoleptic crust-appeal. Obviously the flavor rating of white breads will vary according to composition and baking. Examples are additions of onion and/or other vegetables, meats, and the use of vegetable, meat, or composite broths in the basic doughs.

Oat Meal (23)

This refers specifically to commercial "rolled" oats.

The terms "steel cut" oats, oat "grits," or "Scotch" oatmeal apply to chopped or coarsely milled whole oats (*Avena sativa*) from which the free flour is usually removed. Ahead of rolling, the oats are steamed, subsequently dried. The oat grits require processing of dry, hard oats, to allow removal of free flour. Oats not being degerminated before rolling or gritting, are subject to oxidation and rancidifaction of the germ oil and other components, which accelerate deterioration of the flavor characters after the cereal has been crushed. Therefore old oats, almost regardless of how it is packaged, tastes musty.

The kinesthetic factors of rolled oats or oatmeals substantially vary with how they are cooked. They are usually overcooked. "Mush" is the common name for the dish—and that is what it is.

Sesame (25)

Specifically whole raw sesame seed (*Sesamum indicum*), used in cookery as is. In baked goods, its characteristic nutty flavors vary with whether the cereal is physically submerged or exposed to surface heat.

Decorticated sesame meats, when ground, are called *tahini* in the Middle East, where it is combined with other cereals and/or legumes for dip or spread compositions. It is one of the oldest two-finger dips.

Whole Wheat Flour (28)

Specifically the flour commercially produced, usually from a blend of different wheats. Variations between flours, not only that from whole wheat but from ground wheat that has been refined, are many. Physically, wheats vary from small and soft to large and hard, and their intrinsic flavors varietally vary, and perhaps most of all, their growing conditions, the use of straight wheats or blends. After that come storage and processing. Because whole wheat flour retains the cereal's germs, it is subject to rapid deterioration, which may be the primary reason why it is not more popular.

Pastes (20–65, av. 32)

Most commercial paste flours and pastes including the American production of Italian-type pastas are usually milled from hard wheat. Here again the flavors of such compounds vary with the kinds of wheat and their processing. Some of the specialty packs of pastes have egg solids as well as other ingredients.

Barley (34)

Specifically decorticated whole barley (Genus *Hordeum*), has a flavor rating between oats and wheat. When cracked or coarse-ground its flavor deteriorates. Its inclusion in Scotch barley broth should prompt exploring cooks to try barley in other concoctions. In cookery it softens more readily than either oats or wheat, and the final texture may be more agreeable.

Wheat (36)

The FN (36) is based on soft varieties of whole wheat soaked 24 hours, then steam-cooked. Incidentally cracked wheat should be soaked about twelve hours before cooking.

Hard wheats may have to be soaked twice as long. However all wheats (as well as other cereals) after soaking should be immediately cooked; because under conditions favorable to fungal growth they will start fermenting.

Obviously at the option of the cook prolonged soaking or maintenance of cereals in conditions that favor fermentation may be desired for some cookery purposes.

Whole Wheat Bread (38)

Fabricated cereals and cereal by-products are covered in Volume II on cookery.

Sorghum (40)

Sorghum (*Sorghum vulgare*) is also known as African millet, Egyptian corn, kaffir corn, and milo maize. While this grass is especially cultivated for fodder, the grain is sometimes used in bakery products. The juice of the fodder is used for syrup.

Rice, Natural (43)

The flavor rating of 43 is assigned to undecorticated seed usually marketed as "brown rice." Simply cooked or steamed natural rice (*Oryza sativa*) has intrinsic flavors according to variety (and there are many) that are substantially above those of the same varieties of rice that have been decorticated and polished. Like wheat, rice falls into two groups: soft, those that tend to become soft and expansive in cookery; and hard, those that remain firm and more or less retain their natural form.

The cookery section of this work (Volume II) covers different methods of processing both polished and natural rice with considerable detail of white rice cookery designed to retain grain separation and avoid coagulation.

The first wash water of polished rice, which is high in free starch, is processed in the Orient for *congee* (sometimes spelled "Kanji") where it is used for beverage and thickening purposes.

Water Chestnut (43)

The vernacular names are "water caltrops," "Jesuit's-nut," etc. (Bailey 1943). The petiole of the root of an aquatic plant (*Natans*, Linnaeus), the pulp of which is potato-like but more dense and higher in sugar with an agreeable nutty flavor. It is mainly used in cookery as a component of Chinese and Asiatic dishes, but may be most agreeable when roasted. The labor of paring these bulbs is largely responsible for their rarity in American markets. They are commonly available canned, brine-packed, ready to use. They may be judged one of the best root vegetables.

Wild Rice (47)

Wild rice (*Zezania aquatica*) isn't rice. It got its common name because of its resemblance to natural rice. It is the seed of an aquatic perennial grass.

Corn Flour (49)

Corn flour is decorticated and degermed corn that has been milled to flour. It is distinguished from corn meal, which is cracked but neither decorticated nor degermed and is usually marketed in several grades of fineness with a minimum of free corn flour, and corn starch which is the by-product of the decorticating and degerming process.

Millet (50)

The seed of this cereal grass (*Penicum miliaceum*) has long been used in the Middle East and Southern Europe—usually in combination with other cereals, for bakery products. It may be the most important cereal not commonly produced or marketed in the United States. Millet is being grown in Ohio and is being introduced into other areas.

Buckwheat (55)

Buckwheat (Genus *Fagopyrum*) is the pyramidal seed of a grain plant. In the Near East natural buckwheat is crushed or parched (there its most common name is *Kasha* or cognate terms) and used in cookery as we use wheat. Buckwheat can be compared with natural rice and wild rice, but has some qualities superior to both, particularly texture, nuttiness, and appearance.

Kasha, a term of Russian origin which has crept into many languages, refers to cooked buckwheat *groats.* Commercial buckwheat groats go through about the same process of "roasting" as wheat that is processed for bulghur, and is commercially available so roasted in three grinds: fine, medium-coarse, and whole. The roasted groats have much better keeping qualities than the crushed natural "grits."

Bulghur (55)

Bulghur is made from whole wheat that has been roughly crushed, the free starch removed, moistened, aged for mellowing, then heat-dried. Bulghur (also spelled bulgur and bulghour) is produced under some trade names, e.g., *Ala.*[2]

Shredded Wheat (60)

This refers specifically to *Shredded Wheat* produced by National Biscuit Company. Steamed wheat is cooled and somewhat aged (for mellowing), rolled and shredded into slender strands, and then formed into biscuits, wafers, etc.

About the same procedure is followed in producing *Wheat Chex* (Ralston Purina Company). The flavor of the different products varies, first, with the kinds of wheat, then with the different pre-preparational steps, and finally with how they are baked or toasted.

Shredded wheat has long been used in the Middle East (where the process may have originated) for baked confections. Prominent examples are Egyptian, Greek, Lebanese, Syrian, and Turkish combinations of shredded wheat, honey, and ground nuts. Incidentally many so-called breakfast foods that

[2] Fisher Flouring Mills Company, Seattle Wash.

are crisp-baked too, should be considered as components for many composite foods for their kinesthetic and garnish as well as their nutritional values. Example: consider such crisped cereal products for stuffings instead of bread; or combine bread and crisped cereals to avoid mushiness in a stuffing.

Corn Meal (63)

Specifically commercial corn meal. Read the discussion on corn grinding processes under FN 75.

Corn meal is the product of processing the whole grain so that it is free from skin or germ particles; this accounts for it rating lower in flavor than *whole* ground corn meal.

Polenta (66)

Corn is ground, the free flour removed, moistened for mellowing, and then heat-dried to make polenta. It is usually marketed in three grinds: coarse, medium, and fine. The process parallels that to which wheat is subjected for the production of bulghur. In Italy whole corn is so processed, but in the United States producers usually decorticate and degerm the corn to be used for polenta. Whole-corn polenta, because of its inclusion of the germ, has a relatively short shelf life.

Corn Flakes (68)

This flavor rating is based on commercial corn flakes.

Corn (50–90, av. 75)

This refers specifically to United States maize or Indian corn (*Zea mays*).

The flavor range of corn varies between 50 and 90, by varieties as well as growing conditions, from a low of the white hybrids through some of the colored natives of the United States, Mexico, and Peru—through yellow, orange, red, purple, to blue-black. Sizes of "ears" range up to about three inches in diameter and about 15 inches long. The kernels vary from elliptical under $^1/_8$ inch in diameter and $^3/_{16}$ inches long to peg-shaped, from $^1/_8$ inch square and a $^1/_2$ inch length to $^1/_2$ by $^3/_4$ by $1^1/_2$ inches! The widest range of types is found in the mountainous areas of Peru, which may be the area of origin.

The bulk of American corn cultivation is toward a low-to-medium corn flavor which is in notable contrast with the Indian, Mexican, and particularly some of the Peruvian mountain-grown corns. According to areas and growing conditions, some of those corns have seasonal color variations and vary from light to heavy corn flavor and some of them are distinctly nutty in flavor.

Flavor trials based on crushed dry corn, soaked overnight and pressure-cooked, with just enough water to equilibrate; this requires 1.85 to 2.15 parts of water to one part of crushed corn, according to the kind and condition of the corn.

The term "corn" is an outstanding semantic example of a word that means different things to different people in different countries.

Etymologically, "corn" is synonymous with *grain*. A "corn" or a "grain" is whatever it is synonymous with, a "worn down," hard particle, as sand or salt. In the United States the cereals—wheat, rye, barley, oats, etc., are collectively called *grain*. In English usage corn may refer to any cereal; e.g.: a *cornfield* in England is a field of any cereal that is grown in the country; in the United States, one of maize.

"Egyptian corn" refers to sorghum.

Whole kernel dried corn seems to store indefinitely; but after crushing, oxidation (particularly of the germ) takes its toll and it rapidly deteriorates. This is particularly true of "stone ground" corn meal.

Commercial corn meal is usually refined and may be free of both skin and germ particles. This in turn implies that commercial corn meal will not be as corny in flavor as stone ground meal.

Popcorn

Popcorn (*Zea everta*) is a sub-variety of corn, the ears of which vary in shape from small elliptical about one and one-half inches long to relatively thick ears about six inches long; and in color from white and yellow through orange to dark red and blue-black. The kernels of popcorn are usually smaller and more densely packed on the ear than the common varieties of sweet or field corn.

Rye Bread (50–100, av. 80)

Some of the commercial bland offerings as rye bread will rate as low as 50, and the sweetish Swedish rye may rate around 65. German rye with a fairly high percentage of caraway seeds and salt rates 90, and Russian rye and some of the European "black breads"—which actually are almost black—may rate at 100 or more.

Straight rye is too glutinous to make a porous bread, and it is too high in acid to be agreeable. So rye bread usually has 50 per cent or more of soft wheat flour.

Rye (98)

In appearance and composition rye (*Secale cereale*) resembles wheat but is browner. It is used almost exclusively as *one* of the components of "rye" bread. Whole rye, sometimes difficult to find, like buckwheat and natural rice, can be processed to simulate wild rice.

Pharmacognosy.—One of the reasons for this cereal being unpopular is that the grain is subject to *ergot* which is the dried fruiting body of a parasitic fungus that develops in the process of florescence (Anon. 1960). The dangerous principle, *ergotine,* is *not* heat-labile; so that even after baking in bread, serious illness may result. It can be fatal. Industrial processing of rye for flour starts with avoidance of diseased grain, so there are no known instances of United States commercial rye bread causing ergot poisoning.

Pumpernickel (90–110, av. 100)

Made principally of rye flour with a greater or lesser proportion of wheat flour for lightness.

Here it should be realized that part of the cereals that go into many, not only of the cooked breads but very dark breads, are baked or roasted before being ground to flour or meal.

CHAPTER 11

Legumes

COLUMN 6

Introduction

Pork-and-beans is one of our most popular canned foods. But the use of dry beans and other legumes is largely neglected by the American housewife. Bean cookery has far more interesting and gratifying possibilities than most of us are aware. A little investigation of the potentialities of bean cookery should be rewarding. Legumes are nutritious and palatable. There are literally countless combinations in the field of legume cookery. It should be favored as one of the cornerstones of cookery. The legumes can probably be classified as second only to meats and dairy products in protein content and in the variations possible in their application and usage. Scaling the chart, using different legumes as points of reference, will disclose many optional combinations.

All legumes are fruit seeds, technically, the fruit or seed of a pod-bearing plant. All the grains are seeds. Of the legumes, our usage is mostly confined to their seeds, comparatively little of the whole fruits.

As usually offered, cereals and legumes are *dehydrated*, having the moisture natural to them in their "dry" state. Understand that all fruit seeds have casings or shells, the skins of which in the case of cereals and legumes have more or less mucilaginous constituents which are usually imperceptible, but which are generally removable by simple soaking, an important bit of knowledge for preparational steps. Further, the skin and husk of some legumes have bitter and other undesirable flavor components that should be reckoned with for good cookery techniques. So, soaking or blanching some cereals and legumes not only steps up their moisture content, but leaches some, if not all, of the undesirable flavor elements contained in their skins.

Legumes are consumed fresh, both shelled and unshelled. They are consumed dry in the shelled form. Other than peas and lima beans we ordinarily use few shelled fresh legumes. On the other hand, there is far greater usage, particularly in Europe, of shelled raw beans and peas, such as favas (broad beans), garbanzos, and most of the snap beans.

Varieties and Comparisons

Garbanzos and most of the string beans are used dried and shelled. Green and yellow snapbeans are widely used in this country, but it is only within the past few years that we have started to use the Chinese peas, another of the edible-pod legumes.

The differences in texture and flavor between the kinds and varieties of beans will be a revelation to the inquiring cook who has not previously explored the subject with an experimental attitude.

There are only 30 or 40 different beans and peas available in most of our metropolitan areas, but they will serve to represent the hundreds of legumes that can be read about in international cookery. The subject should be approached by reading about the formulations of other people, particularly how they vary bean combinations within their different seasons. Like our usage of potatoes, many other peoples use beans in and with other foods, but are more sensitive to seasonal concocting possibilities.

In size the individual seeds range from just over one-eighth inch for Chinese *mung* and some of the Central and South American varieties, to the one-inch and longer kidney types. The flat seeds vary from lentils to the more than inch-long favas, the horse beans of Southern Europe. The round beans and peas cover a wide range, but the largest common ones are the garbanzos.

Oriental productions of bean purée, like Chinese bean cake and Japanese *tofu* are covered in Volume II.

Lima Bean (25)

These beans (*Phaseolus lunatus*) are marketed in three sizes: small ("baby limas"), medium, and large.

White Bean (28)

P. vulgaris includes snapbeans, green or yellow, white-seed (haricot, navy), green-seed (French *flagiolets*), and red-brown seed, kidney or Spanish *frijoles*.

The dried white seeds of this variety are commonly marketed in the United States as "navy beans." They are marketed in three sizes: baby or small, medium, and large.

Pink Bean (34)

The so-called "kidney beans," varying in color from light pink to dark red, are sub-varieties of *Phaseolus vulgaris*. The scarlet runner bean is *P. multiflorus*. The brownish-red beans are sometimes called "frijole beans."

Pea (35)

The flavor norm is based on dehydrated whole green peas (*Pisum sativum*). Commercially dried peas are marketed in several grades of yellow and green, split and whole.

Crushed or split peas, because of oxidation, particularly of the germ, rapidly deteriorate. Like all other legume seeds, immediately after removal from the pods, their flavors fade, first in the rapid loss of sugars, and second by development of off-flavors which are perceptible as sour and sulphurous odors within the first few hours of processing. This means that ordinarily dried peas (as well as other legumes) have only a small portion, perhaps less than 25% of the sugars they had at the moment of harvesting, and their aromatic components are substantially altered.

Soy Bean (41)

The soy bean is technically a pea. It has a nutty, earthy flavor which seems to appeal more to Asiatic people than to us.

In China they are the basis of *soy* sauce; in Japan the *shoyu* sauce.

Both the soy (*Glycine hispida* (also G. *soja*) and the mung beans are used in the Orient for "bean sprouts."

Garbanzo (43)

In Southern Europe, Northern Africa and the Middle East, garbanzos (*Cicer arietinum*) are one of the oldest and most widely used legumes. They are also called "chick peas" or *ceci.* Used whole, crushed, or seived for a purée or thickening, the pulp is the bulk basis of many popular spreads and dips.

Black Bean (48)

Some of the best sub-varieties of black beans (*Phaseolus vulgaris*) that are frequently found in foreign markets, particularly Central America, seem to be unknown in the United States. The best of them are a little larger than a plump grain of wheat.

Lentil (60)

While every Christian child has heard of lentils, (*Lens esculenta*), ("Then Jacob gave Esau bread and pottage of lentils," Genesis, 25:34), comparatively few have eaten them. This pea should be much more popular.

Fava (70)

In England, called "broad beans" (*Vicia faba*), here, "butter beans," "horse beans," etc. The plant is a shrub, not a vine. Immature, they are used like snapbeans in Spain and Italy. Some writers mistakenly say that the pods are inedible.

CHAPTER 12

Solid Vegetables

COLUMN 7

Introduction

Most of the vegetables in this class are roots, but note the inclusion of some fruits that can be properly considered as solid vegetables, such as bananas, corn, cucumber, eggplant, pumpkin, squash, tomato, and zucchini. Roots frequently used in foreign cookery but infrequently cooked in the United States include the *daikon* (Japanese) and other radishes, parsley, and chicory roots. Cassava, taro, and water chestnut are representative of the increasing importation of Oriental root vegetables. The use of raw peanuts is a comparatively recent entry into vegetable cookery.

A number of root vegetables marketed in Europe and elsewhere are practically unknown here; chicory may be the most important omission from our markets. Sugar-beet roots and several varieties of parsley roots are used in Southern Europe. In foreign markets there are far more offerings not only of "baby," tiny or immature vegetables in the different seasons, but much more appreciation of varietal modifications. There is much more awareness of *seasonal* vegetable possibilities. Comparatively few American markets offer baby beets and carrots.

Some kinds of vegetables are varietally limited: salsify, celeriac, plantain, rutabaga, parsnips, artichoke, kale, Brussels sprouts, asparagus, etc. Most of the other vegetables are grown in many varieties, but only a few of each are marketed on any extensive scale.

One English seed catalog lists about 40 varieties each of potatoes and cabbage. Some American seed houses offer from 10 to 20 different varieties of beets, carrots, onions, tomatoes, etc.

All of the solid vegetables in Column 7 are flavor rated on the basis of their being steamed.

The flavor values of all vegetables and particularly the root vegetables are attributable to specific growing conditions: first, the fertility of the soil; second, the climate with emphasis on moisture; and third, methods of cultivation. There are many subvarieties of potatoes, but comparatively little in the way of flavor differences, but that little may be primarily attributable to richness of the soil in which they are grown. Neither good root nor other vegetables, for that matter, can be produced in exhausted soil. Carrots experimentally grown in humus- and fertilizer-free sand are very low in flavor factors. They would be rejected if a buyer were to first taste them.

In general, the stem end of a fruit is more flavorsome than the distal or flower end. Some notable exceptions are present in the squashes (genus *Cucurbita*) where the reverse is true. (See notes under Squash, this column.)

The fundamental principles of selection are particularly applicable to root vegetables: a food is chosen for nutritional satisfaction or for aesthetic satisfaction or both. Puréed root vegetables satisfy nutritional needs, but far broader in the field of kinesthetics are the appraisal and usage of roots in natural solid conditions. In form and texture the contrasts between potatoes puréed or mashed against whole steamed or baked; eggplant pulped against eggplant slices fried or halves unskinned and baked; tomatoes skinned, cooked, and liquefied compared with whole baked green or ripe tomatoes provide examples of physical changes of state that meet one or the other of our basic selection requirements.

Ordinary cookery of all vegetables should attempt, as far as possible, preservation of their intrinsic structural characters for their kinesthetic values. There is far more animal satisfaction in chewing and crunching almost all foods in contrast to drinking them or swallowing them in a more or less liquid, viscous condition.

Solid vegetables that are high in moisture, such as Jerusalem artichokes, potatoes, and cucumbers, require low temperature cookery under a watchful eye, or they will physically disintegrate. Most such high-moisture vegetables are best dry-cooked, which makes it possible to partially reduce their moisture and raise their kinesthetic values.

Chinese Artichoke (20)

The Chinese artichoke (*Stachys sieboldi*) or French *crosnes* is finger-small, orange in color, and delicately nutty in flavor.

Jerusalem Artichoke (22)

The Jerusalem artichoke (*Helianthus tuberosus*) or Indian potato (not to be confused with globe artichoke, *Cynara scolymus*) is a small eccentric potato-like root developed from one of the native American wild sunflowers. The tubers are very low in texture, high in moisture, and delicate in flavor. If wet cooking is employed careful control is required to retain texture and flavor. (See Jerusalem Artichoke, FN 62, Column 9 Vegetables, Raw Salad.)

Potato (24)

The flavor norm is based on an average of California and Idaho potatoes as commonly marketed. Beside differences in physical conditions attributable to times of harvesting and storage of boiling and baking potatoes, there are marked variations of total sugar components ranging from slightly under 1 to almost 6 per cent. Those variations are effects of harvesting (according to month or season) and handling practices, primarily the temperatures of storage. For example, Wright (1932) showed potatoes stored for three months (November, December, and January) at between 60° and 70°F. not only started sprouting at the end of that period but from an initial content of one per cent sugar started losing sugars to almost 0.5 per cent at the end of January. The same potatoes stored for the same period at 36°F. did not sprout and developed about 3.7 per cent total sugars. The same potatoes stored for the same period at 32°F. not only did not sprout but they developed almost six per cent total sugars. In other words, depending upon storage conditions, there is a decrease in starch and an increase in sugars. Von Loesecke (1960) says, "Potatoes can be, and are, 'desugared' after storage by exposing them to a temperature of about 70°F. for from 1 to 4 weeks. This procedure is followed in conditioning tubers to be used for potato chips and frozen French-fried potatoes" (Harris and von Loesecke 1960).

Some varieties of yellow meated potatoes (common in Central and South American countries but so far as the author knows not marketed in the United States) have substantially higher flavor levels than our commonly marketed white potatoes.

Commercially processed and dehydrated potatoes may provide the outstanding example of a desiccated vegetable having some points of superiority over the same vegetable in its natural condition. In the different forms in which they are marketed, dehydrated chips, cubes, flakes, and granules, they have a minimum of free starch so when they are used in cookery they retain their particulate forms under conditions where raw potatoes (in the same forms) tend to disintegrate. So, commercially dehydrated potato chips and dice tend to retain their identity without breaking down in compositions such as stews when comparatively long cooked. Further, commercially dehydrated potato products flavor rate higher than raw potatoes, which condition is attributable to the use of selected varieties and grades of potatoes and by cooking (and other factors of processing) altering the chemical composition of the tubers.

Onion (27)

As a rule, small dry onions are more pungent than the large ones, and the red ones are stronger than the white ones. Scallions (baby onions) are listed under green cooked and raw salad vegetables. Note particularly that in wet cookery onions lose most if not all taste and smell components. In dry cookery some pungency may be retained, but the flavor is altered. Most noticeable is caramelization of their sugar content.

Cucumber (30)

Widely used in foreign cookery, cucumbers seem to be here overlooked. Like most varieties of zucchini, before cooking them in the round they may first be blanched to remove most of the strong skin flavor, and then processed, like zucchini: either whole or halved, stuffed or plain, or sliced.

Kohlrabi (32)

One of the root vegetables like carrots and salsify that should be harvested before they become woody, perhaps before they are half grown.

Daikon (33)

The Oriental white radish (*Raphanus sativus,* or *longipinnatus*) is mild in flavor, like young white turnips. It is the root vegetable most favored for pickling in China and Japan.

Turnip (35)

Specific reference is to the white turnip. The yellow turnip, also called *rutabaga*, is on a higher flavor level (46). Here is an example of white and yellow varieties of a vegetable having substantially different flavor characters. White turnips as they age develop cabbage-like (sulfurous) flavors and are usually lower in sweetness than the yellow varieties.

Squash (36)

The flavor levels of squash are substantially different between varieties and growing conditions. In wet cookery much of their intrinsic flavor value is dissipated. Dry cookery, by concentration (by evaporation of moisture) retains much of their flavor components and to some extent caramelizes the sugar. Baked Hubbard squash is kinesthetically far more agreeable than the mashed pulp either wet or dry cooked. Halved Acorn squash simply baked or stuffed and baked is usually preferred to the mashed pulp by itself. The flower end of the squash is more flavorful than the stem end. In immaturity the thready, somewhat gelatinous connective tissues in the seed mass are much higher in sweetness and aromatics than the pulp under the skin. Accordingly the small squashes should be cooked in the round by either wet or dry process; then the seed mass in the baby specimens should be left in when serving if the seed shells are soft, but removed if the seed shells are tough. Sections of larger squashes and pumpkins should be cooked with some of the seed mass which may be best done by foil enclosure. Some of the nutty flavor components of squash seeds will be imparted to the pulp if the seeds are crushed before inclusion in the process of cooking.

Squash Seeds.—It may be that the seeds of all the different kinds of squashes are edible. But their values vary with variety, size, and condition and how they may be decorticated. The seeds of squashes (as well as many other vegetables and fruits) can be considered the same as nuts. The seeds of most small melons are too small or tough shelled to be handled like nuts, but though some shells of larger-seeded melons resist splitting (and some kernels have no flavor value) other varieties have soft or paper-shelled seeds that are comparatively easy to shell. Such squash seed kernels are widely marketed in the Orient and in Mexico, simply baked and salted, or candied. Some squash seeds are mildly agreeable when raw, but most should be cooked. Some kinds are not agreeable under any treatment. Most squash and other seeds do not acquire their characteristic nut flavors until they have been heat-processed, usually by baking or roasting. Crushed or ground, cooked or baked, the seeds should be considered as *seasoning* components of some sauces, stocks, or marinades: they should be removed by straining before the sauce is used.

Corn (38)

The flavor norm is based on several varieties of immature corn appraised by envelope cookery without the addition of water, processed within 20 minutes of harvesting.

Corn loses its sugars rapidly after harvesting. At 68°F. in 24 hours, the depletion of sugars in green sweet corn is about 25 per cent; in 48 hours about 45 per cent, in 72 hours about 55 per cent, and in 96 hours about 65 per cent. At 86°F. the total sugars in green sweet corn is depleted by 50 per cent in 24 hours, about 60 per cent in 48 hours, 65 per cent in 72 hours, and about 72 per cent in 96 hours. If green sweet corn is stored under refrigeration at 32°F.

immediately after harvesting, the total sugars drop 9 per cent in 24 hours, 12 per cent in 48 hours, 18 per cent in 72 hours, and 20 per cent in 96 hours (Harris and von Loesecke, 1960).

Corn on the cob is an example of a "finger food" that owes its popularity to kinesthetic satisfactoriness. We hope that it is sweet but we relish it most for the physical experience of biting, crunching, and chewing the kernels off the cob.

Beside sweetness, corn is one of the vegetables with a wide range of other qualities such as length and diameter of cob, shape of kernels, tenderness or toughness of kernel skin, and color; from 2 to 4-inch long white, through the small golden bantam to large field corn, from white to yellow and red through blue and almost black.

If corn on the cob is low in sweetness, add sugar, either lightly sprinkled on the cob or admixed with melted butter, perhaps with salt and pepper. (See Sugar, FN 100, Column 19, Basic Taste Substances.) If corn on the cob is taste-flat, the cob can be plumped by soaking in water for a few hours and then cooking it in sweetened water. If it is prime corn on the cob, it should be steamed.

Taro (40)

"Pacific" taro (*Colocasia esculenta*) or "Kalo" is the United States crop. The basis of *poi* and *dasheen* in the South Pacific and Oriental areas, taro is the common starchy root vegetable of the tropics and the Orient. It can be likened to sweet potato pulp but is lower in sugar and higher in fiber. Being a good keeper, it is usually available in Chinese- and Japanese-American shops. The pulp is dense, like compressed potato, crunchy with an agreeable nutty flavor. It is one of the most popular (but not cheap) components of Chinese and Japanese dishes. Lightly fried new potatoes are sometimes used as substitutes.

Cassava (42)

The potato-like root vegetable (*Manihot utilissima*) common in the tropics and semi-tropical areas; some produced in the United States. Superficially cassavas resemble large sweet potatoes. The pulp is oyster-white, dense, lower in moisture than sweet potatoes, and lower in body fiber. The pulp texture is somewhat like that of celeriac. Flavorwise it is threshold-sweet, lightly nutty, and kinesthetically agreeable. In wet cookery it tends to resist physical disintegration. Where available it is the most popular starchy root vegetable. **Pharmacognosy:** all varieties of cassava are reported to have more or less hydrocyanic acid; which is driven off during cooking.

Water Chestnut (43)

The vernacular name Singhara-nut is applied to this petiole of the bulb-like root of an aquatic plant (*Trapa bispinosa*) the pulp of which is potato-like but more dense and higher in sugar with an agreeable nutty flavor. It is mainly used in cookery as a component of Chinese and Asiatic dishes, but may be most agreeable when roasted. The labor of paring these bulbs is largely responsible for their rarity in American markets. They are commonly available canned, brine-packed, ready to use. They may be judged one of the best root vegetables.

Rutabaga (46)

Also called "Swede," the rutabaga is a yellow turnip; most varieties of which are larger, mealier, and sweeter than white turnips. In mashed and puréed forms, yellow turnips are favored. In dry cookery the young specimens free of woodiness are good substitutes for baked sweet potatoes.

(See also Rutabaga, FN 60 in Column 9, Raw Salad Vegetables.)

Peanut (47)

Raw peanuts, blanched to remove the paper skin, provide an agreeable kinesthetic component of both vegetable and some meat dishes. They can be substituted for pine nuts in some Middle Eastern rice and wheat, pilaff, and bulghur compositions. Lightly fried or baked, then minced or coarse-ground, they substitute for other nuts in South Pacific and Oriental fish cookery.

Sweet Potato

The Latin names *Ipomoea batatas* (49) and *Dioscorea alata* (52) are given to evidence the fact that sweet potatoes and yams are different vegetables. Superficially they have points of resemblance, but the body and flavor characters are different. Most sweet potatoes have thin skins, whereas yams have heavier, thicker skins; some varieties have skins about an eighth of an inch thick that in baking develop shell-like conditions. The pulp of sweet potatoes tends to be mealy and low in fiber, whereas yam pulp has some jelly-like characters. Sweet potatoes are relatively low in sweetness compared with the high sweetness of most yams. Some varieties of yams grow to weights between 5 and 100 pounds.

Pumpkin (50)

Immature pumpkin may be wet or dry cooked like other members of the squash family.

Breadfruit (56) (*Artocarpus incisa,* Linnaeus); **Jackfruit** (*A. integrifolia,* Linnaeus)

While commonly called fruits both breadfruit and jackfruit are generally used in a cooked condition as a vegetable: none of the fruits of the different varieties seem to be sweet enough or otherwise appetizing to eat out of hand or treat as most other fruits.

There are perhaps 40 species of the genus *Artocarpus.* Most of the smaller, often seedless-fruited trees tend to be called breadfruit; while the taller and narrower trees with much larger fruits are usually called jackfruit. The small varieties of breadfruit weigh from 1 to 5 pounds, are from 4 to 6 inches in diameter, and in form are between globular and pyriform. The medium to large fruited varieties yield fruits up to about ten inches in diameter and 20 pounds in weight.

The jackfruits may be up to 18 inches or more in length and weigh between 20 and 40 pounds. The jackfruit tree is one of the few, the fruit of which is pendant from small branches close to the trunk. Most of the jackfruits have large seeds, the meat of which may be considered as between pumpkin seed and chestnut, which seeds may be preferred to the pulp, which is rather coarse and not as flavorsome as that of breadfruit.

When close to maturity both breadfruit and jackfruit are hard; at maturity both have varying degrees of softness which in cookery pass into mushiness.

In body structure there is no common solid vegetable or fruit that can be approximately compared with breadfruit and jackfruit for most factors of surface or deep tissue characters.

The rinds vary in color from light green to brownish; surfaces typically muricated, sometimes reticulated (tiny to one-eighth inch diameter knobby, sometimes slightly pointed in a web-like cortex); at maturity they are usually sticky to the touch. Some of the hard-shell avocados have somewhat knobby skins which remotely resemble small breadfruit. The pulp may be likened to medium-firm squash but is more spongy, with delicate long fibrous tissue suggestive of the anonas.

Flavorwise they are slightly nutty, more or less sweet, and slightly acid. When fully mature they may be fairly sweet and sub-acid.

Horticulturally, breadfruit may be the most important fruit-vegetable tree not propagated on a substantial scale in the United States. All varieties are evergreen, the leaves are fig-like but much larger and the trees (somewhat comparable to fig) are both bushier and higher, up to about 60 feet. Further it is one of the best hardwoods. While some of the varieties require humid tropical growing conditions, others should do well in some of our southern and southwestern states.

Banana (35 to 85, av. 65)

The banana is listed here as a solid vegetable, because that is the way it is commonly used in the areas where it has long been grown. Botanically, bananas and plantains may be divided into two designations, but distinguishing between them by form or color is difficult. Bailey (1943) lists *Musa paradisiaca* as the plantain, the fruits of which are to be cooked and the common bananas to be eaten raw as *Musa sapientum* and *M. cavendishii.* The eating-out-of-hand bananas are frequently used in both wet and dry cookery, where the fruit is common.

Plantain—Basic types have relatively few (5 to 8) fruits or fingers in each hand or cluster. Fruits have 3 and 4 sides, rather than 5 as do most bananas, and vary from short to long and larger in diameter than most bananas; stems elongated, flower ends stubby. In the just underripe state the pulp is starchy and low in sweetness. A few plantains are low in sweetness even when ripe, with the skins black. Most red bananas are in the plantain group. It is not hard to distinguish superficially between basic plantains and the common varieties of eating bananas. The difficulties enter the picture because there are so many crosses between the different genera. Examples: some of the plantains have short stems, five sides, and are narrow and long. Some bananas are red, short, and stubby. About the only way to tell the difference in many cases is to cut the fruit and taste it. Even this is not definitive, because some plantains are quite sweet when mature, even before blackness appears on the skin.

Only in cookery, wet or dry, is there a notable difference between plantains and bananas. Bananas soften quickly while plantains tend to remain firm. The low-sweetness plantains when wet or dry cooked behave and taste like some root vegetables, particularly some potatoes. The sweet plantains and immature bananas in cookery behave and taste like some sweet potatoes, but have characteristic banana aromatic components.

Usage.—Baking either plantains or green bananas, keeping the skin on, or as with sweet potatoes, removing skin and combining baked pulp with other foods will provide agreeable options which can be plotted on the Gustametric Chart. See Banana FN 48 in Column 10, Fruits, Raw.

Carrot (75)

In wet cookery, intrinsic flavors of carrots are altered. The flavor levels of some rise while others fall. Flavor levels tend to fall in wet cookery and rise in dry cookery. Note particularly that carotene is almost insoluble in water. Experimental cookery of whole or crushed or diced carrots will reveal that only about 5 per cent of carotene content passes off into the water. This indicates that a soup or stock composition for a bouillon or consomme in which carrots are cooked will have carrot flavor components, but will contain little carotene. For the carotene content of carrots, carrot solids should be eaten.

Beet (77)

Beet roots, cooked in tap water, will result in dull colored vegetables and purplish liquor, because the average tap water is slightly on the acid side, with a pH of approximately 6.3. Adding sufficient soda to put the water on the alkaline side should result in a bright color of both the beet and the liquor. The beet is one of two vegetables (the other is *chiso,* the Japanese red mint) the cooked juice of which is widely used for coloring in food composition. See Sugar Beet, FN 92, this Column, Beet Root, FN 88, in Column 9, Raw Salad Vegetables.

Eggplant (80)

Related to potato and tomato. The name was applied to the prototype South American white fruits the shape and size of eggs. In Asia and the Orient there are many varieties of the narrow, elongated type, ranging from white through green, violet- and purple-streaked, to uniform violet and light to dark purple variations. Most of them are denser and have higher flavor levels than the bulbous varieties offered in American markets. Only recently has there been any substantial introduction into American markets of the narrow, elongated varieties, most of which have characters superior for cookery and especially for frying techniques, compared to the bulbous and more spongy kinds familiar in America.

Tomato (90)

The term "tomato" stems from the original Peruvian name. When the Italians first took the tomato from Spain, they called it *pome di more* (Moor's apple). This the French distorted into *pomme d'amour* ("love apple"). Flavor variations of varieties and subvarieties range from almost tasteless from some of the white, to strong tomato flavors in some of the very small berry-like clustered fruits, original wild types. Some of the new green, yellow, and orange introductions provide interesting subacid to mildly acid tomato flavor variations. What may be voted the best of the new hybrids are the variations of the golden kind. The Italian *pommadora* and pear tomatoes, both yellow and red, are highest in sweetness and in solids and lightest in acidity, lending themselves to sautéeing and preserves better than most of the standard tomatoes, which are much higher in moisture and lower in solids. In the field of tomatoes we are confronted with the American trait: the marketer catering to common "demand" for size and external appearance factors rather than intrinsic eating values. Consequently growers produce tomatoes for size and color rather than flavor (see also Tomato, FN 60, Column 19, Raw Salad Vegetables).

Sugar Beet (92)

Before sugar was commercially crystallized from either beets or cane, outside of China, sugar beets, or *mangels,* were grown in Europe and processed for syrup. Those sugar beets (*Beta vulgaris*) are still the principal source of sweetness in a syrup form in much of Central Europe, but here is a notable point: European home gardeners use baby sugar beets as a vegetable. They are white and much more fibrous than the red beets we are familiar with, but they are also much higher in sweetness. Home gardeners may be well advised to try an experimental planting. In cookery sugar beet roots have their own distinctive flavor characters which are unlike those of the red beets. They are quite agreeable (see Beet, FN 77, this Column).

Zucchini (95)

The skin of most zucchini being strong in grassy flavor should be blanched to avoid most of those objectionable flavors. Even dipping in boiling water for 10 or 15 seconds will strip it of its grassiness (see Zucchini, FN 85 in Column 9, Raw Salad Vegetables).

Parsley (98)

Several varieties of parsley are propagated solely as a root vegetable, popular in Europe. Rarely encountered in the United States (see Parsley, FN 140 and Parsley Root, FN 92 in Column 9, Raw Salad Vegetables).

Celeriac (100)

This is the celery developed as a root vegetable. The heart greens but not the leaves can be desirable soup stock components. The leaves should be considered as spice vegetable matter and used with restraint; they are very high in celery flavor and are quite bitter.

Garlic (110)

In wet cookery garlic loses all of its pungency but retains enough of its peculiar flavor to make it rate very high (see Onion, FN 375 in Column 9, Raw Salad Vegetables).

Chicory (115)

The root of what is commonly called endive, like the different salsifies, is a good vegetable if used before it is half grown. Baked or roasted chicory roots are used as a coffee extender, not necessarily an adulterant. Some of the best so-called "French" and "Italian" coffee compositions include a little chicory. It tends to raise the body and agreeably supplement the flavor of "high" coffee roasts (see Chicory, FN 95, in Column 9, Raw Salad Vegetables).

Salsify (125)

The common salsify is *Tragopogon porifolius. T. scorzonera* may be considered a black-skinned salsify. *Scolymus hispanicus* is the vegetable known as "golden thistle" or "Spanish oyster plant." All of the so-called "salsifies" are of the family *Compositae* (Bailey 1943). Salsify is one of the most agreeably flavored root vegetables, but not popular because of the work required to surface-clean them. Like parsnips, their flavor may be worth the labor.

Radish (150)

All of the radishes, white through the different colors to black, are used in cookery abroad. Some of them with high skin flavors may be preliminarily blanched. All of them lose their pungency in wet cookery, and some or all pungency in marination, depending on the kind of marinade (see Radish, FN 130, in Column 9, Raw Salad Vegetables).

CHAPTER 13

Green Cooked Vegetables

COLUMN 8

Introduction

Attention is directed to the possibilities suggested by the juxtaposition of Columns 7, 8, 9, and 10, comprising most of the vegetable group, in the way of interchanging raw and cooked vegetables. Within limits their degree of cookery can be agreeably varied in food services, from the raw state to partly cooked, which is a modified stage in the preservational process, to a cooked state. However, the cook should take cognizance of the change in flavor level between the raw and the process-modified condition of any given vegetable or fruit. Study of comparative flavor levels on the Gustametric Chart will point out, and individual experimentation should confirm, that some vegetables and fruits, as well as other foods, have higher flavors when cooked than when raw, whereas others have lower flavor levels when simply wet cooked. Further, flavors of most foods are raised by dry cookery, to a degree varying with the method of dry cookery. Raw carrots are charted at 65; steamed they rate at 75, but baked they would probably be around 85. Many of the vegetables which have substantially higher flavor when raw than when steamed would have a level between the two when baked: celery raw is 90, steamed it is 80, and baked it may be around 85.

Simple cookery of vegetables in water is a custom that seems restricted to the United States and some but not all of the English-speaking peoples. The majority of other peoples use meat stocks or fats when available. Particularly in continental Europe and the Orient a stock-pot is maintained for general utility; it may be said that the primary purpose of pot liquor is its service as a carrier, a base liquid for common cookery. Secondarily it provides the starter for most soups and sauces. So into the *pot-au-feu* of the French kitchen, the almost universal pot-on-the-fire, go odds and ends of meats and vegetables and some fruits, as well as residual liquors from different concoctions. It all goes into the common stockpot to provide a base liquor for everyday cookery.

Here are some examples to illustrate the point: spinach or other leaf vegetables, as well as the solid vegetable varieties when wet-cooked or braised in meat-stock will be found far more acceptable by the majority than spinach simply water-cooked and salt-seasoned. "Boiled beef" when simmered in vegetable and meat stocks will be judged more flavorful than beef prepared with plain water. However, the development of the stock-pot idea for everyday cookery should proceed with due consideration of the flavor values of individual components; particularly must dominating components be avoided or minimized. Too high a proportion of high-flavored vegetables such as celery leaves and carrot greens, or animal meats such as lamb, or the fatty fishes, will make the stock taste too green, too muttony or too fishy.

Most green vegetables should be blanched ahead of cookery, to reduce grassy flavors. Many leafy vegetables are not now popular because of the dominance of raw green flavor components. Most of those undesired flavor factors are concentrated in the epidermis, particularly in the case of leaf vegetables, and can be substantially reduced and in some cases almost entirely removed by relatively short blanching processes. This is particularly true of the bitter vegetables such as mustard greens, cardoon, kale, some varieties of snapbeans and spinach. Just dipping some of these vegetables into boiling water for from 3 to 5 seconds will remove the superficial flavor constituents that are most objectionable. Naturally, for a skin-deep leaching of root vegetables or fruit, longer blanching periods are required, but by careful pre-preparational blanching, many can be raised from just palatable to really likable.

For emphasis it is repeated that blanching may vary from in-and-out dipping in scalding water—merely scalding the surface of the food—to several minutes' immersion in boiling water or in an atmosphere of steam.

Along with blanching, paring is often advisable. The lower part of asparagus spears can be made edible by shaving them with a vegetable parer. This is a procedure almost universally overlooked here in America, where we discard about half of the asparagus, but quite common in Europe where the butt ends are either stripped and used or saved to be cut up for stock make-up. In southern Europe artichokes are marketed with long stalks because the cooks use the stalks separately and process them as they do asparagus, shaving away the outer fibrous covering. Then the inner stick is cooked very much as is asparagus. It is particularly good when braised or sautéed with some meats.

Column 8 is constructed on the basis of specific flavor norms determined at a temperature of 98.6°F. after wet cookery. All of those vegetables served cold and particularly with seasoning additives, as in salad compositions, will have different flavor levels. All are used by some peoples in simple cold form or as components of salads with other vegetables, particularly with raw salad vegetables or cold meats. Examples include the many variations of herring salad where a small percentage of marinated herring dominates both cooked and raw salad vegetables.

There is an indented column within Column 8: the more or less "solid" items adjoin Column 7, the Solid Vegetables, and the vegetables with loose green leaves are indented.

Cauliflower (20)

Note particularly that simply steamed cauliflower flavor rated at 20 may be compared with broccoli, which is 75, as an example of two different varieties of the same vegetable having radically different flavor characters. Accordingly, prime cauliflower should not be blanched ahead of cookery, but most broccoli may be more acceptable if it is preliminarily lightly blanched.

Aquatic Plants (35)

An average flavor rating of the commonly used aquatic vegetables (seaweeds) will be about 35. Thoroughly washed, fresh aquatic plants are surprisingly low in intrinsic flavor values. (See Aquatic Foods Chart.)

Bean Sprout (37)

The sprout of the *mung* bean (*Phaseolus mungo*) is most favored in Oriental cookery, but other beans are also used for sprouts (soy beans for example).

Mushroom (25 to 95, av. 38)

Agaricus campestris is the mushroom almost exclusively propagated by commercial growers. Our usage of mushrooms is with rare exceptions limited to them in the immature state, as "button," "slices," "stems," or "pieces." It is emphasized that the difference in flavor levels between immature and mature mushrooms is great. Accordingly, many foreign food compositions call for mushroom "caps" which is really a specification for mature or ripe mushrooms for their ripe, full mushroom flavor. (See Column 9, FN 35.)

Bamboo Shoot (40)

This is one of the common ingredients of Oriental dishes, ordinarily available canned, ready to use without further cookery. It is occasionally available fresh in Oriental stores. Flavor values are light; kinesthetic values are medial.

Snowpea (45)

The edible pod pea which in the baby state is edible in the round.

Pea (46)

The flavor norm is based on shelled immature peas, envelope packaged and blanched *in the pod*, and appraised within 20 minutes of harvesting.

Perhaps more than any other vegetable, peas rapidly lose their sugars from the moment of harvesting. Just bruising or lightly crushing the pods seems to cause some deterioration. A lug box of peas in the pod gathered under atmospheric temperatures of 70° to 80°F. will develop internal temperatures up to 140°F. within 30 minutes. That is much too hot to permit the hand being kept in the middle of the mass. Further, by respiration, enzymatic burning of sugars, a lug box of peas as it develops heat gives off a sour and sulphurous odor.

A few years ago peas intended for canning were "vined" in the field and transported to canneries in lug boxes or bulk. Now most canners remove the pods from the vines in equipment alongside the cannery so that the peas are removed from the pods, processed and canned in something like 20 minutes.

Culling the chemical abstracts revealed no specific data on the loss of sugars in peas subsequent to harvesting but checking with several packers leads to the conclusion that the loss of sugars in peas is more rapid and greater than the investigations show to be true of corn. (Refer to Corn, Column 7, FN 38.)

The gist of these notes is: Peas are at their best when eaten raw or processed within a very few minutes of gathering. At normal temperatures peas in the pod lose 25 per cent of their sugars in 24 hours and 50 per cent in 48 hours. What may be equally critical is, as time goes on, certainly within 48 hours of harvesting, peas in the pod develop off-flavors.

In the past, preferences have been for infant, tiny (French: "*petit*") peas, but hybridization has developed large, so-called "giant" seeds with superior flavor characters, especially sweetness, and tenderness of seed skin. Here note that some of the old varieties of peas have not only tough skins but those skins are responsible for some off-flavor notes.

Okra (50)

Also called "gumbo," this may be the most mucilaginous common vegetable. In the southern States it is one of the essential components of gumbos and other Creole dishes. Young okra pods (*Hibiscus esculentus*) are firm and if lightly cooked are agreeably crunchy and only slightly gelatinous. It is with prolonged cookery that okra becomes mushy or "gumbo" in consistency.

Palm Heart (52)

The so-called "cabbage" of this palm (*Oreodoxa oleracea*) is commonly used in the tropics and the Orient as a component of meat and vegetable compositions and for salads (Bailey 1943). Its availability in the United States is almost entirely limited to the pre-cooked product in cans. In texture palm heart can be likened to bamboo shoots, like undercooked, rather fibrous asparagus.

Snap Bean (57)

The term "snap beans" refers to immature beans which are to be cooked whole, broken, or sliced. While there are many sub-varieties of *yellow* beans ranging from short, narrow and thin to long, narrow and plump, those sub-varieties are rather limited in number. Almost all of them have white-meated seeds. Of green snap beans there are not only many sub-varieties varying in shape in both the pod and the seed from tiny to very long, but from narrow to broad; and the seed meats vary from white to green. Especially marked differences occur in the many sub-varieties of English broad beans. The flavor factors of the snap bean pods varietally vary from earthy to grassy, and the seeds vary from bland through nutty to earthy. The earthiness of snap bean pods can be lessened if they are blanched ahead of cookery and the blanch water discarded. Experience indicates that most of the earthiness of snap beans is skin deep. So, long soaking or quick blanching will remove the bulk of what is an objectionable cover flavor. If shelled beans, the seeds of snap beans, are to be separately cooked, those seeds should be blanched and the blanch water discarded ahead of cookery. The seeds of all snap beans have a relatively heavy coating of wax. Here two factors should be contemplated: (1) wax does not metabolize; and (2) much of the clayey or earthy flavor of bean seeds is residual in the wax that covers the seed skin. Obviously, then, if that wax is removed (by the simple and fast process of blanching) the over-all flavor of the resultant dish will be more agreeable.

TABLE 3

CABBAGE-LIKE VEGETABLES[1, 2]—FN 55[3]

Broccoli	(*Brassica oleracea*, var. *botrytis*)
Brussels Sprouts	(*B. oleracea*, var. *gemmifera*)
"Cabbages"	
Celery Cabbage or Pe-Tsai (first attracted attention in U. S. about 1925)	(*B. pekinensis* or *B. Pe-tsai*)
Chinese Cabbage or Bokchoi	(*B. chinensis*)
Common or True Cabbage	(*B. oleracea*, var. *capitata*)
Cauliflower	(*B. oleracea*, var. *botrytis*)
Charlock	(*B. arvensis*)
Collard or Kale	(*B. oleracea*, var *acephala*).
Kohlrabi	(*B. oleracea*, var. *gongylodes*, or var. *caulo-rapa*, D. C.)
"Mustards" (Bailey 1943)	
Black Mustard	(*B. nigra*)
Chinese Mustard—"California peppergrass"—excellent greens	(*B. juncea*)
Tuberous Rooted Chinese	(*B. napiformis*)
Mustard (in China, tubers used as winter veg., intro. to France from Pekin 1882)	
Pot-Herb Mustard	(*B. japonica*)
Wild Mustard, a weed from Europe	(*B. alba*)
Rape	(*B. napus*)
Rutabaga	(*B. napobrassica*, or *B. campestris*, var. *napobrassica*)
Turnip	(*Brassica rapa*)

[1] From Bailey (1943).
[2] The greens of the vegetables in this list (the *Brassica*) can all be used as cabbage is used.
[3] The norm of cabbage is arbitrarily established at 55, which is assumed to be fair center of the average *heading* varieties. *Bokchoi*, the Chinese cabbage, may be lowest in flavor, the mildest of the heading varieties; and mustard greens highest, above kale and collards, and other *non-heading* varieties.

Chard (60)

Chard is a hybrid beet developed for large and succulent leaves and broad, tender spines. In some cookery the leafy matter is stripped from the spines which are then cooked like asparagus or braised like celery. (See Beet Greens, FN 78 in Column 9, Raw Salad Vegetables.)

Beet Greens (63)

The heart and young leaves of young red beets are generally processed in cookery like spinach. The young leaves of sugar beets (the *mangels* of Central Europe) are likewise used.

Spinach (65)

Flavor norm is based on steamed spinach; note that in a raw state it is rated at 80. (See Spinach, FN 83 in Column 9, Raw Salad Vegetables.)

Leek (67)

Leek loses all its pungency in wet cookery. (See Onion, FN 375 in Column 9, Raw Salad Vegetables.)

Scallion (70)

Flavor level here is based on stalks. Scallion greens flavor rate lower than the stalks. Scallion loses all its pungency in wet cookery. (See Onion, FN 375 in Column 9, Raw Salad Vegetables.)

Asparagus (75)

The flavor norm refers to white asparagus. The flavor level of green asparagus will be considerably higher, especially if not pre-blanched. In general, asparagus should be pre-blanched, discarding the water, then steamed, not water-cooked.

Broccoli (75)

The name means "cauliflower" in Italian. In the United States, the term is applied to the yellow, green, and purple subvarieties of cauliflower. Broccoli should be pre-blanched ahead of steam cookery. This is one of the vegetables that require careful processing for the best results.

New Zealand Spinach (77)

This vegetable is an annual creeper (*Tetragonia expansa*), the leaves and young shoots of which are used much like spinach (Bailey 1943). It is one of only two true succulents commonly used as vegetables; purslane is the other. Like purslane and spinach, it is used both raw and cooked.

Purslane (78)

Purslane (*Portulaca oleracea*) is one of the oldest common potherbs of Europe, where it is used in cookery compositions as a leafy vegetable like spinach and raw in salads and for garnishing. It is common in the United States, where it is called pussley, "pigweed," and other more or less disdainful names because of its lush, spreading, weedy growth. Purslane may be the most neglected common good green leafy vegetable: it resembles New Zealand spinach in texture but is higher in kinesthetic and other flavor values. In sweetness it parallels beet greens. (See Column 9, FN 83.)

Endive (Chicory) (82)

Both the "Belgian" and the common endive hearts are among the leading lettuce vegetables that lend themselves to braising procedures. Thick slices of dense heads of iceberg lettuce, and young cabbage are parallel in cookery options, but they will flavor rate differently. (See Chicory, FN 115 in Column 7, Solid Vegetables.)

Rhubarb (85)

In the United States, rhubarb is used largely as a pie fruit, secondarily as a compote—as an accompaniment or a dessert. In Europe, particularly in the Teutonic areas, as a sweet vegetable, it is used as a component of many food compositions, particularly heavy stews.

Pharmacognosy.—Rhubarb is the common vegetable that is highest in oxalic acid. The leaves should never be used in cookery, because they are particularly high in oxalic acid.

Celery (85)

The flavor norm is based on average bunch celery, including a small portion of the root, but trimmed of upper parts of spines and leaves. The heart cluster will flavor rate lowest. Both the root section and the outer spines, particularly if greenish or green will flavor rate higher than the norm. Celery should be cooked wet or dry so that it retains some of its kinesthetic values. For stock or soup, the upper spines and leaves should be used with restraint. As a spice herb, those parts, like carrot tops, can flavor rate higher than parsley (to which celery is botanically related). Incidentally, the stringy outer stalks of bunch celery (frequently discarded because of their stringiness) are easily *de*stringed by partially clipping each stalk; like removing the strings from some snap beans.

Fennel (85)

Finocchio is the Italian name for this vegetable. Fennel heart, becoming more and more commercially available, usually used like raw celery, should be investigated for its possibilities in cookery, particularly as an inclusion with some of the meat dishes. In heat processing, it loses most of its volatiles, but enough remain that, together with its high sweetness and low bitterness, make for an agreeable vegetable dish, particularly when braised with meat broths. The greens are usable in salads, soups, etc. (See Fennel, FN 90 in Column 9, FN 90 in Column 16, FN 280 in Column 18.)

Sorrel (88)

Also called "dock," "herb patience," and "spinach rhubarb" (*Polygonaceae*) (Bailey 1943). The leaves have been used as substitutes for spinach and the stalks as substitutes for rhubarb.

Collard

See Kale, FN 95, this Column.

Watercress (95)

The possibilities of watercress (*Roripa nasturtium aquaticum*, Bailey 1943), as a cooked vegetable are commonly overlooked, which is puzzling because of the frequency with which tourists encounter it in many different ways of cookery in other countries. It is one of the most common vegetables of world-wide distribution. As a cooked green leaf vegetable, it is far more frequently encountered abroad than spinach, chard, and beet greens put together. It loses most of its bite and bitter components in the process of cookery, and if at all properly done, it has kinesthetic and flavor values that will be found agreeable. The garden cress commonly called "peppergrass" is *Lepidum sativum* and should not be confused with watercress. Garden cress, rarely produced in America, is commonly used in Europe, both in cookery and as a garnish. Both garden cress and watercress, minced, provide a peppery vegetable component for dips and sauces for seafood.

Kale (95)

The FN of kale is based on young flat varieties. The outer leaves rate much higher in cabbage flavor. The curly varieties of kale flavor rate higher. Kale and collards, like most of the leaves and green sections of the cabbage group of vegetables, should be pre-blanched to strip them of most of their grassy and some of their sulfurous flavor components.

Globe Artichoke (100)

Parboiling is the popular procedure for preparing artichokes (*Cynara scolymus*, Linnaeus) but the young or infant flower heads (which is what artichokes are) are best carefully steamed to retain agreeable kinesthetic values. The outer leaves and trimmed stalks cooked to softness and then puréed and strained, can provide a vegetable base comparable to avocado for dips, spreads, mousses, etc. (See Globe Artichoke, FN 62 in Column 9, Raw Salad Vegetables.)

Grape Leaves (110)

Young grape leaves have long been used in the Near East in wrapper cookery. An example is the Armenian *dolma,* a rice or wheat composition rolled stick-like in a wrapper of grape leaves. Even in maturity, grape leaves are high in sweetness, but for cookery they are gathered when young, before the heavier fibers become tough. The grape is one of the fruits the sugar of which is synthesized in the leaves. This is why grapes removed from the vine before they are mature will not sweeten in storage.

Pimiento (115)

It is important to realize that the flavor norm is based on steaming the whole vegetable, seeds and all. The seeds are peppery even in the so-called "sweet" pimientos. The term "pimiento" is properly applied to the different varieties of the capsicum, the pod peppers. The term "pimento" comes from *Pimenta,* a genus of the *Myrtaceae* family—the allspice tree. Technically, therefore, "pimento" refers to allspice, not to capsicum peppers. Some of the mild varieties of pimiento which happen to include the largest specimens are the blandest and relatively high in sugars. Pre-preparation usually requires removal of the seeds and the inner ribs. It seems that the smaller varieties increase in pepper hotness as they reduce in size, the hottest being the tiny cayennes and the peanut peppers, which are so hot that they are rarely used in cookery. Their usage is usually limited to pickling and extremely cautious employment of minute or trace quantities for the hottest seasonings. The small and usually long green pimientos that are so very hot in raw or simply cooked conditions are mostly pickled or marinated; the marination processes are directed at reducing the pepperiness while yielding a kinesthetically agreeable finished product. Italian *peperoni* are examples of the results of relatively simple vinegar marinades, some of them carried to the extent of almost eliminating the bite.

Pharmacognosy.—These and other vegetables high in piperine or other caustic chemicals are prohibited in ulcer diets. The strong peppers provide one of the best examples of organoleptic perception of pepperiness being classified as predominantly due to pain stimuli rather than simply flavor impulses. (See Pimiento, FN 95 in Column 16, Spice Vegetables, and FN 92 in Column 9, Raw Salad Vegetables.)

Cardoon (125)

A variety of artichoke (*Cynara cardunculus,* Linnaeus) propagated for the fleshy heart-bunch celery-like section. Common in Europe, it is most popular in Italy where it is used in many concoctions and braised like celery. It should be parboiled and the water discarded ahead of any cookery use. It is too bitter to be eaten raw.

Mustard Greens (150)

They, together with the infant flowerets, like all other comparable cabbage-like vegetables, should be pre-blanched; otherwise they are much too bitter and grassy.

Chicory Greens (190)

The bitter components of chicory greens, like those of many of what we usually think of as salad vegetables, are not substantially dissipated in cookery. As a generality, it is recommended that the outer leaves be rejected for both raw and processed usages, including pickling. Here is an instance where folklore in cookery has developed the almost universal practice of stewing such bitter green leafy vegetables in meat broths, an example of the meat flavors to some extent masking an otherwise objectionable taste. Again bear in mind the Biblical tradition concerning bitter herbs: the idea of dipping bitter vegetables in fruit or meat concoctions. (See Chicory, FN 95 in Column 9, Raw Salad Vegetables.)

Dandelion (150–350, av. 200)

The flavor range is from relatively mild to very high in some of the wild varieties, but they are all so high in bitterness, like Chinese bitter melon, as to be intolerable to all but the grossest tastes. Even high and long blanching doesn't take enough of the bitterness out of dandelion greens of any kind to make them generally acceptable.

CHAPTER 14

Raw Salad Vegetables

COLUMN 9

Introduction

This classification is purposely extended by listing vegetables either unknown or unthought of for salad purposes by most Americans, but commonly used abroad.

Consider the two adjoining columns for their potential inclusion of different items in salad compositions, as well as most of the vegetables in Columns 5, 6, 7, and 8, the fruits in Column 10, the fruit juices and infusions in Column 14, and some of the carriers in Columns 11, 12, and 13. However, most of the items classified in Columns 14 through 24 should be considered as seasonings for salads, particularly all of the items in Column 16, the raw herbs and spice vegetables.

While the heading of this column is "Raw Salad Vegetables," an elemental consideration is that, with rare exceptions, salad *compositions* include processed components, primarily dressings.

Next, while the term "salad" stems from references to compositions of raw vegetables, historical usage has applied the term to conglomerations of not only fruits and leaf vegetables, but vegetable and animal foods in conditions varying from raw through cooked to different stages of preservation. The term "salad" is so loosely applied as almost to frustrate definition. It would probably be easier to classify the different usages rather than attempt to confine the term to one order of food service. The line of least resistance is to arrange raw salad vegetables in columns and to suggest *salads* as a classification of cookery; thus one or more raw salad vegetables with or without dressing can be stipulated to be generically a salad, but fruit salad is an extension of the salad idea; and a composition such as tuna salad is a liberal extension of the term "salad."

Chartwise, using any of the raw salad vegetable placements as a base, the assemblages of animal and other vegetable, as well as seasoning matter can be logically composed.

The development of man's tastes for raw vegetable salads is a remarkable phenomenon in his food behavior. Primarily a carnivore, by the processes of civilization he grudgingly has become an omnivore and by force of the "it's-good-for-you" school of nutrition, together with the arts of seasoning, he has come to eat green leafy and other raw vegetables.

In analyzing why we eat green leafy vegetables as well as some other foods that alone are definitely disagreeable we go to the roots of accounting for taste and arrive at the inevitable conclusion that our tendency is to balance the flavors in a meal. We try to satisfy the five cardinal tastes; after that, the secondary and tertiary taste and flavor factors. In our vegetable salads, particularly with green leafy components, we get the bitter and some of the floral vegetable elements which, combined with seasoned dressings, can provide as in no other single dish all of the desired cardinal tastes—saline, sweet, sour, bitter.

Unsalted celery stalks are appreciatively munched by everybody, but almost no one finds escarole acceptable without seasoning. It's too bitter. It must be accepted as a truism that many of us eat green leafy salads only for the dressing.

The "bitter herbs" of Biblical narrative were dunked in some form of dressing.

In general, only very young, immature vegetables are considered adaptable for raw salad make-ups. We tend to avoid both the texture and the flavor of mature vegetables in salads. The exceptions are fruits which are used both immature and mature. Always allow for maturity of herb and spice inclusions. Also, a large class of foods generally overlooked, both raw and blanched, includes some of the vegetable blossoms like those of squash, and flowers like nasturtiums.

The majority of raw salad vegetables are within the flavor range of 50 to 100.

The majority of the spice vegetables and other seasonings are over 100. The flavors of most raw vegetable salads total higher than most other basic dishes.

Selection, assembly, and composition of raw salad vegetables provide a field of discrimination—more of what is actually visual art can be applied here than in any other single classification of food assemblage. We may here be entering into exploration of the possibility of what is actually the art of flavor composition, art in the sense of creating compositions that are aesthetically satisfying. Here we should recognize the potentialities possible with combination of visual, smell, taste, and texture arrangements for an aesthetically satisfying result. Salad pictures constitute one of the several applications of what may be technically defined as art in food presentation.

Be particularly aware of the fact that raw salad vegetables include all of the raw vegetable embellishments, not only to basic but to secondary dishes. A broader classification would include the processed vegetables, including fruits which have customarily been alluded to as the condiments and garnishes.

The word *condiment* is derived from the Latin, meaning that which gives relish to other things, from *condire,* to pickle, season. The word *garnish* is derived from the French *garnir*, meaning to ornament, adorn, fill, mount, etc.

As garnishes and condiments, the raw salad vegetables provide complement and contrast as accompaniments or components of basic dishes as well as accessory food compositions. Speculation about arrangement of individual dishes in the literature of food elaboration, ferreting out the reasons underlying the inclusion of vegetable garnishments, must result in the conclusion that discriminating cooks have wittingly or unwittingly used salad vegetables for complements and contrasts to satisfy whatever they had in their grasp of food aesthetics. Appearance was probably the first consideration, with flavor factors secondary.

Appearance

The first consideration is mass, perhaps in terms of black and white configuration; second is color; third is visual-textural registrations. There is a wider range of variations of mass and color in what may be properly included in the classification of raw salad vegetables than any other single classification of foods, not excepting fruits. Not generally recognized, certainly not commonly taken advantage of, are the extreme variations in both mass and color of the green leafy vegetables ranging from tiny to large, and from white with a tinge of green to the darkest green, and in texture from smooth to rough. Consider the mass and color variations, the textural impressions ranging from the inner leaves of the Belgian endive to the pink- and red-green of some of the curly lettuces; the feather delicacy of fennel and coriander greens through the smooth and rough parsleys, the masses and colors of the root vegetables ranging from white to black through gray-white through yellows and oranges and pinks and reds; and the same to greater or lesser degree for the melon group. If we accept some of the fruits as herein properly included, particularly mushrooms and tomatoes, the mass and color range covers practically the whole spectrum, allowing for the inclusion of Columns 8 and 10 in contemporary salad compositions. The most elaborate color wheel becomes our palette, and there are no limitations of mass. The possibilities of configuration are almost infinite.

What is much more difficult to compose agreeably is the combination of textures. Flavor neighbors in Column 9 are kinesthetically unrelated. For example, cucumber and lettuce, also cabbage and carrot. Here some writings of Chinese epicures may be suggested because the Chinese have historically been more sensitive to textures in food and have longer discriminated among kinesthetic variables than any other people.

Vegetables to be used raw that rate over 100, including the spice vegetables in Column 16, should be reduced in proportionate usage as their flavor rating ascends. Recall that 100 is the mean average flavor acceptance of both the quantity and the intensity factors. Above 100 are encountered the vagaries of individual tolerance. While most people will take a little more or less of high flavored foods, the bulk of their food will flavor rate well under 100. The admixture of green vegetable and other food matter rating above 100 is to be approached with a restrained hand. Careful weighing of both quantity and quality of the flavors is advisable.

Pre-preparation

The initial procedure is cleaning each vegetable and in some classes cleaning each part of each vegetable. Bear in mind that raw vegetables constitute living vegetable matter that if not marketed and used for a considerable period after harvesting, is subject to varying degrees of deterioration, but may be improved by freshening. The advisable procedure involves rehydration to restore the moisture lost in the period of transportation and storage. Resuscitation of salad vegetables is best accomplished in cool water in the range of 45° to 60°F. If water under 45°F. is used, revivication is arrested. If over 60°F., some vegetables will wilt.

Preparation and Service

If salad vegetables are cut or macerated and held for an appreciable time ahead of service, they should be chilled, kept in cold storage, to maintain firmness and provide maximum kinesthetic factors. Further, to provide an optimum of kinesthetic agreeableness, salad vegetables should be served in the cool temperature range. They tend to lose their crispness and crunchiness at higher temperatures. The appearance factors likewise vary with temperature.

Cauliflower (10 to 75, av. 25)

Varieties and conditions from the youngest buds of white, to mature purple, include sub-varieties of which broccoli is representative. (See Column 8, FN 20.)

Cucumber (30)

This rating is based on peeled specimens. The bulk of the flavor of the entire gourd family is in and immediately under the skin. Peeling them leaves only the relatively bland body and watery cores, especially when young. Cucumbers range from baby "pickles" and gherkins to the more grassy-flavored green varieties, as well as the hybrids, ranging from the white through the light to dark green strains. The latter have relatively mild flavors and more tender skins. *Kinesthetic factor:* refrigeration adds to crunch appeal. (See Cucumber, FN 30 in Column 7, Solid Vegetables and Zucchini, FN 85 in Column 9, Raw Salad Vegetables.)

"Mango melon" is a South African term for a small round to slightly elongated squash that when small and under half grown (1 to $2^1/_2$ inches in diameter when they are quite round and pale grey-green) cuts, tastes, and somewhat resembles cucumber with slightly denser flesh. When submature or mature, when the tough shell varies from just yielding to resisting indentation, it cooks and tastes like a high-moisture acorn squash.

"Snake cucumber" may be thin, narrow, and straight to thick, curved, and goose-necked, and long. Most hybrids are smooth-skinned, some of them corduroy-ribbed. The texture and flavor of snake cucumbers are between prototype cucumbers and squash. Prime specimens will look, taste, and eat like unusually firm cucumber.

Mushroom (10 to 150, av. 35)

Puffballs, coral, and spike types in early stages may rate between 5 and 10, tasteless to most people. Almost all fungi in maturity acquire earthy and woody flavors. Any fungi rated over 75 would probably require development of taste for acceptability. When rated over 150, the woodland flavors of must and mold are probably within the tolerance of only old country mushroom addicts.

Within the flavor range of 25 to 75 there are probably more kinds and varieties and sub-varieties of mushrooms that may be eaten raw or processed—marinated or cooked—than all the more common vegetables and fruits counted together. Few American salad compositors know the utility of some of the common mushrooms in raw salad make-ups.

The variety almost exclusively grown for the American market and one of the most commonly picked in the field by amateurs, *Agaricus campestris*, in its immature button state has a flavor best described as mildly nutty and is almost universally acceptable. Some of the uncommon mushrooms range in flavor from light but earthy with floral characteristics, like *Cantharellis cibarius*, to the rich rootiness of some of the *Boleti*, the honeycomb mushrooms.

Squash (25 to 65, av. 45)

Flavor level varies with variety and condition according to degree of maturity and whether peeled or unpeeled. *Note:* the entire squash family is prone to absorb unpleasant flavors from the ground. No other group of vegetables betrays origin from improverished soil so much as the gourd family. (See Column 7, FN 36.)

Pathology.—There are some instances of gourd vegetables having absorbed toxic matter due to growing conditions.

Asparagus Tips (25 to 75, av. 45)

These flavor rate from a low of 25 for blanched white buds to perhaps 75 for partly open gree-purple flowerets. Important: taste-test of purplish buds will avoid going over 75, where bitterness may be disagreeable.

Turnip (48)

Variation of flavor is over an extreme range according to variety and maturity. Some older turnips can be used for salads by removing the core. (See Column 7, FN 35.)

Lettuce (15 to 115, av. 49)

This range is accounted for by the blandness of the hearts of immature bland varieties of lettuce (*Lactuca sativa*) to the bitterness of the outer leaves of some of the colored ones in maturity. Some of the heading varieties such as Iceberg are mild. Open escarole is bitterest. (See FN 95.) On a dry basis some lettuce has 35 per cent of sugar and is comparatively high in fiber and ash. Most of the vitamin potency is in the outer leaves. The kinesthetic factor is primarily responsible for the use of lettuce and some of the other green leafy vegetables in salads. The senses concerned with feeling and sound are in this field most noticeable. The crunch factor of some states of lettuce is usually of higher appeal than the other phases of sensory perception. Visual appeal may rate second.

Broccoli (53)

The Italian name for cauliflower, but in the United States it is generally applied to the green and purplish hybrids (of cauliflower) that are much higher in flavor characters than the parent stock.

Romaine (55)

"Cos lettuce" (*Lactuca romana*) is possibly the best kind of lettuce for out-of-hand dipping. Should be chilled to retain its crispness.

Tomato (60)

The new developments in the white, yellow, and green tomatoes in the long as well as the round varieties when as and if they are marketed provide the salad artists with agreeable color, form, and flavor material. (See Tomato, FN 90 in Column 7, Solid Vegetables; FN 60 in Column 10, Fruits, Raw.)

Rutabaga (60)

Rating is based on immature garden varieties. The type commonly called "Swede" varieties, unless used in the baby state, flavor rate higher. When mature, they are more or less earthy in flavor. (See FN 46 in Column 7, Solid Vegetables.)

Globe Artichoke (62)

Baby artichoke hearts, quartered, are nutty and only faintly bitter, and should be much more frequently used in raw salad compositions. Artichokes (*Cynara scolymus*) would be much more widely grown if it were known that they are extraordinarily hardy in some of the coldest areas, provided the root and crown area is heavily mulched and otherwise protected through the cold weather seasons. Variety commonly marketed in America is "Large Green Paris." For those to whom the bitter taste is agreeable, the very young leaves can be utilized, if with restraint, especially with highly seasoned meat dishes, where a little bitter partner could be companionate. (See Column 8, FN 100.)

Italian Artichoke.—A smaller globe artichoke, round, and mauve or purple. Comes from around Venice. Italians use it as we do asparagus, with the stems.

Caution.—*Globe artichoke roots are violently purgative.*

Cardoon (130)

In cultivation, the thickened leaf stalks or ribs are blanched and used as a potherb. The root is also edible. A variety of artichoke (*Cynara cardunculus*, Linnaeus), used exclusively as a green vegetable.

Jerusalem Artichoke.—The root of the indigenous wild sunflower of North America, called "Indian potatoes" (*Helianthus tuberosus*) by early American settlers. (See Artichoke, FN 22 in Column 7, Solid Vegetables.)

Carrot (50 to 90, av. 69)

Harvested as seedlings from 1/4 to 1/2 inch in diameter, which home gardeners use when they thin plantings. Stubby and dwarf varieties such as Danvers and Oxheart are high in sweetness and good in the small stages. More mature carrots may be cored for raw salad inclusion. The carrot is another vegetable which quickly betrays growing in impoverished soil. The best forms may be developed in sand, but unless the soil is "fed" the product will be virtually tasteless. The hearts of very young carrot greens can be used in salad make-ups, not only for appearance but because of the quite agreeable flavor resembling caraway which is also present in carrot seeds.

Processing.—Blanch and cool some carrots to reduce strong carrot flavor, much of which is in or directly under the skin. As with other root vegetables, the preparational process of marination modifies their flavor and lends variety to their inclusion in raw salads.

Cabbage (35 to 95, av. 70)

The flavor and color range is from hearts of heading white varieties to mildest usable outer leaves of green and red partly open varieties and subvarieties. Most of the outer leaves, particularly the tips, are too strong in cabbage flavor for acceptance in cold salads. Soaking cabbage in cool water for half an hour or longer, then chilling it, tends to firm it, making it kinesthetically more agreeable. (See Cabbage, FN 55 in Column 8, Green Vegetables.)

Chard (76)

This vegetable varies between light green and dark red sub-varieties and strains.

Beet Greens (60 to 100, av. 78)

All of the heart greens of the many different varieties of beets are usable raw in salads. Americans, unlike most Europeans, rarely use the tender greens of sugar beets which may be the best of all beet greens. (See Beet Greens, FN 63 in Column 8, Green Vegetables.)

Purslane (80)

Resembles New Zealand spinach in texture, but the stalks have agreeable kinesthetic values, and are fairly high in sweetness. One of the most agreeable and, oddly enough, neglected of our salad as well as cooked green vegetables. In America it is disdainfully named "pigweed." It is one of the oldest vegetables in European usage. (See FN 78 in Column 8, Green Vegetables.)

Spinach (83)

Like beet greens, the heart greens of spinach make good raw salad components. (See FN 65 in Column 8, Green Vegetables.)

Zucchini (85)

Should be used only when very young and peeled. The skin of most varieties has a disagreeable odor, above the tolerance of most people, particularly in the more mature stages. They can be rendered quite acceptable for raw salad purposes by proper blanching. The same applies to cucumbers, in which the undesirable flavor is concentrated in the skin, which is largely removable by blanching. (See Zucchini, FN 95 in Column 7, Solid Vegetables.)

Celery (50 to 150, av. 87)

Greenish outer stalks flavor rate high. The trimmed root rates around 95. (See Celeriac, FN 100 in Column 7, Solid Vegetables.)

Beet Root (88)

Use most varieties when quite immature. (See Beet, FN 77 in Column 7, Solid Vegetables.)

Fennel (65 to 200, av. 90)

Sweeter than celery, more fibrous, and a little of it goes a long way. Most children, when offered a free choice between fennel and celery, will pick fennel. The outer greens with their high flavor should, of course, be sparingly used. (See Fennel, FN 85 in Column 8, Green Vegetables; FN 90 in Column 16, Raw Herbs; FN 280 in Column 18, Spices.)

Chervil Root (92) and **Parsley Root** (99)

Two of the root vegetables widely used in Europe but neglected in America. Sub-varieties are grown primarily for the root rather than the greens. As raw salad components, chervil, parsley, and other such bitter roots are usually used shredded or cut to thin sticks. (See Parsley, FN 98 in Column 7, Solid Vegetables.)

Pimiento (60 to 150, av. 92)

Some of the new strains have less of the objectionable grassy flavor and more sweetness than some of the older ones. Hybridizers aim to breed out the pepper-hotness of the capsicum ancestors. Pimientos rated over 150 are included in pepper (FN 800). In other words, "sweet peppers" include only those with ratings under 150. The pepper-hot pimientos of our Southwest and some of our Southeast usages should be recognized as being stronger than a sweet pepper. Most of them are far above the maximum tolerance of most Americans. (See Pimiento, FN 115 in Column 8, Green Vegetables; FN 95 in Column 16, Raw Herbs.)

Chicory or Endive (85 to 200, av. 95)

Belgian endive (*Cichorium intybus;* French: *escarole*) which is a product of a cultivation technique of a sub-variety, is mildly bitter and kinesthetically agreeable. A number of pink and red strains of half open Belgian endive are becoming increasingly popular in Europe but are almost unknown in America: one of the most agreeable colorations in salad vegetables. Escarole unquestionably requires cultivation of a taste for its acceptability. Even the hearts are usually too bitter for the uninitiated. (See Chicory, FN 115, in Column 7, Solid Vegetables and FN 190 in Column 8, Green Vegetables.)

Chervil Leaves (110)

The mildest and sweetest of the parsley-like spicy vegetables. Very close to coriander in flavor, but of course about 50 points lower in the flavor scale. Has a light licorice flavor note. (See Chervil Root, FN 92, this column.)

Parsnip (115)

Should be much more generally used in raw vegetable salads. Use only immature roots. The heart greens are usually too grassy and bitter for salad usage.

Radish (75 to 250, av. 130)

Varieties range from some of the very mild Oriental kinds, like the Japanese *daikon,* which in some sub-varieties resemble white turnips through the rank of yellow, pink-orange, red, to the black peppery ones. Of the root vegetables, radishes vary over the widest flavor range. Some, like horse-radish, are altogether unacceptable raw. Radish is one of the extremely deceptive vegetables in visual appraisal as to its anatomical or flavor characteristics. Most often radishes cannot be flavor gauged without biting into one and then it may be too late. (See Radish, FN 150 in Column 7, Solid Vegetables.)

Parsley (140)

This rating applies to the flat-leafed mild varieties of parsley (*Petroselinum hortense*) not the curly-leafed varieties that are much too dominant in flavor. (See Parsley, (Root) FN 98 in Column 7, Solid Vegetables; and FN 99 this Column.)

Celery Leaves (150)

(See Celery Leaves, FN 150 in Column 16, Raw Herbs.)

Coriander (160)

The fresh herb has characteristics of sweetness and coriander herbiness much more pronounced than the seeds. It is very fragrant. (See Coriander, FN 160 in Column 16, Raw Herbs, and FN 225 in Column 18, Spices.)

Mint (175)

Rating allocated to peppermint, not spearmint. The latter is much too high for acceptance for raw eating (See Mint Chart, FN Table 8 in Column 16.)

Leek Hearts (180) **Scallion** (300) **Shallot** (350)

See Onion, FN 375, this Column.

Nasturtium (200)

One of the oldest raw vegetable salad inclusions. Both the leaves and the flowers are much used abroad; very little used in America. The young flowers are sweet and lightly spicy, and flavor rate below the leaves. It is lightly sour in flavor, with a slight pepper bite. (See Nasturtium, FN 210 in Column 16.)

Watercress (230)

Even the mildest cultivated sub-varieties are too peppery for most tastes. The stalks are more peppery than the leaves. (See Watercress, FN 225 in Column 16, Raw Herbs.)

Dandelion (150 to 350, av. 250)

Some of the cultivated sub-varieties may rate as low as 150, but some of the wild field dandelions are much too bitter for most people's acceptance. (See Dandelion, FN 200 in Column 8, Green Vegetables.)

Onion (Genus *Allium*) (375) and the **Onion Group**

Leek Heart (*A. porrum*) (180).—Rating is based on hearts. Use only the heart core for salads; the leaves are too fibrous and may be too strong. (See Leek, FN 67 in Column 8, Green Vegetables.)

Chive (*A. schaenoprasum*) (75 to 400, av. 275).—Within this variety are a number of chive-like greens of the onion family which rate from just perceptible onion flavor to strong garlic flavor. The chive we know best is tube-like. There are a number of Oriental sub-varieties that are like blades of grass and more like garlic than onion in flavor. They are called "garlic chives."

Scallion (*A. ascalonicum*) (300).—Scale ranges with varieties and sub-varieties and strains from almost leek-like mildness to a biting onion flavor. The scallion gives the entire range from very small to large, from white through yellow to dark red, from tender to tough; and, of course, from very mild to very strong. The word "scallion" (like "shallot") in contemporary usage may also apply to sprouts (i.e., before the stalk develops a bulge) of several different varieties of common onions. (See Scallion, FN 70, in Column 8, Green Vegetables.)

Shallot (*A. ascalonicum*) (350).—Rated for the bulbs which can be described as onion-like but lower in the flavor scale. Sliced or slivered shallots are favored abroad for relatively light salad compositions.

Onion (*A. cepa*) (175 to 600, av. 375).—Onions vary extremely in the raw state. Generally the large bulbs are milder than the small ones. Color is not a good index of flavor appraisal. Some of the yellows are milder than some of the whites; even some of the reds are milder than some of the lighter colored varieties. Thinly slicing onions and exposing them to atmosphere by oxidation will substantially reduce the inherent onion flavor. Onions are susceptible to what amounts to instantaneous enzymatic reduction of some of their dominant flavor constituents. Marination also alters the flavor profile.

Garlic (*A. sativum*) (500).—There seems to be only one approximate flavor level for garlic. Even the immature bulbs approximate the flavor of the mature ones. But one of the strangest findings of the experimenter is that what is commonly thought of as strong garlic taste actually is strong garlic smell. The taste alone of garlic is very, very mild. Almost all offensiveness is contained in volatile matter. Hold your nostrils closed and bite into raw garlic, and it will be found both mild and sweet. (See Garlic, FN 110 in Column 7.)

Pepper (Hot Pimiento) (800)

Some varieties of pimientos (Genus *Capsicum*) are pepper hot. They range in form from small and plump to long and narrow and from white and yellow through green to red and purple. The majority of the hot pimientos are narrow, but there are a few exceptions: one is the small yellow or red cherry-like capsicum, and the other is yellow, yellow-green or green, or red small to medium inverted bell shaped. As a rule the seeds are much hotter than the pulp, which is hot enough. Hot pimientos are listed in this column because very finely sliced or shredded or even juiced, they may be desirable salad inclusions. But a warning to the unwary is to taste pimientos for salad inclusions, to avoid mistaking the mild pimiento for some of its red hot brethren. In other words, an innocent green pimiento may be loaded with peppery dynamite. (See Pimiento, FN 900 in Column 16, Raw Herbs; FN 115 in Column 8, Green Vegetables.)

CHAPTER 15

Raw Fruits

COLUMN 10

Introduction

Most U. S. Department of Agriculture standards of identity in fresh fruits apply to factors of appearance: varieties to a limited extent; form (size and conformation); and some physical grading, particularly in packing. Flavor factors are not covered.

Fruit is the class of foods with the widest range of flavor factors. With the exception of salt (NaCl) all of the cardinal and secondary tastes are present to some degree in most fruits. The tongue tastes of sourness, sweetness, and bitterness are usually dominant. Astringency is secondary, and the aromatic tastes are supplemental. Whether the kinesthetic factor precedes the other taste factors or follows them is a matter of personal opinion.

"Beauty may be only skin deep," is a phrase generally applicable to fruits. Beauty of skin and perfection of form, carelessly appraised, may conceal at best a poor body, and at worst one that is physically defective. Too often a beautiful shell has a rotten core. The upholstery is pleasing to the eye, but the structure may be bad. In short, it is a trick of nature to clothe many fruits in bright colors which frequently lure man or beast, frequently cloaking unattractive or sometimes dangerous fruit pulps. Some of the most beautiful apples have almost flavorless flesh. Rangpur limes look like (and are) tangerines, taste like lemons, but smell like limes. Most common is a selection among fruits that appear ripe from the color of the skin but prove to be underripe in flesh. Immature pineapples may look ripe: it takes experience to detect the difference between ripe and underripe pineapples of any variety.

Perhaps the most nearly general human error in appraising fruits lies in the assumption that mature fruits are *uniformly ripe*. With few exceptions, fruits marketed as structurally mature will vary in flavor factors. Accordingly the stem end of most (though not all) fruits will be more flavorsome than the flower end. According to kinds and varieties, fruits develop their sweetness and sourness largely from the stem end, and secondarily from the center. But it is emphasized that the flavor components of a fruit do not uniformly diffuse radially from the center. There are many examples that demonstrate this differential ripening phenomenon peculiar to most fruits. Melons such as muskmelons or cantaloupes, honeydew or casaba types appraised for this phenomenon will clearly prove the point. The stem end is always sweeter and the distal or flower end is always less sweet. The flesh along the perimeter of the cavity is always sweeter and becomes less sweet as the rind is approached.

Sourness and sweetness may be coupled in such appraisals, but bitterness is often, but not always, associated with the outer flesh as the appraisal approaches the rind or skin. Some varieties of peaches are bitter around the pit and, of course, the skins are almost always puckery. Some nectarines are not bitter just around the pits, but they have more or less astringent and bitter skins. Terpenes, present notably in mangoes and pine nuts, give a flavor of turpentine at any stage of maturity.

Location of the volatile esters, the components of fragrance, vary from fruit to fruit and from inside to outside. Some apples are almost entirely surface-fragrant, the fragrance of their flesh being subliminal. Other apples are either not surface-fragrant or just barely so but have highly aromatic flesh. Plums, cherries, and most grapes have either subliminal or no surface fragrance. Perhaps the least fragrant of all fruits, outside or inside, stem or distal end, is the avocado group. An example of extreme variation between varieties is tomatoes, that vary from no perceptible fragrance to highly aromatic, and, of course, from bland to highly flavorsome, from soft and watery to firm.

The floral fragrances of most pears develop only under favorable conditions and are evanescent. Some varieties of pears have fragrant skins, while others are practically aromaless. The flesh of some pears when picked at the optimum (which may be immature) is fragrant, and that of others is not.

Ungraded fruits according to U. S. Department of Agriculture standards should be considered according to their individual merits. In a majority of instances those standards do not permit marketing of fruits that the farmer calls "dead ripe" or what horticulturists term "tree-ripe." Like the vine fruits such as melons, bush and tree fruits are almost invariably harvested at or approaching specific stages of *immaturity*. The simple reason for marketing such immature fruits is that the majority of mature, tree-ripe fruits will not ship well. Their shelf life is too short.

Many fruits that by marketing standards are rejected as overripe or not conforming to size or form patterns probably are the best fruits. The exceptional offerings may be in the farmer's wayside stand, and some of the village and town markets. But tree-ripe fruits in their prime are not generally found in markets.

One of the odd marketing disqualifications is oversize. Many, many jumbo specimens of different varieties are culled in packing-house procedures, because too few can be put in a standard package, like oversize apples, oranges and grapefruit, and some of the melons. Misshapen fruit that may otherwise be good to excellent is rejected. Shriveled or excessively russeted apples of some varieties are rejected, but the farmer may prefer them because of their flavor qualities. Shriveling of a tree-ripe apple, frequently the last of the season, is an indication of what may technically be described as "storage-ripening." Most of the sugars in apples, as in grapes, are transported from the leaves. Comparatively little of the starch in apples is hydrolyzed into sugars until the apple is tree-ripe. Here the qualification is made that the starch in apples functions as storage material for the sugars photosynthesized in the leaves, transported to the fruit through the trunk and branches and also to hold and develop the volatile esters. Thus, starch, not being soluble, seems not to hydrolyze into sugars in the apple until the fully ripe or what may be termed the overripe stage. Here a qualification is that if apples ripen and shrivel on the tree they gradually sweeten, but if they shrivel in storage, there will be little if any increase in sweetness. An opposite example is that of pears, which should be picked at a specific stage of immaturity, stored in a cool and dark area whereupon their starches hydrolyze into sugars. Most standard varieties of pears, if allowed to mature on the tree, will soften and brown-rot in the core. Even the cooking and winter varieties should be harvested ahead of maturity, or they will have a short shelf life.

An observation applicable to most vegetable foods as well as animal foods is that resting or storage of foods under controlled temperature conditions is an almost universal commercial practice for both chemical and physical reasons. When fruits of the field are gathered they are usually allowed to lose their field heat before marketing.

Marinades

Frequent reference is made to immature fruits. What to do with fruits that are not sweet enough to meet the purpose for which they were bought presents a problem and a challenge to the cook, which can often be met by resorting to marination of one kind or another. With some exceptions the different fruits can, when immature, be satisfactorily marinated. The kind and character and the periodicity factors vary with different fruits and circumstances, using from very light to heavy liquors and from short immersions to long pickling.

That many fruits are familiar as "preserves" shrouds the puzzle of why so many fruits which are not commonly preserved are neglected.

If Column 20 *Preserves* is related to Column 10 *Fruits, Raw* and the two are lined up across the Gustametric Chart and the straight edge procedure followed, a number of oddities become apparent: cucumbers are preserved in varieties ranging from small pickles to strips and whole specimens, from sweet to sour and salty. Watermelon rind is likewise frequently pickled or preserved, but muskmelons with their greater range of food characters, in the same family with cucumbers and watermelons, are almost never encountered in pickled or otherwise preserved form. This provides one of the many paradoxes in our food behavior—why people who after all are observant and imaginative remain in a groove and neither look nor investigate to right or to left.

What may be thought of as the borderline of marinades are fruit sauces which in turn can be divided in two parts: (1) sauces for fruits, and (2) fruits as sauces.

(1) **Sauces for Fruits.**—When other vegetable or animal sauce components are added to fruits, they are classifiable as a kind of marinade. If a muskmelon is found to be immature and thereupon sugared and each half filled with sauterne and subjected to refrigeration overnight that would be called marination. Clipping enough off one end of a muskmelon to enable removal of the seed body and filling the cavity with ice cream is a common practice. Not common is filling the cavity with a beverage, allowing a period for internal marination, and then serving the melon with straws. With this kind of procedure and with some liquors the pulp is more or less a side issue. Scooping out the core of a really good pineapple and filling it with brandy is a good marination practice, though not approved by some people. A point is made that where, as here, liquor penetration is made by radiation from the center of the fruit, the marination is partial and only the inside is pickled.

Sauces poured over fruits and allowed to stand from a short to a long period are common practices.

(2) **Fruits as Sauces.**—Fruits as sauce components start with substantial particulation, to balls and chunks, slices and segments which are added to other sauces. In another type, the fruit may be reduced to liquid consistency, from juice through the different conditions of purées to coarse pulps, which are then incorporated into either vegetable or animal sauces. The use of immature fruits in sauces, particularly for animal dishes, is common abroad but infrequent in America. Here is another paradox that ignores parallel possibilities. We use pineapple with duck and ham while we ignore peaches and apricot combinations. Muskmelon may be puréed in a blender and then combined with some other cold or hot vegetable and meat sauce. This kind of thing is one of the purposes of the Gustametric Chart: to suggest exploration of parallel and complementary flavors that may be nomographic. Many of the combinations will create a queer first impression but will eventually lead to agreeable results—always with the qualification that proper combinations require

skill. Here again the sweet-sour balance potential of fruit purées in the different marinades and sauces is stressed.

Verjuice.[1]—From the earliest times underripe whole fruits, their pulp or juice, have been used as sour components in cookery. For verjuice many old European cookbooks specified preparations of hard green apples and plums, but reading between the lines, it must be obvious that most other immature and of course sour fruits were used for the same purpose.

Taxonomy.—For convenience Column 10 is primarily concerned with raw fruits; but it must be realized that each entry has components (flowers, fruit, and seeds) which may enter the areas of other classifications. Most conspicuous are the fruits in Column 10 overlapping the vegetables in Column 9. It is common practice to combine raw vegetable matter of the kinds and varieties shown in Column 9 with fruits shown in Column 10.

The dried fruits, processed fruit products, the seeds and nuts are grouped with the classifications of seasonings and condiments, in Columns 18 and 22. Likewise some flowers and fruits which are commonly classified as herbs and spices are accordingly grouped in Columns 16, 17, and 18.

Flower and fruit infusions and juices are grouped separately in Column 14.

Man often reaches for fruits because he associates floral qualities with them. Or, to put it another way, he attributes fruity qualities to flowers rather than flowery qualities to fruits. Analysis of the enjoyment of fruit in organic order starts with the visual factors, then smell, then taste, followed by other organoleptic reactions. Here we come to the abrupt realization that beyond the very few cardinal tastes, the components in fruits that most attract us are concerned with sight and smell. Both flowers and fruit as food appeal most to what we may call aesthetics in our food behavior. In the final analysis we may decide that it is the floral values of fruits that we prize above any other grosser taste.

When we reject beautiful but "tasteless" fruit that refusal is based on a lack of "fruitiness"—that is how we usually think of it. Technically, however, the rejection may be based on a lack of the floral qualities associated with a specific fruit. The first cultivated strawberries of the season, for example, are sometimes devoid of "strawberry" aroma. In contrast some of the earliest peaches are among the fruitiest and are highly aromatic. But most fruits are more aromatic later in the season.

In the lands of their origin, discriminating people have from earliest times used orange blossoms as part of the service of oranges. Citrus flowers, principally orange and lemon blossoms, are among the oldest and most common in usage in Mediterranean countries. Flowers of the

[1] Literally "green juice."

jasmine family, both the many different fragrant jasmines and varieties like gardenias, have supplemented fruit services and beverages. Jasmine in tea is a contemporary example where a floral spike raises the flavor level of the infusion.

Wild flowers as food, with the qualification that the phrase "wild flowers" includes the buds, have been among the foods of man from his arboreal days through the primitive developments of yesterday and today. They still are among the foods of preference and necessity of many contemporary civilizations as well as the existing primitive peoples.

The wild foods of many peoples are surprisingly high in flowers. One of the anomalies of our food behavior is our tendency to reject flowers *per se* as food matter while we accept them in processed conditions as seasoning matter, if we call them herbs and spices. Worst of all is our attitude of disdain with some overtones of pity toward the gatherers of wild food, "peasant" customs of gathering what we call "weeds." The majority of country folk in most lands, like most of our rural forebears, if we knew it, gather some wild flowers as food, because they have a keener sense of aesthetic values than most of us in what we call "higher cultures," who have had little or no experience with wild flowers as foods.

Papaya (30 to 40, av. 38)

Papaya[2] has one of the narrowest flavor ranges and comparatively little difference in flavor characters between varieties. However, papayas not commercially grown are, like other melon fruits when grown in exhausted soil and under unfavorable climatic conditions, poor in flavor. Neither color nor shape is a fair index of flavor. The nose test is the most reliable, if the fruit is ripe. This is one of the few fruits commonly harvested substantially immature, to allow shipping. Further, they are usually unripe when marketed, and only a knowledge of the feel and smell of an almost ripe, possibly good papaya may reveal its intrinsic worth. For economic reasons the marketed varieties are the small ones. Varieties that range between 20 and 30 pounds are usually seen only in some of the areas of origin, like Cuba. In immature conditions papayas are usable in cookery. Reference is made to Caribbean and Central American cook books. The seeds of the papaya, which are almost universally discarded, have a flavor reminiscent of capers and lend themselves to marination over a wide flavor range.

Pharmacognosy.—The seeds and rind are high in papain, a commercial "meat tenderizer."

Avocado (30 to 45, av. 40)

Fruits average in size from the finger varieties, weighing around an ounce, to some that weigh about three pounds, from soft to hard skin, and from light green to purplish-black. Surface appearance is no index of quality, and practically all varieties are odorless.

[2] *Warning:* The ulcer patient should consult with his doctor about the advisability of eating raw papaya.

The skin of *underripe* avocados is glossy. The surface acquires a characteristic dullness as it approaches full maturity. Hard, actually underripe avocados can be softened by holding them in an oven around 150°F. for about 30 minutes, varying with the degree of their hardness.

While we usually use avocados as components of raw salads, in the tropics they are commonly used as dessert fruits with or without sugar or other higher seasoning additives, as well as in cookery. The widest range is under the heading of *guacamole* in Mexican cookery. If an avocado is found too hard, green, or underripe to use for the salad for which it was intended, it can be cut or pulped and used in a sauce, soup, or stew.

Loquat (42)

The loquat (*Eriobotrya japonica, Lindley*) which ripens in spring, varies in shape from spherical to pyriform, in color from pale yellow to deep orange and in the best varieties is sometimes three inches long. The skin is thin and smooth, but tougher than that of an apple. The flesh is firm and meaty in some varieties, more melting in others, almost white to salmon-orange in color, juicy, and of a sprightly flavor suggestive of a cherry. The seeds, which are about $^3/_4$ inch long and dark brown in color, vary from 1 to 8 or 9 in number, 4 or 5 being common (Bailey 1943). Introduced from China and Japan, it has become a hardy and quite frequently encountered resident of much of the southern half of the United States. Most varieties stand up under climatic conditions to around 20°F. or slightly below. While most popular eaten out-of-hand, it is widely used, particularly in the Orient, for preserves and to a limited extent in cookery.

Pear (45)

While there seem to be almost as many variations between pears as between apples, classifying them is almost equally difficult. Morphologically, they are just as variable, from small, round to flattened, and up to comparatively huge, more or less pyriform. Some of the smallest Seckel pears weigh about an ounce, and some of the Pound pears weigh more than a pound. The flesh ranges from soft and tender to hard and woody. In flavor they vary from bland to mild. There seems to be no variety of pear that can be said to be highly flavorsome. There are substantial differences between flavors of different pears, but none of them are really high in flavor. With the exception of some of the so-called "winter" varieties like the Pound pears, most of which are more popular for cooking than for eating out-of-hand, all pears intended for cookery or preserving are best selected when sub-mature. In the processes of cookery or preservation, most pears lose practically all their floral esters.

Sapota and Annona (45)

Annonas, sapotas, and other members of this large botanical family (containing 335 genera and 600 species) are sometimes colloquially called "custard apples." While most of them flourish best under tropical conditions, some of them do well in some of our southern states, particularly California and Florida. Where they do well, they are among the most popular fruits. With the exception of cherimoyas and some of the hardier sapotas, most of the annonas are only locally marketed. That is the reason why the sweetsop and the soursop, which are easily grown in many of our southern states, are not more widely known and enjoyed. With acclimatization and particularly with development of hardy strains, many members of the Annonaceae will unquestionably be popularized in the United States. The annona is one of the few fruits that do not lend themselves to preservation. Its use in cookery is limited. It does not even lend itself well to salad compositions, and is almost solely considerable as a fruit to be eaten out-of-hand when tree ripe.

TABLE 4

ANNONA—SAPOTA
("Custard Apples")

Soursop	(*Annona muricata*)
Custard Apple	(*A. reticulata*)
Sweetsop	(*A. squamosa*)
Cherimoya	(*A. cherimolia*)
Sapota, Sapodilla, Sapote or Marmalade Tree	(*Sapota achras*)
Acana	(*S. dissecta*)

[1] Verrill and Hyatt (1950).

Banana (35 to 60, av. 48)

In the tropics bananas (*Musa paradisiaca*, var. *sapientus*) range from finger size weighing a couple of ounces to some varieties with occasional specimens of five pounds. This is another fruit commonly harvested when quite immature and marketed underripe to mature in storage. Even when picked "dead ripe" from the native plant it has only a little higher flavor level than one that has matured in storage; not much sweeter but it has substantially higher aroma. The difference between bananas and plantains is apparent only to the expert. Both are perennial herbs almost identical in appearance, but the flavor of plantains when ripe, particularly the red varieties, is generally substantially higher than that of bananas. (See Banana, FN 65 in Column 7, Solid Vegetables.)

The small so-called "apple bananas" (in the Hawaiian Islands called "Chinese bananas") are, like some of the plantains, higher in flavor characters then the larger, commonly marketed varieties.

TABLE 5

BANANA—PLANTAIN

Banana, dwarf	*Musa nana*
Plantain	*M. paradisiaca*
Banana, common	*M. paradisiaca*, var. *sapientus*

Muskmelon (30 to 60, av. 50)

Melons such as muskmelons, Honeydews, and Cranshaws (Genus *Cucurbita*, Family Cucurbitaceae Bailey 1943), are assumed to be fruits of the different botanical varieties of *Cucumis melo* as distinguished from *water*melons which are fruits of *Citrullus vulgaris*. Extreme flavor variations occur according to growing conditions and maturity. Varieties include the smooth skinned, small and round to the three foot banana-like fruit. One variety like a mango has flavor characters between the cucumber and the muskmelon. The original musk-scented forms might be assembled into one group including the nutmeg or netted melons, and the cantaloupe or hard-rinded melons, although the name "cantaloupe" has become generic in this country for all musk-scented melons. The so-called "winter melons" might be grouped under *Cucumis melo*, var. *inodorus* (Bailey 1943); mainly known to us as casabas and some of the casaba hybrids such as Cranshaws and Honeydews, but note that "Honeyball" is a late season but not a winter melon. There is no clear differentiation between muskmelons and cantaloupes. However the core form of many cantaloupes is triangular, and some of them are pink to salmon-pink in flesh color.

Relative maturity is perceptible around the stem and in the color of some varieties, but not all. Tactile testing is reliable only for some varieties. All cantaloupes and muskmelons, and some of the winter melons are surface fragrant at maturity.

Flavor qualities are detectable to a limited extent by aroma, but melons like many other fruits may have attractive aromas but unsatisfactory flavors. Some melons provide examples of the presence of delicate volatiles and that is all. The flesh may be anything from substandard to flat-bland. It may be said that the esters might indicate a fringe of 50 and the flesh 30 or less. Grant that a good melon, like a good fruit of any kind, is best enjoyed by itself.

Most melons are harvested immature, and some varieties do not mature satisfactorily after immature harvesting; therefore a large per cent of melons reach the consumer in a condition which calls for ingenuity for their satisfactory disposition.

Melon flesh in various states of maturity is usable in and with other classes of food, starting with fruit and vegetable salads, on through meat groups. Underripe, not too sweet, melon chunks agreeably combine, both flavor and texturewise, with animal meats and fish and poultry over a wide range. They may provide both sweet and sour notes for balance needed. One of the oldest European customs is accompanying melons with thin slices of quite salty, usually country-cured ham. The idea of using melon balls and cubes with beans may be startling to the person who has long used them in cereals and salads, but the different texture characters as well as the flavor should be considered for complementing some of the basic food assemblies. Color composition is the other element where the melon has appeal, varying from the light greens and whites to the yellow pinks and salmons.

Apples (52)

More varieties of apples are familiar to most people than any other fruit, but not generally comprehended is the great range of varieties and qualifications peculiar to some of them, nor the applicability of apples and apple products in cookery. Some of the best varieties are not marketed because they are small or do not otherwise conform to set standards, perhaps because of skin characteristics, inherent blemishes or color faults. With the exception of some crabapples the large pink-meated apples are practically unknown in our markets. Some apples with aromas suggestive of bananas or berries which have agreeable acidity characteristics seem only to be known by grower-fanciers.

Immature apples in marinades and preserves are in common usage abroad but such use is uncommon here. As components of sauces, apples together with plums provided the *verjuices* of our ancestors. Commercial "green apple pie" rarely contains green apples. Apple pulp from combined immature and mature fruits is one option of the sweet-sour balance compositions.

All of the standard apples have whitish flesh when ripe but there are some sub-varieties or hybrids that have pinkish flesh: e.g., Pink Pearl, which has a pallid pink, occasionally blushed skin and *pink flesh.*

The flavor of apples should be judged by tasting the skin together with the flesh, not by eating peeled segments.

Some apples are without superficial aroma, in either skin or flesh, but are lightly aromatic in the process of eating. Many apples are skin-fragrant, and others, the skin fragrance of which is subliminal, have flesh fragrance.

Detailed coverage of apples is given in U. S. Department of Agriculture publication 24 F.R. 4681, with specific standards of identity covering some of the common varieties and sub-varieties and detailing factors of color, size, texture, and some marketing standards.

Watermelon (54)

Variations in size and shape of watermelons (*Citrullus vulgaris,* family Cucurbitaceae) are from small to large, spherical to round and long and very large. The smallest are three or four inches in diameter. Flesh from white and yellow to watermelon pink and red. Skin colors vary from white through yellow and light green to dark green. One of the midget watermelons (Tom Thumb) is green while sub-mature, but turns golden yellow at maturity. There are no known superficial indications of flesh flavor qualities. Comparative ripeness can be determined by thumping a melon as an index of the physical condition of the pulp, and in some varieties pressure on the skin to check comparative yield pressure. Skin fragrance is usually absent.

The so-called Chinese watermelon is *Citrullus vulgaris,* var. *citroides* (Sanders 1956) which the Chinese use for "melon candy." It is commonly grown and used for preserves in the tropics and South Africa, where it is referred to as "citron." While those citrons have hard white flesh, even when mature they are so low in sugar as to be almost tasteless and are commonly used in the areas of production only for preserves and cookery; however, all members of this family (cucumbers, common melons, such as muskmelons, and immature watermelons of all varieties) are also usable as preserves or "pickles."

The radical developments of hybridization of watermelons are in two directions: first, skin and pulp color from white through yellow and golden, and second, seedlessness. Lippert (1960) reports tests on five lines of seedless watermelons with sugar levels of between 11 and 12 per cent and satisfactory general features of flesh flavor, texture, and color.

Raspberry (45 to 75, av. 56)

Colors range from white, yellow, pink, red to purple-black. Some of the tart, amber colored raspberries resemble wild thimble-berries in form, but the latter are shrubs, not vines. (See Blackberry, FN 80 in this Column.)

Blueberry (58)

Some of the new hybrids have marked size and form improvements, but are not necessarily better in flavor than the wild varieties. The term "blueberry" applied to huckleberry is a colloquial misnomer; the two berries are unrelated.

Tomato (60)

The chart placement of the tomato (*Lycopersicum esculentum*) straddles Columns 9 and 10 to emphasize its consideration within the classification of raw salad matter as well as that of fruits. Since its post-Columbian introduction to civilization, the tomato has become more nearly universal in distribution and usage than any other fruit; and it has influenced cookery more than any other vegetable.

The great variation among tomatoes is illustrated by an attempt to describe them, e.g.: *Mass:* from round, $^1/_4$ inch berry to round and large, to long and narrow; skin tender to tough. *Skin color:* white through different yellows and greens, through pinks and different reds. *Flesh color:* white, yellow, green, pink red. *Texture:* watery to firm and mealy, from high in seeds to seedless. *Taste:* subliminal, especially in immature, forced cultivated specimens, to sweet and sourish. *Aroma:* from subliminal through cucumberish to tomato-fragrant.

Discrimination between varieties is most important for the consumer, but it is unfortunate that so very few different varieties and strains of tomatoes are marketed. Only tomato fanciers, home gardeners, or other specialists who grow their own can begin to explore the almost infinite possibilities of tomato usages, raw and cooked, in a field where there are thousands of different varieties and strains.

As "love-apples" they were dubbed poisonous by many European peoples until well into the 19th century, yet it is hard for us to imagine European cookery, especially that of Southern Italy, without tomato sauces. Tomato ketchup was not popularized until after the turn of the 19th century. Tomato purée and tomato paste were not commercially produced on any substantial scale, in either Southern Europe or America, until the late '20s. Only within the past few years have commercial producers standardized production with tomatoes bred for specific food factors. There is more quality control applied to tomato growing and packing than any other single food.

"Green" tomatoes have a flavor level of 33, varying from 30 to 40. They are used sub-mature rather than hard green in cookery, since sugars and acids are not sufficiently developed until maturity has been almost reached, just before color appears in the pink and red varieties. Tactile test will show suitability for cookery of the white, yellow and green varieties in the sub-mature stages. This is especially important for "green" tomatoes to be used for frying. They must have high enough intrinsic flavor to be worth while.

Fig (62)

The two white varieties generally marketed in the United States are Calimyrna and Kadota. The Mission (so-called "black fig") and its sub-varieties ranging from tawny through green, purple-green and brown, are infrequently marketed fresh because of their relatively short shelf life. Prime figs served chilled as a component of ice creams and sherbets make one of the best combinations.

In southern Europe, particularly in Italy, fresh figs (*Ficus carica*) served cold are frequently accompanied by thin slices of prosciutto; which is an example of the tendency to supplement a sweet-sour food with one that is saline.

Peach (64)

Color varies from white to dark red. In mass peaches vary from small. round ($1^1/_2$ inches in diameter), to large (5 inches), from about 2 ounces to 1 pound, from slightly flat to elliptical. Epidermis is smooth to fuzzy. Pit types are freestone, part freestone, or clingstone. Color varies from white through pink to suffused red and striated pink to red. Taste varies from low to high sweetness, low to medium acidity; smell from subliminal to highly fragrant.

This is one of the fruits where some of the early varieties are superior in flavor characters to most of the later varieties. As a rule the earliest peaches are quite small but can be very good. Growers might center more attention on developing flavor and aroma for taste appeal in the later varieties rather than concentrating on size and color for eye appeal. (See Table 6, Plum Fruits following Plum, FN 72, this Column.)

Apricot (65)

There are comparatively few varieties of apricots (*Prunus armeniaca*). Blenheim and Moorpark are the favorite commercial apricots in California, which is the principal area of American production. At maturity and under favorable growing conditions, prime apricots of all varieties have flavor characters that are on an approximately even flavor level. Thus prime apricots grown anywhere in the world are just about equally good. For *glacéeing* and high-sugar preserving, the apricot, because of its firmness, is probably the most favored fruit in areas of its production.

Nectarine (67)

Bailey (1943) specifies the freestone nectarine *Prunus persica* var. *nucipersica*, once known as *Persica violacea*, and the clingstone variety (old name: *Persica laevis*) with overall designation that it is a smooth-skinned peach. The principal differences between nectarines and peaches, other than the nectarines' having smooth skins, are that prime nectarines are denser in flesh and much higher in flavor than most peaches. Up until comparatively recently, nectarines were smaller than most varieties of peaches, but within the last few years, some nectarine hybrids are as large as quite large peaches.

Litchi (68)

Litchi (*Litchi chinensis*) is a globular, knobby appearing fruit (about 0.75 to 1.5 inch diameter) with the coloration of a large, round strawberry, from light green to pink-red. The pulp is like a firm jelly, the delicate flavor of which qualifies it as one of the best of all fruits. In China there are four varieties which differ somewhat in their fruiting habits, and in the size of the seeds, but the pulp of all four varieties are about the same. (See also Litchi, Dried, Column 22, FN 110.)

Longan (68)

There are several varieties of longan (*Euphoria longana*), the fruits of which, other than being smaller (about 0.75 inch diameter) are practically identical with the litchi. Both longan and litchi fruits, shelled and pitted, are available in Oriental and specialty shops, usually canned in light syrup. While the canned fruits lose much of their delicate aromatics and texture, they are quite good.

Strawberry (68)

The strawberry is next to the blackberry in world distribution. In the wild states it varies from tiny round to elongated, but all of the wild varieties tend to be small. The forms of the cultivated varieties range from small round to elongated, pointed or ridged, to large and eccentric, some of the largest being several inches in diameter. In color most of the wild varieties at maturity are pink to red with a few practically pure white strains. In Turkey and on the west coast of South America some pure white strains are commercially produced to some extent.

Cherry (70)

Sweet cherry is *Prunus avium* and sour cherry is *P. cerasus*. Fruits of sweet cherry vary from quite small to relatively large, but all are more or less heart-shaped. Color varies from white, yellow, so-called "golden" through white-pink, pink and red to red-black in the Black Tartarian. Flesh consistencies vary from soft to firm and somewhat crisp. Juice varies from almost colorless to dark red. The different cherries tend to have distinct flavor notes peculiar to specific varieties or sub-varieties. In this they differ from other plum fruits. The members of *P. cerasus* (sour cherry) are rather small, quite round; in color, light to medium cerise. While they are classified as "sour cherries" at full maturity under favorable conditions many of them are high in sweetness. While most generally used cooked or preserved, some sour cherries when tree ripe are good out-of-hand eating fruits. Cooked pitted or unpitted, pulped or mashed, because of its tartness and fairly high sweetness, the sour cherry is a good option as an accompaniment or an inclusion with or for meat dishes where the sour-sweet balance factor is considered.

Plum (60 to 150, av. 72)

All the many, many varieties of prunes are plums (*Prunus domestica,* or *P. prunophora*) but not all plums can be prunes. A rough generality is that a prune is a plum with high enough sugar content to dehydrate naturally. Color of skin varies from whitish buff through yellows, pinks, and reds to dark purple; color of flesh from yellowish to purple. In texture skin varies from thin and delicate to tenuous and rubbery. Flesh is soft and pulpy to firm and slightly fibrous. In mass plums range from one-half inch for some wild varieties and the "cherry plums" to about three inches for some hybirds; in shape from round to elliptical, with some plums slightly pointed. Pit-types are freestone, part freestone or clingstone, pits from small and round to large and long. In taste all plums are sour when immature. In maturity they vary from mildly sweet to very sweet, from subliminally bitter to very bitter, from non-astringent to puckery. The plum is one of the very few fruits that is almost non-aromatic.

Usage.—Some wild varieties and some that are colloquially called plums (like "Catalina cherries") are in raw states quite high in bitter characters, so high as to be unpalatable to most people, but in cookery most of the bitterness is dissipated. Plums are useful in all states from green through immature, mature and preserved, in any combination, whether raw salad, sauce, or soup, where it is important to control the sweet-sour-bitter balance.

Grape (73)

Labrusca (Genus *Vitis*) is the name assigned to the wild fruit known as Fox-Grapes (Bailey 1943). They are usually too sour for out-of-hand eating, but they can repay the labor of preparation required for tart preserves or a very rough, "foxy" wine. *V. vinifera* is the wine grape. Evolved from the native Fox-Grape species are Concord, Catawba, Niagara, Delaware, and Worden and several others, some of which are characterized as "slip-skin" grapes. Practically all of the derivatives of our native Fox-Grapes varying from white to almost black and from small to medium-sized berries, are juicy, almost to the point of wateriness. Further, many of them are higher in pectin than varieties of grapes from other parents, so they make more consistent jelly. Most grapes grown for wine production are varieties of *V. vinifera* that originated in the Mediterranean area and developed in Europe. Some of them are discussed in Column 15. Commercially most grapes are classified as either "wine grapes" or "table grapes," probably because most grapes grown for wine are not specially good for out-of-hand eating. All of the so-called "table grapes" and their many, many varieties have been developed from wine grape parents with one common objective: to breed out some objectionable characteristics such as small berry size and small bunch size, large seeds, and tough skins; while at the same time keeping or modifying characteristic parent grape flavors. In the process of hybridizing several seedless strains have been evolved, such as white Thompson Seedless and black Monucca, which have small to medium long berries and

TABLE 6

PLUMS AND RELATED FRUITS

Almond	*Prunus amygdalus*
Apricot	*P. armeniaca, or P. prunophora*
Cherry	
Sweet	*P. avium*
Sour	*P. cerasus*
Nectarine	*P. persica* var. *nuciperisca*
Peach	*P. persica*, or *P. amygdalus*
Plum	*P. domestica*, or *P. prunophora*

several with yellow or golden, round berries. The seedless grapes are among the highest in grape sugar. Other than the Thompson Seedless, which may be the most popular single variety of grape, the table grapes most commonly marketed from California (the principal area of American production) are the white to Golden Muscat and Malaga types, the pink to flame Tokays and the purplish-black Missions (and their hybrids) and the black Hamburg. For home production of juice or for everyday cookery, wine grapes and many of the varieties that produce fairly well in more or less unfavorable areas such as the Eastern and Southeastern United States (primarily because of too much rain and not enough sun) are better than most so-called "table grapes." Almost all of them are higher in acidity though lower in sweetness. So, for quick juice production or cookery, the wine grapes and their close relations can provide juice with more and higher specific flavor interest than table grapes.

As marketed, very few grapes of the *Vitis vinifera* species have perceptible surface fragrance. Right off the vine, many grapes are lightly and quite pleasantly fragrant, but they quickly lose their surface fragrance as they lose their field heat.

Currant (74)

The red currant is *Ribes rubrum* and the black currant is *R. nigrum*. The fruit of *Ribes* should not be confused with "dried currants," a different fruit; the dried currants of commerce are the dehydrated berries of a species of grapes originating in Corinth, anciently called the "grapes of Corinth." The variety grown in California is Zante Currant. Rarely eaten out of hand, because they are so sour, the true currants, varying from white through red to black varieties, are good for preserves when considering the sweet-sour balance.

Mango (75)

The mango (Genus *Mangifera*) is probably known to more people throughout the world than any other single fruit. It is more important in the tropics and the semitropical areas, both for out-of-hand eating and cookery than the apple is in America. There are probably more widely grown varieties of mangoes than there are of apples. One Indian nursery catalog lists and describes more than 175 mangoes. In form they range from small round to large conical; from light yellow through green to pink blush and brilliant, some of them almost purple. All have very large, long flattish seeds. The skins vary from thin to thick and delicate to tough, from smooth to the roughness of avocado skins. Surface fragrance varies from subliminal to high. The pulp of all when ripe can be described as having the density of an average peach; some are very low in stringy pulp fiber while others are fibrous to the point of being woody. The flavors of all mangoes can be said to be spicy in the range from low to almost overpowering. The flavor notes may start with peachy-floral, with a background of mace, to and through various levels that suggest pineapple and clove. When prime, all of them are high in sweetness and light in acidity. All of the bitterness of mangoes seem to be concentrated directly under the skin. The skins themselves, especially when not prime ripe are particularly high in terpenes. If an underripe mango is bitten into, it will taste like a mouthful of turpentine. The skins of some of the ripe mangoes can be just as distasteful. Street vendors in tropical Mexico pare what look like stone-green mangoes for the buyer who from a tray sprinkles salt and adds a dash of red hot pepper sauce to the mango, and appreciatively eats it there and then. If the tourist follows this process, he will have a *memorable* example of this first step in educating his taste for that kind of thing. However, a slice of almost mature mango with just a little salt, lemon juice and *one* drop of tabasco can be anything from just tolerable to good or at least interesting. In cookery, mangoes are most used in the state between three-quarters grown and sub-mature. For preserves, principally what we call "chutneys," half the quantity used are sub-mature and half mature.

Persimmon (78)

Diospyros virginiana is the native species, and *D. kaki* is the Chinese-Japanese species. All of the persimmons native to America have fruits that are more or less like small tomatoes in form, distinctly flat, both the flower and stem ends. All of the Oriental persimmons are flattish at the stem end, and most of them are conical. Commercial production of persimmons is almost limited to the Japanese varieties. Hachaya is the most popular and Fuyu ranks next. A prime Hachaya fruit is probably the ideal persimmon for fruit anatomy (other than having seeds), for size, color and basic flavor characters. Fuyu, besides being one of the few rather rare flattish persimmons (in this respect resembling the native American species) is seedless and non-puckery (the orchardists' catalogs say); however, it is non-puckery only when fully mature.

Persimmons are remarkable for these qualities:

(1) An unripe persimmon is the fruit most frequently cited as an example of astringency in demonstrating flavor perception.

(2) All varieties of the persimmons with the exception of Fuyu are practically

unusable until they are past the standards of maturity common for almost all other fruits. They should be allowed to remain on the tree past maturity. With few exceptions, immature to botanically mature persimmons are not used in cookery (the exceptions are in the field of preserves) because the specific flavor values of persimmons are not available until they are in various states of post-maturity. The notion that persimmons, especially wild ones, are only good when frostbitten, is a fallacy. However, it is true that substantial post-maturity, plus chilling or freezing will accelerate their chemical decomposition, primarily the conversion to sugars.

(3) Almost all varieties of persimmon except Fuyu are preferred for out-of-hand eating when they are more or less over-ripe, when the body solids have decomposed from the naturally mature state to the characteristic gelatinous conditions just short of spoilage. All varieties of persimmons perfectly demonstrate a case where *dead* ripeness of a fruit is the preferred condition. All persimmons will dehydrate like prunes. They are high in sugars and most varieties when properly dehydrated are almost non-astringent.

Color is not an infallible index of post-maturity until the shades or tints which characterize the different varieties deepen to the color that denotes the preferable state of post-maturity peculiar to each variety. With the exception of Fuyu, tactile testing is the only process that is reliable for distinguishing between simply mature and post-maturity.

Fuyu and a few other small to medium round and flattish persimmons are secondarily marketed, but have somewhat inferior flavor characters. Many of the American wild persimmons, while smaller than Oriental ones, are sweeter. Dehydrated persimmons imported from China and Japan are available to a limited extent in some food specialty shops, particularly the Oriental ones.

Usage.—Persimmon pulp, raw or cooked, or baked with opossum or raccoon has been a traditional American combination. Properly processed, persimmon pie is on a blindfold test almost indistinguishable from yam pie. For dessert use in cakes or pastries and particularly for frozen desserts, persimmon pulp is one of the most rewarding inclusions.

Blackberry (80)

There are many forms of the genus *Rubus*, subspecies and varieties, with many hybrids and intergradients abounding (Bailey 1943). American blackberries (*R. flagellaris*) also called "dewberries," range from small round to long; while most of them are black, some are white. The raspberry (*R. idaeus*) varies from white through light to dark pink and purple, the so-called "black raspberry." The loganberry (*R. loganbaccus*) is deep red and long. The boysenberry closely resembles the loganberry. The wineberry (*R. phoenicolasius*) varies from tan through pink to bright red. Salmonberries and thimbleberries are wild variants of the blackberry family. They and some others are relatively close to raspberries in flavor and texture. (Raspberry is FN 56, this column.)

Guava (82)

Locally the different guavas (*Psidium guajava,* Linnaeus) are named according to the forms they suggest, such as "Apple Guava," "Pear Guava," or "Strawberry Guava." The pulp and the juice of all guavas are spicy to varying degrees, some of them almost pungent. The guava has a specific flavor character different from most fruits. The notable exception is cherimoya, and possibly other Annonas, whose flavors would resemble guava. Guava juice in cans or frozen provides an exotic option for inclusion in fruit juice compositions, and particularly frozen desserts. The orange-pink color of both juice and pulp is agreeable for fanciful food compositions.

Quince (86)

Perhaps the quince (*Cydonia oblonga*) is the fruit least popular for out-of-hand eating. It may be rated as barely tolerable. Like persimmons, they vividly illustrate high astringency in fruit. Up to and beyond maturity they may be anything from strongly to violently puckery. It is only when quinces remain on the parent bush fairly long after maturity that they lose some, but never all, of their astringency. Cookery dissipates both the astringent and the bitter notes. While it may be the worst fruit for raw eating, from the standpoint of texture and color it is one of the best fruits. While the poor varieties are distinctly sandy and minutely pitty (like some pears), they tend to retain good, firm texture and rather agreeable salmon-pink color, together with the flavor notes unique to quinces. The quince is one of the few fruits, the color of which is radically altered in cookery processes. From creamy white or lightly lemon, it cooks to different hues of salmon-pink. For preserves and especially glacées, because of its firmness and color peculiarities, it is one of the best fruits.

Tangerine (88)

See note on citrus fruits under Orange, FN 120 this Column.

Grapefruit (90)

See note on citrus fruits under Orange, FN 120 this Column.

Pomelo (95)

See note on citrus fruits under Orange, FN 120 this Column.

Pineapple (100)

The variety of pineapple (*Ananas sativus,* Bailey 1943) most extensively marketed in the United States is called "Red Spanish" or "Spanish." The smooth Cayenne or Porto Rico, and the small Queen occasionally appear in our markets. All of these varieties and their different strains have characteristic pineapple color when mature. They vary in size from the small Queen that may weigh less than a pound to large specimens of the other varieties that average around three and a half pounds. The Queen is generally grown in South Africa and some of the Asiatic countries. The Red Spanish prevails in Hawaii, Mexico, and most of the Caribbean countries. The largest but not necessarily the best pineapples are the so-called "black skinned" group which at maturity are very dark green and weigh from 5 to 10 pounds, and occasional specimens are more than 15 inches long. They are the Black Jamaica, Black Prince, Black Tortuga, etc. In the Western Hemisphere they are principally grown in Jamaica and some of the Caribbean islands, and abroad the popular varieties are grown in Kenya and some of the central African areas. While almost all varieties of pineapple are durable shippers, and they do mature in transit and storage, they are at their best when they are picked prime ripe and immediately used. The almost overpowering floral esters of a freshly cut prime ripe pineapple vanish with anything approaching protracted storage. It isn't necessary to sniff such a pineapple to determine its ripeness; when cut, its fragrance will suffuse a large area. While the pineapple is and always will be one of the most popular fruits for normal fruit services, it has within only the past few years become the fruit most popular for use in cookery. In some of the relatively new commercially produced crushes, pulps and concentrates, both canned and frozen, pineapple lends itself to sauce and purée production as well as bastes where sweet and slightly sour flavor notes are required. For bastes, pineapple crush or purée serves well because being high in solids in solution and suspension, it is syrup-like and will readily adhere to baking or roasting meat surfaces. Because of its peculiar properties, a pineapple slurry functions not only as a baste but also as a binder for other seasonings which in most other compositions tend to separate or to run off.

Pharmacognosy.—Oxalic acid crystals in raw underripe pineapple account for the stinging sensation (which is not due to sourness) in the process of eating. The sensation is attributable to a trauma or physical injury of the taste buds and other sensory receptors. It should be remembered that the majority of people knowingly or unknowingly have an extremely low tolerance for oxalic acid. However, it is important to realize that the oxalic acid crystals, painfully apparent in underripe pineapple, decrease as the pineapple matures which in turn indicates that the oxalic acid is low in ripe and particularly low in commercially packed pineapple.

CITRUS FRUITS

Orange (Genus *Citrus*) (120)

There are few fruit families in which the members have so many differences. Technically, *Citrus* is a botanical genus of the *Rutaceae* with a number of different varieties and in turn each variety has a surprisingly large number of sub-varieties and strains. However each member of this very large genus, regardless of how distant the relationship, has characteristics that are *congeneric.* This word "congeneric" and what it implies should be borne in mind in appraising many and often confusing characteristics of citrus fruits. For example, two citrus fruits may have skins that appear similar yet have entirely different pulp. One will be sweet and the other sour. One will be classed as an orange and the other as a lemon or even a lime. The mandarin group of citrus fruits includes tangerines, while some of the varities of oranges superficially resemble different members of the mandarin group, but not until internal physical comparisons are made are the differences revealed. So, some oranges look like mandarins just as some mandarins (especially if they have been skin-dyed for marketing) look like oranges. While one of the outstanding characteristics of the whole mandarin group is that they are supposed to be flat at both ends—usually indented in the flower end—some of the new mandarin hybrids are almost as round as oranges. To add to the confusion, the mandarin group, especially tangerines, are supposed to have orange-colored pulp, but some of the best of the mandarin hybrids have pulp almost as yellow as some of the Valencia oranges and perhaps just a little bit more orange colored than most lemons. The huge "ugli fruit" is a mandarin hybrid that looks like an oversize grapefruit, is marketed up to six inches in diameter and five inches high, is muddy colored and bluntly peaked at the stem end, has a bulbous body and an uneven green and yellow skin over the underbody. The rind is thick and spongy. However, the unprepossessing fruit that is aptly named "ugli," has the largest and possibly the best pulp body of any of the mandarins. The very juicy, mildly acid but not insipid golden flesh, has the gelatinous character common to the best mandarins. It is commercially grown in Jamaica and South Africa but, so far as the author knows, is not produced or marketed in the United States.

Among the most deceptive of the citrus fruits are the sweet limes which look like diminutive oranges but are as nearly tasteless as they can be in an orange-lemony kind of way. The Rangpur "lime" is so named because of its use as a lime. It looks like a small roundish tangerine, tends to be fairly deep orange in color and in flavor is a combination of orange and lemon. The pulp has no taste that we think of as lime-like. Botanically it is related to the mandarin orange. Variations between oranges are far more extreme than those between strawberries, even on the same shrub—bearing in mind that botanically an orange is a berry.

TABLE 7

CITRUS FRUITS (*Family—Rutaceae*)

Citron (Bushukan or Foshekan)	*C. medica*, var. *sarcodactylis*
Lime	*Citrus aurantifolia*
Orange, Sour ("Seville" orange)	*C. aurantium*
Pummelo (Pomelo or Grapefruit) (Shaddock, Pampelmous)	*C. maxima* or *C. Grandis*
Lemon	*C. limon* or *C. limonia*
Mandarin Orange	*C. sinensis*, var. *deliciosa* also called *C. reticulata*
Calamondin (Fr. brt. orange) (red $1^1/_2$ in. dia.)	*C. mitis*
Satsuma Orange	*C. sinensis*, var. *unshiu*
Commercial Orange in Florida	*C. sinensis*, var. *Dancy*
Tangerine	*C. sinensis*, vars. above, or *C. reticulata*
Sweet or Grove Orange	*C. sinensis*
Bergamot (Cult. in Calabria for Eau de Cologne)	*C. bergamia*, Risso
Kumquat (Cumquat)	*C. japonica*, Swingle
Otaheite	*C. taitensis*
Papeda	*C. histrix*, Swingle

By and large the thin-skinned oranges are supposed to be superior. Some oranges, some lemons, some mandarins and some grapefruit of thin-skinned varieties are best. But some of the very best of the different members of the different families of the citrus group are thick-skinned. Some of the best naval oranges are huge, and they are thick-skinned. On the other hand, the Ponderosa lemons, some of which weigh more than a pound, are not only thick-skinned but indifferent in pulp quality. Some of the Eureka lemons are large and thick-skinned and good in lemon quality. In the grapefruit family it is true that some of the thin-skinned members have excellent, juicy pulp but some of the pomelos (the true grapefruit) are huge, some weighing nearly two pounds, and they have very thick skins. The flesh is as firm as the most solid of the navel oranges. The total flavor characters of those pomelos (at present available only in China; those grown in the United States are not close in quality) are in the top quality classification of citrus fruits.

The bitter components in the citrus fruits are altered in storage. Freshly picked oranges will be judged relatively bitter and sour compared to oranges from the same picking sampled a week or ten days later. It is not that the sweetness builds up so much as that bitterness and sourness tone down. This is especially noticeable in grapefruit and oranges. Grapefruit properly stored, sometimes for months, to the point where the skin is partially dehydrated and shriveled, may be so low in bitterness as to be almost bland. The same is true of lemons; their sourness seems to change in character as chemistry alters the stored fruit.

Both tangerines and mandarins, their varieties and strains, are becoming more and more popular for their high sweetness and the jell-like flesh character. Both tangerines and mandarins are at their best when post-mature. Both tend to be sour until they are fairly well past maturity.

Selecting Citrus Fruits in Market

(1) Form should be proper to that particular kind of orange.

(2) The color rule is that the darker, brighter colored oranges of the same variety are better than the lighter ones. (N.B.: Many oranges today are dyed and waxed, and one should be careful.)

(3) Skin should be smooth and non-scabrous, without skin defects, which are indices of pulp defects. They show deficiencies in the soil. As a general rule skin defects such as scabs and blights may be indices of metallic or other deficiencies in growing conditions which very definitely adversely affect flavor. Skin should show storage, i.e. should be no longer glossy, yet not shriveled—simply aged-looking.

With all the variability of kind, variety, seasonal conditions, and growing conditions, the average person is fairly safe in relying on fruit that has been name-stamped by a reputable organization or a cooperative. The reasons are that such fruit must meet standards of identity which, while they may vary from area to area, are, in the case of citrus fruits, almost parallel in the basic requirements of the sweet-sour-bitter balance, and, of course grades for size, form, and color.

Selection in Orchard

Selection should be made from the crown on the sunny side of tree. Foliage should be heavy, dark green, glossy, not curled at edges, indicating a well-nourished, uninfested tree which has not been windblown or frost-bitten.

Crown oranges are deeper in color, both outside and inside, more fragrant and sweet, than those within and at the bottom of the shrub.

Hybrids and Strains

Citrangequat, Limequat, Bearss lime, Perrine, Meyer lemon are examples of many varieties and strains in the genus; there must be 50 varieties of tangerines, and 20 or 30 of mandarins. Tangelo is a hybrid of mandarin and grapefruit.

Cranberry (*Vaccinium ericacae*, var. *macrocarpon*) (150)

The cranberry is the fruit of the dwarf shrub *Vaccinium;* the small fruited wild varieties of northern Europe and North America are *V. oxycaccos.* The low bush, small fruited wild cranberry or wolf berry of Europe and eastern North America is *V. vitis*, var. *ideaea.* The large or American cranberry, *V. macrocarpon,* is the only variety that is cultivated. Of this variety there are more than a dozen sub-varieties or strains of which the so-called "black" strains yield the best color.

The flavor norm of 150 is based on the juice pressed from raw cold berries, the *p*H of which is around 2.5; acids (as citric 2.40). Reducing sugars 4.20.

Cranberries may be used either raw or cooked:

Raw cranberries are used for garnishing, as a color component for embellishing salads and other food compositions, but they are much too sour to eat as is. Cold pressed raw juice as a sauce or beverage component is one of the options to effect a sweet-sour balance.

Cooked or blanched whole berries may be used for garnishing, as cranberry sauce or preserves. The heat-extracted juice is used for jelly or beverage purposes. While commercial cranberry sauce in several different forms is widely used in cookery, it should be realized that all those products are sweet. Their principal usage is more or less restricted as food supplements. What is overlooked is the potentiality of not only cranberry "sauces" but the cold- or heat-extracted juice of raw or frozen cranberries as a sweet-sour balancing component of food compositions, with emphasis on the contribution of agreeable cranberry pink color which is attainable with careful processing.

Pomegranate (200)

This is one of the Biblical fruits historically more liked for its juice. Contemporarily that juice is most widely used as the syrupy beverage base termed "grenadine." The fruit is globular, topped with a crown-like calyx, and the interior consists of numerous seeds enveloped in firm to hard and white to ruby-red pulp (Bailey 1943).

Pomegranates introduced into the American colonies in the 17th century went wild, resulting in some mutations which when crossed with some of the foreign parent varieties have resulted in extreme variations in form, color of skin and pulp, and especially acidity and sweetness of the pulp. While some of the foreign varieties have white or yellow skin (and one is reported to be practically seedless) all of the American varieties have skin colors that range from white with a pink blush, through pink, red-striped to dark red. The pulp of the commonly marketed varieties ranges from pink to ruby red. The juice of some of the pink varieties is lightly sweet and sub-acid, whereas the acidity of the red-juiced varieties seems to increase with depth of color. Some of the newer dark red hybrids are from 3 to 5 inches in diameter and the ruby juice has a wine-like character like a high-acid rose wine with a pomegranate note.

The pomegranate may be the most bitter common fruit. There is no easy way of avoiding inclusion of the bitterness in either pressing the fruit for juice or eating the seed segments out-of-hand. Any inclusion of the rind or the thin skin that surrounds each seed segment conveys extreme puckeriness. It is emphasized that both the rind and the seed enveloping membrane are more astringent than immature persimmons. This is one of the fruits the juice of which is qualitatively improved by 2 or 3 weeks' storage after harvesting. (See Pomegranate, FN 115 in Column 14, Beverages.)

Pomegranate juice, because of its high acidity and bitterness, is outstanding in many compositions requiring correction of the sweet-sour balance.

Lemon (250)

Many lemons that have been allowed to cling to the parent shrub long after maturity are high enough in sweetness and low enough in sourness to be just barely acceptable for out-of-hand eating. Half of one will probably be enough. However it is emphasized that such post-mature lemons lose most of their strong acidity. For cold drinks the juice of such lemons can provide what may be described as a winey, a pleasantly acidic fairly sweet but not too sour component. (See note on citrus fruits under Orange, FN 120 this Column.)

Lime (350)

This rating is based on the so-called "true lime" frequently called "Mexican" or "wild" limes in American markets, the fruit of which is usually round but may be slightly elongated and pointed. The pulp is lime green, and while the skin may vary from dark green to light lemon (when post-mature) the pulp is always lime green, the tint of which lightens only after prolonged storage, when the skin becomes yellow to almost brown. All of the true limes (with the exception of Tahiti types such as Bearss) have the flavor note that is peculiar to limes. No other fruit that can be considered common has a lime component in its flavor characters. (See note on citrus fruits under Orange, FN 120 this Column.)

CHAPTER 16

Carriers

COLUMNS 11, 12, 13

The different carriers are flavor rated in Columns 11, 12, and 13 and only briefly discussed. They are more broadly covered in Volume II. They are placed where they are in the Gustametric Chart because they are bases of most concoctions—the free liquids with which foods are cooked or which are added to foods. The flavor components of carriers influence the food of which they are a part.

Definitions

Carrier.—A liquid by whose agency other food matter is held, sustained, or transferred in solution or suspension.

Infusion.—An admixture of animal, mineral, or vegetable food matter in a liquid.

The foods and the conditions of foods contained in Columns 11, 12, and 13 may properly be considered as subdivisions of one classification of food: *infusions.*

Incidental to these considerations must be the realization that all carriers are compounds, but all compounds are not carriers, so these three Columns—11, 12, and 13—are limited to considerations of liquid carriers.

The classification of liquid carriers is tabulated in three subdivisions more or less conforming to traditional nomenclatures. As within other classifications, specialized definitions or restricted meanings are given to some terms. The word "infusion" is applied to the classification as a generic umbrella with thorough awareness that its meaning is technically restricted in some fields. The tea trade would provide an example, where its real sense is vegetable matter *dissolved* in water. In its wider interpretation here, solid additives to liquids that may or may not combine are included in the term. Oil and water may be admixed one to the other and constitute a carrier. They may not chemically or physically combine, but either one may be suspended in the other. In other words, the term "infusion" allows for solutions and suspensions as well as the states of matter in between. Technical juggling of words, technicalities of nomenclature, begin bobbing around when one looks for words to express compound physical and chemical functions. For example: if a chunk of meat is added to water which is then brought to the boiling point, what word designates the liquid, and what the solid? For greater simplification, the water-fat part is called the "liquid carrier." The meat may be called the *infusorium*—that which has been added to or infused in the starting liquid (water). When the composition becomes cold the water is the substratum atop which is the fat and usually some meat. At the bottom of the water mass there will be some sediment; in the top of the fat mass there will be some flotsam. Recognizing the different elements of the subject and distinguishing between mixtures (infusions, suspensions, and separations) the final product in this example may be seen as only one common substance. By suffusion whatever intrinsic flavor the meat may have had as been partially conveyed or transferred to the liquids that functioned as carriers in the process of cooking.

CHAPTER 17

Beverages

COLUMN 14

Introduction

Most of the liquids or liquorous foods that are generally considered beverages are listed in Columns 14 and 15 by individual or type names or terms. Omitted from either of the two classifications of beverages is any broad discussion of their compositions. Example: alcohols and syrups (included in Column 11) are components of beverages.

In the watery carriers, Columns 11 and 12 there are liquors varying in solid content from low to high (from marinades to soups) that may circumstantially be used as drinks but they are not commonly classified as *beverages.*

Column 14 is headed "Non-Alcoholic Beverages" and the column alongside of it, Column 15, is labeled "Liquors, Alcoholic." A qualification to the consideration of fruit juices as beverages is that they are not absolutely non-alcoholic. It may be that the majority of commercial soft drinks are non-alcoholic but conversely it is probable that the majority of natural fruit beverages have some alcoholic content. With a few exceptions, examples are sarsaparilla and root beer, the beverages listed in Column 14 are considered relative to contemporary usage. Here a qualification is that all of the beverages in Column 14 according to ordinary contemporary production are innocuous drinks. In the past and even today according to unusual circumstances, many of those beverages were and still are more or less alcoholic.

All fruit juices, when submitted to conditions favorable for fermentation have enough sugar by themselves to develop into rather heady beverages. Mixtures of fruit juices combined with crushed grain and especially with crude sugar provided some of the Colonial low alcoholic beverages. While many commercial soft drinks such as soda pop are carbonated, many of the Colonial fruit wines and root "beers" were consumed when they were only partially fermented with their intrinsic carbonation. Illustrative of this point is the fact that almost all the fruits listed in Column 10, "Raw Fruits," have provided wine bases. Examples of what may be considered unusual fruit juices manipulated to low alcoholic beverages are persimmon and pineapple wines. Parenthetically it must be obvious that all of the true fruit brandies are based on fruit wines.

Water (0)

Tap water is not chemically pure water. It is a shocking fact that the domestic water of some communities here in the United States as well as many rural water supplies are from polluted sources. While this work is not directly concerned with public health and sanitation involved in the source of domestic water supplies, it enters our picture when appraising the variation in flavor characters of natural water itself or as it affects cookery. Chemically pure (usually distilled) water is devoid of organic or inorganic matter other than H_2O and, of course, is tasteless. With mineral, animal, or vegetable components, its flavor varies from subliminal through agreeable to disagreeable. Soft waters are low and hard waters are high in inorganic matter. Good water should be devoid of organic (animal or vegetable) matter. Impure water substantially affects the flavor of anything with which it is used.

Contrary to generally held impressions, average tap water is not *neutral.* It averages about pH 6.3, so it is weakly acid. It is important to realize that on the pH scale tap water is subliminally sour to most people. It is below the threshold of sourness to them. Knowing that tap water is generally not chemically pure and that it is lightly sour, we should preliminarily appraise and treat any natural water to be used in or with food.

Recommended Procedure.—Ahead of a trial, look at the inside of your toilet reserve tank for sediment at the bottom and feel for slime on the float. You may be amazed and shocked at the revelation. At least you will proceed with subsequent organoleptic trials with some hint of what to anticipate.

(1) In a clean, clear, thin-walled glass, hold tap water to the light and look for macroscopic flotsam.

(2) Raise the temperature of the tap water to the point where it visibly starts vaporizing (about 150°F.) at which point smell it for organic and inorganic components.

(3) Lower the temperature of the water to about 98.6°F. and taste it.

Usage.—If the tests indicate the presence of organic (animal or vegetable) matter, the water should be boiled for five minutes or held at 185°F. for a minimum of fifteen minutes. If water has been chlorinated, then boil it for five minutes or hold it at 185°F. or higher for fifteen minutes, in either case, uncovered. Chlorine, being volatile, will largely go off with the water vapor.

Both of these admonitions are important flavorwise, because both organic and inorganic components of tap water chemically combine with other food matter and usually adversely affect the total flavor of a food. Here it may be somewhat amusing to note English criticism of American tea. The answer is largely that water chlorination in England is not widespread; in America a large number of municipalities chlorinate their water in the distribution systems.

Try brewing two pots of tea, making up one pot with straight tap water and the other with water that has been previously dechlorinated by boiling:

(1) Using a very light darjeeling or jasmine tea, carefully measure into aluminum or other neutral metal tea balls the same amount of tea for each of the two pots.

(2) Place tea balls in clean, heated tea pots and pour in water at not to exceed 185°F. The tannin in tea does not dissolve readily under about 190°F. but rapidly goes into solution above that temperature. Steep for five minutes (at 185°F.) then remove tea balls.

(3) Checking with a clinical thermometer, lower the temperature of the tea

to about 98.6°F. Then look, smell, and taste. The normal taster will thereupon decide that chlorine doesn't agreeably blend with tea.

Coconut Milk (10 to 20, av. 13)

The hollow fruit of the tropical coconut palm *Cocos nucifera* contains a cloudy liquor. This liquor, colloquially called milk, in nuts approaching maturity, tends to be bland and flat, almost flavorless. The milk of very young nuts, being fairly high in sugar, readily ferments in favorable conditions.

Soda Water (25)

Soda water (also called seltzer) is water (H_2O) carbonated with carbon dioxide (CO_2). The flavor level of 25 is due to the kinesthetic effect of gas bubbles bursting in the mouth and past the olfactory perceptors. The flavor norm will vary with the amount of carbonation in the beverage as it is being tasted, smelled, and swallowed.

Critical:

(1) As carbonated beverages are allowed to become warm they "flatten." Carbonation rapidly evanesces after a container has been opened and the beverage exposed to atmosphere. Evanescence is accelerated as temperature rises.

(2) Avoid agitation of carbonated beverages; either in the process of pouring or by stirring in a receptacle. Depending upon the extent of agitation the entrained CO_2 is dissipated from sodas resulting in comparatively flat soda drinks. As a component of mixed drinks chilled soda water should be added last with little or no stirring. Incidentally, tulip-shaped glasses theoretically restrict the escape of CO_2.

(3) Soda water may be judged most lively if it is consumed at a temperature below 60°F.

Grenadine (Pomegranate-Juice Syrup) (25)

Abroad it is one of the more popular bases for children's beverages. With lemon juice and soda it is one of the teetotaler's standbys. It may be the origin of pink lemonade.

Bartenders use grenadine for sweetening and pink coloring.

Orgeat (Syrup of Almonds) (33)

This emulsion of bitter and sweet almonds, sugar, lemon peel, and water is one of the neglected seasoning syrups. Abroad it is widely used not only in beverages but in desserts and bakery products. It should be considered as a supporting or strengthening medium on and with raw and cooked fruits, particularly with peaches and other fruits, the pits of which taste almond-like. It is one of the favored components of Swiss and Austrian pastries, ice cream, and cream-base desserts.

Tea (50)

The term tea is largely applied to a drink made by infusing the leaves of *Thea chinensis* (or of a congeneric variety of the *Camellia* family) in hot water, for a beverage having characteristic aromatic, bitter, and stimulating constituents.

Tea is used as a general name for an infusion made in the same way as with

Thea: (1) As a substitute for *Thea* (refer to Maté, FN 58); (2) for medicinal purposes.

The main tea producing countries are Africa, Ceylon, China, Formosa, India, Indonesia, Japan, and Pakistan.

Most of the teas that are "varietally" labeled come from India: Assam, Cachar, Darjeeling, Dooars, etc. which are the names of districts.

The tea trade distinguishes not only between the countries of origin but the elevations of the tea estates (whether they are up-country, mid-country or low-country: from perhaps 10,000 feet down to almost sea level) and according to seasonal conditions. There are distinct differences between early, mid-season, and "autumnal" teas from the same district. While what the trade considers the finest qualities in teas tend to come from higher elevations there are many exceptions. The most delicate teas may be produced from choice leaf tips in virtually all producing areas. In general, the heavier teas come from the lowlands but color in tea is largely according to what part of the bush the leaf tips or the leaves come from: a given bush at any elevation will yield light-colored leaves from the upper outside leaf tips and quite dark tea from the lower or coarser inner leaves. Variety, district, and growing conditions are factors influencing the color of tea but light tea or dark tea can be produced from the same bush.

Teas are classed according to their method of preparation as Green, Black, or Oolong. There are two main groups of grades into which the dried tea leaves have been sifted.

Leaf grades are divided into Orange Pekoe, Pekoe, and Souchong. Broken grades are divided into Broken Orange Pekoe, Broken Pekoe, and Broken Pekoe Souchong. In some instances Pekoes are made from the smaller leaves and Souchong from the larger and coarser ones.

Some Chinese teas are marketed in forms that are twisted or curled or rolled, which may be called gunpowder tea.

There are two distinct classes of scented teas: one in which freshly gathered flowers are mixed with the drying tea, and the other where the scenting flower is added to the dry tea. The flowers favored in China for scenting tea are jasmine, gardenia, orange, and other citrus blossoms.

There are some smoke-cured teas, the flavor of which is imparted by the kind of fuel used. Sometimes woods with herb or balsamic esters or peat are used. Some Lapsang Souchong and others that are peat-smoke-cured convey a wistful suggestion of Scotch. In panel trials it was found to appeal more to men than to women.

Strange as it may seem it is factual that there are more connoisseurs of tea than there are of coffee; because more people drink tea than drink coffee and it is much easier to distinguish between different varieties and grades of tea than is the case with coffees.

Further there seem to be more ways of producing compound tea beverages than coffees. Both the methods of producing the beverage and the kind of additive vary (sometimes startlingly) with both areas and peoples. In Northern India melted ghee or butter is added to strong tea; the resulting composition, leaves, and liquor, may be the sole food matter of a meal. In the Levantine countries some of the pungent mints are added to tea, and in Europe there is considerable admixture of some of the lighter herbs starting with woodruff and some of the native wild herbs. However, tea epicures in all the heavy tea-consuming countries (except the United States) tend to cling to varietal preferences, particularly of the lighter, more floral ones.

Commercial blends of teas both in the countries of origin, in Europe and America are (like coffees) according to the teas that happen to be available and that will, according to trade standards of identity and individual quality control meet the requirements of the professional tasters of each producer. The many differences of kind and variety and other factors affecting the quality of tea (just as they do coffee) mean that a given specimen of straight tea or blend is never quite the same as any preceding or subsequent pack.

Preparation of Tea.—There are two basic ways of preparing an infusion of tea:

(1) Steeping and its variations; stirring or whipping tea leaves or tea powder in hot to boiling water;

(2) The use of instant tea in the form of an extract or other conversion.

Here again there are more schools of thought and individual ideas on how to prepare tea than how to prepare coffee. The most involved ideas are those of the tea cult of Japan which is more concerned with ceremonial precepts than it is with preparation of a beverage. The Chinese follow the simplest procedure by pouring hot, not boiling water atop dry leaves in a pot. Further the Chinese do not follow any set ideas about period of steeping times. The only idea that is fairly generally held is that tea should be made in a non-metallic vessel, preferably in glass or porcelain.

As with all infusions, composition of the water used is an important consideration. Contaminated water or tap water that has been chlorinated or fluoridated should be boiled long enough to drive off the volatile contaminants before making tea with it.

The esteemed floral values of tea are volatile; they evanesce from any vessel that is open to atmosphere at a rate that is proportional with the temperature of the water added, and time.

Experiments.—(1) In a lid-closed pyrex pot pour cool to tepid or warm water atop tea leaves (or a "tea bag"); bring the temperature of the brew up to 165°F. and immediately pour off the tea liquor and appraise the product. Compare the product of that experiment with the controlled production of tea infused with boiling water but which has been allowed to steep for the frequently recommended minimum of three minutes.

(2) Infuse the tea in any cooking vessel but steep the tea at a temperature of 185°F. for three minutes.

Compare the products of the last experiment with either or both of the first.

A Glossary of Tea Trade Terms

This is provided because most of the factors involved in appraising tea are summarized and connotate much of the technology not only of the tea trade but the extensive literature about tea.

Terms Describing the Appearance of the Tea

Brownish.—Leaf which is brown in color. Underwithered leaf fired at too high a temperature produces a brownish tea.

Blistered.—Leaf swollen and hollow inside. Blisters are formed in the firing of leaf which has been too rapidly dried in the first fire.

Black.—Leaf which is black in color. Fully withered leaf gives black tea, but that produced in North-East India is not usually black in color because of the light wither and certain other conditions of manufacture.

Bold.—Indicates that the pieces of leaf are big, and that they might be cut smaller.

Choppy.—Leaf chopped in the breaker or cutter rather than in the roller. Used in regard to a B.P. made by cutting a leaf tea, e.g., a Pekoe or O.P.

Clean.—Leaf free from fiber and dust.

Crepy.—Indicates that the leaf is crimped in appearance.

Even.—Leaf true to grade and consisting of pieces of roughly equal size.

Flaky.—Leaf which is not twisted, but in flakes. Results from hard rolling of under-withered leaf, or from the manufacture of hard leaf.

Grey.—Greyness results from too rapid firing or too much rubbing during sorting and cutting.

Silver Tip.—Grey colored "tip." Over-withered leaf usually gives grey "tip."

Stalk.—Usually indicates the presence of red stalk. Results from coarse leaf and too hard rolling.

Tippy.—Containing a large percentage of golden "tip." The hair on the young leaves smeared with fermented leaf juice is responsible for "tip."

Uneven.—Tea composed of uneven, irregular pieces, indicating bad sorting.

Well-Twisted.—Fully withered leaf gives well-twisted tea.

Terms Describing the Infused Leaf

The tea taster uses the term infusion to denote the infused leaf.

Bright.—Bright red in color, denoting a good tea. The liquors from such infused leaf are also usually bright. This color is referred to as the new penny color.

Coppery.—Bright copper-colored infused leaf, often given by second flush and autumnal teas.

Dull.—Brownish in color, denoting a poor tea. Dull colors result from over-withering, over-fermentation, or poor leaf. The liquors of such infused leaf are usually dull in color.

Green.—Greenish in color. This characteristic results from under-withering, under-fermentation, or insufficient rolling. The liquors from such infused leaf are raw or thin according to the fineness or coarseness of the leaf.

Mixed or Uneven.—The infused leaf contains red, black, and green colors. Results from uneven withering, fermentation, or rolling.

Terms Describing the Liquors

The tea infusion is referred to by the taster as the liquor.

Brisk.—Having a "live" characteristic. May indicate some degree of pungency.

Bright.—Bright and clear in color. In the early-season teas the brightness is of an orange tinge, and in the later teas a rosy-red clear color.

Body.—See Thick.

Color.—Denotes good color, bright red, and clear.

Dull.—Brownish liquors, which are not clear or bright. May result from over-withering, over-fermentation, or incorrect firing.

Flat or Soft.—Lacking in briskness and pungency. Results from over-withering, over-fermentation, or incorrect firing.

Fruity.—Suggests a taint. May be due to over-fermentation on an infected floor.

Full.—A strong tea with no bitterness. One which will cream down well.

Hard.—Suggests pungency. This is a desirable quality met in Assam teas.

Harsh.—A liquor which is bitter. Results from under-withering, under-fermentation, but generally from under-rolling.

Light.—A liquor lacking body or thickness.

Mature.—No rawness or flatness.

Muddy.—Dull liquors suggesting over-fermentation.

Pungent.—Having astringency without bitterness. This is a very desirable quality.

Raw, Rasping.—See Harsh.

Rich, Ripe, Round, Smooth.—See Full.

Strength.—A combination of thick liquors and pungency or briskness.

Sweet.—A light liquor that is not plain.

Plain.—Dull, with rather a sour taste.

Thick.—A concentrated bright red liquor.

Thin, Weak, Washy.—A diluted liquor of little value. Such liquors may result from under-withering, under-fermentation, and not enough rolling. High temperatures during manufacture produce thin liquors. Thin liquors usually indicate poor leaf.

Terms Describing General Characteristics

Aroma.—Denotes that the infusion and the infused leaf have one of a certain number of smells which are highly valued. Such aroma is connected with flavor.

Bakey.—A slightly high-fired tea.

Burnt.—A taste of burnt organic matter in the infusion and a similar smell in the infused leaf. Denotes too high firing temperatures, usually in the second fire.

Coarse.—A liquor with certain undesirable characteristics. Results from coarse leaf.

Cream.—The precipitate obtained as soon as a strong tea cools.

Dry.—A characteristic in the liquor which is evident when tea is not discharged from the dryer as soon as it is fired.

Flavory.—A tea showing a taste associated with certain seasonal, district or "Green fly" teas.

Gone-off.—A moldy or tainted tea, a flat or old tea. Usually denotes that tea has been packed containing too much moisture.

Hay Flavor.—A characteristic which often precedes autumnal flavor.

High-Fired.—A burnt tea but one not so badly high-fired as to be described as burnt. Results from keeping tea in the dryer at 200°F. or more after it is fully fired.

Malty.—A desirable quality. May be due to slight high-firing.

Mushy.—A soft tea, suggesting it has been packed too moist.

New.—A tea which has not had time to mellow. Usually denotes some rawness in the infusion which may disappear when the tea is kept.

"On the Nose."—Indicates some aroma. Maltiness is noticeable on the nose.

Plain.—Lacking in tea characteristics. Suggests coarse leaf.

Point.—Some marked desirable characteristic, perhaps briskness.

Quality.—Denotes the presence of desirable characteristics.

Smoky or Tarry.—Tastes of smoke. May be due to leaky tubes in the stove which allow furnace smoke to enter the dryer.

Stewed.—A dull tea with a taste reminiscent of stew. Results from faulty first firing, usually.

Tainted.—A tea having a strange flavor. May result from infection by microorganisms at some stage of manufacture or on keeping. Usually refers to some flavor quite foreign to tea, e.g., oranges, onions, kerosene.

Woody.—A grass or hay flavor which is undesirable.

Maté (58)

Maté (*Ilex paraguayensis*) is also called Paraguay tea. In South America the beverage is customarily sucked through a hollow reed or tube from a gourd or calabash. This is an outstanding example of the continuance of a primitive custom of food behavior, even to the atavistic custom of sucking out of a family vessel.

Important qualification: in South America maté is *not brewed;* the dry leaves are dropped in a gourd, then hot water is added. Without swirling or stirring the infusion is sucked from the gourd as soon as the liquid is below the scalding temperature. The gourds customarily used for maté being small (usually not more than four inches in diameter), after a few suckings additional hot water is added, until the leaves are exhausted.

In an infusion percentagewise proportional with tea, maté is slightly more bitter and may be more stimulating. The other flavor components of maté are not usually liked by tea drinkers.

As a footnote to maté it is pertinent to observe that besides maté's being commonly thought of as tea in South America, many other countries apply the term tea (or a cognate term in their languages) to infusions made from plants other than *Thea chinensis*. In other countries teas may be designated by territorial or vernacular names. Examples are Abyssinian tea, Arabian tea, Australian tea, Canada tea, Labrador tea, Mexican tea, West Indian tea, etc.

Colloquial names such as goldenrod tea, mountain tea, oswego tea, tend to be applied to infusions produced more for medicinal than for beverage purposes.

Tea-Berry (60)

Also called "checkerberry," "American wintergreen," and "Mountain tea" (*Gaultheria procumbens*). Both leaves and berries are used as infusions for tea; the berries are lightly fruity in flavor.

Passion Fruit Juice (61)

Three distinctly different fruits of the genus *Passiflora* are called "passion fruit." *P. quadrangularis* and *P. edulis* are the two most favored for juice production. The fruits vary in form and size from small, round, or elongated, up to eight inches; and in color from brownish yellow through green to dull purple. The pulp of both is rarely eaten out-of-hand because of its high seed content and the nature of the pulp and seed capsules. The pulp of both is gelatinous and the juice is sub-acid. The flavor of both is lightly suggestive of citrus but has floral notes peculiar to each.

There are several species of *Passiflora* to which botanists ascribe different names, which have quite long yellow fruits. When mature the skin is rather soft and peels easily like a shell; the pulp, encased in a subcutaneous paperlike sac, is high in seeds. That pulp is acceptable for those who find crunching the seeds agreeable, served either with or without sugar and cream. The highly gelatinous pulp resists extrusion for juice.

Cocoa (62)

Cocoa nibs, after roasting and grinding, have between 45 and 55 per cent fat, commercially called "cocoa butter." For chocolate products, enough fat is expressed to permit formation of chocolate slabs; but the fat content of commercial cocoa has a maximum of 28 per cent fat and in a few instances has less than 10 per cent.

Most of the species[1] and hybrids have both red and yellow skins.

The fat content of cocoa suggests comparing some of its beverage qualities with thin or skim milk as compared to common or rich milk. Trial of different cocoas will prove that the higher the cocoa butter component, the more "chocolatey" the cocoa.

Since sugar and sometimes cream are usually added to cocoa as a beverage, qualitative trials of cocoa should first be made without additives, then tried with white, brown, and dark-brown sugars. The brown sugars add flavor components which, in this instance, some may find most agreeable. Since sugars do not dissolve in fats, try sugar syrup for close control of sweetness.

Additives popular with other peoples are spice traces like vanilla, cinnamon, mace, and *coffee.* A topping of whipped cream with or without a touch of vanilla is in vogue in Austria and Switzerland.

In Europe some cordials and liqueurs are added to cocoa. The following additives are frequently used in the foreign countries designated: Aquavit, Scandinavian Countries; Gin, Holland; Brandy, France; Sweet Vermouth, Italy.

Apricot-Peach Nectar (68)

This is one of the many combinations of fruit juices commercially produced under the trade name of "nectar." Some nectars are composed of either one or more fruit juices with no addition of water other than small quantities introduced in steam processing. Where substantial amounts of water are added to fruit juices, the trade names usually have the suffix "*-ade*"; such as, lemonade, grapeade, etc.

Factually, the nectars are somewhat concentrated fruit juices and the "ades" are more or less dilute diffusions.

Papaya Nectar (72)

The natural flavor of papaya juice is so bland that in production the packers always add sugar and fruit acids for the required sweet-sour-balance.

Raisin (72)

Macerated muscat raisins kept in cool water for a few days, sometimes under conditions that promote a little fermentation, result in an infusion which, when served with a dash of lemon juice, is one of the most popular hot weather drinks of northern Africa and some of the other eastern Mediterranean countries. Why it has not taken hold in the United States is a good question. Served cool or chilled, it is a very good hot weather drink.

Cider (74)

Beverages based on the juice of apples fall into four classifications:

(1) Plain apple juice so processed that it approximates the flavor of fresh apples.

---

[1] Species include *C. theobroma, C. criollo,* and *C. forastero.*

(2) Cider
  (A) Plain. Apples crushed and pressed, yielding the liquid in a condition average for that product.
  (B) Carbonated plain cider.
  (C) Fermented cider or apple wine, the fermentation varying from slight to complete. The term "hard cider" is applied to cider when its sugar has been completely or almost completely fermented, where the alcoholic content is relatively high.
  (D) Carbonated, fermented cider.
(3) Apple brandy, commonly called "apple jack": the product of distilling fermented cider.
(4) Mixtures of apple juice, cider, or apple brandy with other beverages. One of the simplest is cider and perry (pear cider). A central European favorite is cider, perry, and rhubarb juice.

It must be obvious that the flavor character of apple beverages vary with varieties and conditions of the apples and methods of production. There are surprisingly many variations of the different kinds of cider productions and they vary not only country-by-country and district-by-district but just as in cookery and in wine production, according to the ability and the equipment of different producers. The ciders of Central Europe and of Britain, it is said, are in the direction of a bitter-sweet beverage. It just about has to be that, for the simple reason that with the exception of some parts of England, apples don't do well in Europe; even in most European market places most of the apples would impress the average American apple grower as being runty, and what the packing houses call "cull" grades. The bulk of them seem to be misshapen with much surface blemish, and the flavors tend to be so-so, neither high in sweetness nor agreeable in sourness and with characteristic surface sourness and bitterness.

Consequently most commercially produced European ciders are modified to correct one or another component. French ciders usually have sweetening added and the bitterness buffered. Central Europe, particularly Switzerland, favors low sweetness, relatively high bitterness, and carbonation. In Britain there is a larger variety of available ciders than in the United States. Not so long ago there were more different varieties of apples grown in the British Isles than in the United States. Their range of ciders varies from the simple and bland to compound and strong, with a large percentage of their production going into carbonated cider. Incidentally, in the British Isles, carbonated or "champagne cider" seems to be on every restaurant menu, together with beers and wines.

"Liquid apple" contains homogenized pulp and is not cider. Only within the past few years have processes developed that resulted in what in trade circles is called "liquid apple"—the juice of apples free from the effects of oxidation. That product is steamed but not filtered, cloudy, and apple-pulp white. It may be homogenized. Its flavor is usually very close to that of apple pulp in prime condition.

Cider is the term applied to the liquor resulting from a process of grinding and then pressing in a hydraulic press. That process exposes the apple solids and liquids to air, which causes oxidation and enzymatic alteration of the natural flavors of the apple to those associated with the term "cider." The liquor slowly browns to the amber hue of ordinary cider.

Commercially filtered cider varies in color from straw to light amber, whereas domestically produced unfiltered cider may be slightly cloudy, with darker color and (being higher in solids) have more flavor. A grayish or brownish cast to cider color can be caused by excessive browning reactions or by the use of spoiled fruit.

In Nova Scotia, New York State, Virginia, and some other states and Provinces, considerable quantities of apple juice are flash-pasteurized by a continuous process, either before or after filtration, then canned or bottled and quickly cooled. Flash-pasteurization not only kills the yeasts and bacteria that cause fermentation, but also inactivates the oxidative enzymes which would otherwise cause rapid deterioration and browning of the product (Tressler and Joslyn 1954). Flash-pasteurized apple juice is a stable product of considerable commercial importance.

Much "home-made" cider is made from "windfalls" and includes, in many instances, infested and partially spoiled apples. Much of this low grade cider is used for making vinegar. Some old-timers still insist that the best cider is made from stored, shriveled apples. Nevertheless, just as the proverbial "bad apple in the barrel" can spoil its neighbors, the use of bad apples for juice can and will spoil whatever good natural flavor the cider may have.

The juice of Gravenstein, Pippin, and other high-acid apples is favored for commercial production. If low in sweetness or sourness, sugar and/or fruit acid is added in commercial production. If preservatives are not added to cider it will, with little or no encouragement, ferment. How "hard" it becomes hinges on content of sugar and to what extent the cider ferments.

Many people use the term "hard" applied to cider as if it were synonymous with "dry" applied to wine. But "hard" refers to alcoholic content of cider, whereas "dry" is not related to alcoholic content, but to sweetness.

The average consumer rejects cider which is so dry that sweetness is subliminal. The types of ciders popular in the United States show that most people here require satisfaction of the sweet-sour balance. The average European taste in ciders requires higher bitterness.

Perry (Pear Cider) (75)

It is an old beverage in England but one that is rarely produced in America, probably because in its natural condition it is too bland. Only by compounding perry with other fruit juices, and sometimes sugar and acids can an agreeable sweet-sour-balance be effected.

Domestic producers of perry usually process it to a partially fermented state. Sugar must be added to the basic cider to permit fermentation or the cider will spoil before it ferments.

Grape Juice (78)

Commercial grape juice, for which Concord grapes are commonly used, gets its flavor and color largely from the hot skins. The cold pressed juice of Concord and most other grapes is not only free from what can be described as the "cooked flavor" of commercial grape juice but such fresh grape juice is usually sickly in color.

With the exception of some of the wine grapes that have red pulp, practically all of the table varieties, as well as some of the wine varieties, have whitish pulp. The color components of grape juice, as well as wine, are largely contributed by color pigments under the grape skin, most of which is extracted by heat or by fermentation.

Only recently have processes been developed where commercially produced grape juice has flavor characters approximating the fresh and natural juice of not only the Concord but other grapes. Because natural grape juice readily ferments and, if low in sugar, spoils, it must be either quickly used or processed for inhibition of fermentative and spoilage organisms.

There should be more awareness of the beverage possibilities in production of juices not only from varieties other than Concord but in the blending of certain table grape varieties according to their different flavor characters. The juice of grapes like Tokay and Malaga, being very low in acid, should be blended with the juices of some tart grapes; and, in their absence, with the addition of citric acid or fresh lemon juice to effect the desirable sweet-sour balance.

The bitterness in all grapes (excepting occasional seeds and stem matter) is in the skins.

Boysenberry Juice (80) (*Rubus*, var. *Boysen*)

Both boysenberries and loganberries are commercially processed for juice, with boysenberry being favored because of its relatively low acidity.

Most fruits of the other members of the rose family either do not have enough sweetness, or sourness, or both to make acceptable beverages. Loganberries and rose hips are high in acids and low in sugars, and the raspberries have neither enough sugar nor enough acid.

Tamarind Juice (83)

The tawny colored syrup is made from the pulp of the tamarind fruit (*Tamarindus indica*). Tamarind syrup is frequently marketed in the United States under the Italian name, Tamarindo. It may be used as a substitute for lemon syrup. It is commonly used as an innocuous beverage base in the tropics and southern Europe. (Refer to Tamarind, Column 22, FN 400.)

Grapefruit Juice (85) (Fresh)

The juice of grapefruit commercially processed sometimes has sugar added to raise it from the blandness that the simple juice would have consequent to the heat treatment required for its sterilization. Therefore, the juice of fresh grapefruit has a different flavor profile from that of canned grapefruit juice.

Ginger Ale (85)

Flavor determination based on the original drink made with ginger, lemon juice, sugar, and yeast.

In Britain it still is called "ginger beer." In a state of low fermentation it is only slightly effervescent. Commercial ginger ale, being very low in sweetness and with very little ginger flavor, is a far cry from true ginger ale. Try fortifying commercial ginger ale with ginger flavor (or crushed candied ginger), lemon juice and about eight per cent alcohol.

Pineapple Juice (88)

The flavor rating was determined on average Hawaiian canned juice.

Canned or frozen pineapple juice is one of the best mixers, particularly in combination with some of the bland fruit juices for beverages and as an ingredient with fresh and canned fruit compositions.

Orange Juice (90)

The flavor norm of California Navel orange juice is 90; that of both California and Florida Valencia orange juice is lower. The flavor characters of commercial canned and frozen orange juices vary with varieties, blends, and additives (sugar, acids, or both).

Lemonade (90)

The juices of limes, lemons, and other sour citrus fruits have flavor norms higher than 90; but compounded in "ades" those juices are so diluted that the basic flavors rate comparatively low.

The flavor norm of 90 is based on the juice of the Eureka lemon. The juices of other varieties are usually less acid than that of Eureka. Some of the hybrids like Meyer are more fruity. What can be very confusing is that sourness as well as sweetness and other flavor characters radically varies within the same varieties under different growing conditions. Thus the Meyer lemon, usually low acid, is occasionally more sour than Eureka.

Limeade (95)

Flavor rating based on the diluted juice of *Citrus aurantifolia.* This is the common semi-wild lime.

The small globular green to yellow fruit differs from the Bearss hybrid, which looks like a green lemon but is more floral in both the pulp and the rind. Both have a distinctly vanilla flavor note.

The Rangpur lime looks like, and can easily be mistaken for a tangerine. The juice tastes like a combination of orange and lemon juices. It provides one of the best citrus beverage bases.

The juice of the sweet lime, *Citrus limetta,* is bland, very low in sweetness, sourness, and bitterness. The fruit is liked by some people, but it is rarely used as a beverage.

Sarsaparilla (97)

It may be that the original American beverage called sarsaparilla had a substantial portion of wild sarsaparilla (*Aralia nudicaulis,* a species of smilax) but like the composition of root beer the variations were probably those of opportunity and inclination varying from non-alcoholic to alcoholic, from innocuous to the potencies of strong brews. The lightest beverages may have been likened to teas made of sarsaparilla and perhaps sassafras and wintergreen. The materials of some of the old compositions beside sarsaparilla root, were sassafras, wintergreen, licorice, sugar, yeast, and water.

Root Beer (98)

The flavor level is estimated by averaging several commercial beverages labeled "root beer." It may be interesting to know that commercial productions of root beer are low flavor level, innocuous beverages when compared with an experimental brew of a representative Colonial formulation of root beer. The materials required for one such composition were sassafras, yellow dock, allspice, wintergreen, wild cherry bark, coriander seed, hops, sugar, yeast, and water.

While the beverage is and was called "root beer" neither the original nor the contemporary bases have more than a small portion of root matter in their composition; further while the original beverage may or may not have been a true beer most of those root beers seem to have been fermented beverages, whereas today true root beer doesn't seem to be available.

Coffee (100)

There are far too many variables in coffee or coffee compositions and coffee brewing processes and techniques to permit any classifications of qualitative merit.

There are too many kinds and grades of coffee to label any of them the best.

Coffee

A. Beans, Whole—*Coffea arabica*
  1. Varieties: *C. arabica, C. liberica, C. robusta*
  2. Sources
    (a) Country: Ethiopia, Arabia, India, Malaya, Brazil, Caribbean countries, Centrial American countries, South American countries, Mexico, British East Africa, Belgian Congo
    (b) District or area
    (c) Grower, Finca, co-operative or broker
  3. Storage factors: Ambient atmosphere (including humidity, temperature) time
    (a) From year and season of production, to processor; usually six months
    (b) Period held by processor; usually three months or less
    (c) Period between roasting and packing; usually a matter of minutes
  4. Grades
    (a) Small, medium, large; bold, hardbean
    (b) Washed, unwashed, naturals
    (c) Straight or mixed
    (d) Graded (Brazil) 1, 2, 3, 4, 5, 6, 7, 8; other countries by description or mark
  5. Condition before roasting (chemical composition other than contamination or pesticides); moisture, ether extract, nitrogen, protein, crude fiber, ash

B. *Roasting*
  1. Cleaning, drying, or preheating
  2. Roasting: straight or blend
  3. Kind of roasting oven
  4. Classifications of coffee by color (colorimeter) and the several roasting processes: light (pale brown), medium (brown), high or full (dark brown), dark, shiny brown (almost black), shiny black, dull black

C. Grinds (particulate specifications)
  1. Regular
  2. Drip
  3. Pulverized
  4. Instant (different types)

D. Package
  1. Can (at atmosphere or in vacuum)
  2. Jar (at atmosphere or in vacuum)
  3. Bag or carton (packing techniques)
  4. Frozen: in container or package

because the goodness in coffee varies with individual taste. Another way of saying this is that it is not possible to *objectively* appraise any single coffee as best, because appraisal can only be *subjective*.

There can be no objective designation of one kind of utensil as the best because that opinion must be subjective.

The professional coffee taster may insist on using boiled (or even distilled) water for the coffee infusion he is to sample. People who use chlorinated (and sometimes otherwise chemically treated) tap water when they brew coffee become accustomed to the flavor imparted by trace amounts of chlorine and/or other chemicals (and who knows, they may actually like it). Coffee brewed with most spring or mountain stream water might to them taste flat.

Only a very few years ago there were marked differences between coffee from different producing areas which led coffee connoisseurs to marked preferences. Many such differences still exist and many of the cognoscenti will exercise their preferences. But food technologists in the coffee industry have within only a few years developed techniques of selection, preparation, and roasting of coffee that have resulted in amazingly high and uniform standards of quality control to the present situation where almost without exception commercial coffee offerings can be rated as very good. The technological developments in coffee start with horticulture: the selection and development of the different varieties of coffee, and their culture to maturity. Stripping the berries of pulp, cleaning and curing the beans in some (but not all) of the different points of origin now follow industrial standards. Consequently very good as well as not so good coffees are imported from countries that formerly produced low grade coffees. Conversely some coffees imported from some of the best (by reputation) coffee producing areas are downgraded by American processors in the course of blending different coffees. What this picture reveals is that some of the countries that were once producers of the "best" coffees have had their production remain static or even deteriorate while many of the coffee producing areas raised their standards and are producing as good or better coffees than the progenitors.

If there is such a thing as "the best coffee" it starts with: (1) the favored kind, blend or brand; (2) the favored grind; (3) the proper amount of ground coffee; (4) water free from adulteration or contamination.

It may be said that there are two common coffee-making faults: the first is using contaminated or chemically treated water and the second is just not using enough coffee—not making the coffee strong enough.

Solids that may be roasted and ground and admixed with coffee before or during infusion are (1) cereals: barley, oats, wheat, etc.; (2) legumes: peas, beans, etc.; (3) chicory, dandelion, and other roots.

Most solid admixtures with coffee are substitutes or thickeners of necessity but sometimes are according to taste preferences.

Parenthetically, outright imitations or synthetic coffee products, "ersatz coffee," are not covered here.

Continuing with solids possibly found in coffee: (4) sugars or other sweeteners; (5) herbs (e.g. mint) and spices (e.g. mace, cinnamon, cocoa).

The liquid carrier in which coffee or coffee compounds are infused is usually water.

Cataloguing of the different kinds of utensils used for "making coffee" as well as the techniques of coffee production are covered in Volume II.

Additives to coffee after infusion: (1) sugar and other sweeteners; (2) milk, cream (butter and other fats in Asia); (3) herbs and spices and fruit juices (e.g., lemon and lemon peel); (4) alcoholic liquors (e.g., brandy).

The coffees that do not meet the qualitative standards of very exacting coffee blenders and roasters go to those who are not so particular or to the many coffee roasters who customarily use what the trade grades as inferior coffees. They go to a surprisingly large number of small-quantity producers of high-roast coffees for what we think of as the foreign trade, for what amounts to foreign tastes.

This is markedly evident in the surging market for *espresso* type coffees for which, because they are over-roasted, the lowest grade coffees are used.

Another large usage for low grade coffees is for the production of low grade instant coffees and some coffee extracts.

Cherry Juice (105)

Juices extracted from the different varieties of cherries can be among the best of all fruit juices, but the quantity packed commercially is rather small. Further, natural cherry juices, being low in sugars and acids, are poor keepers, so they have to be quickly consumed. If pasteurized for storage the flavors of cherry juices are altered. Nevertheless, canned Montmorency cherry juice is an important article of commerce If held in cold storage (between 38° and 42°F.) cherry juices slowly ferment. Accordingly the bulk of commercially marketed cherry drinks are synthetic. (See Wild Cherry, FN 150 this Column.)

Cranberry Juice (110) See Cranberry, Column 10, FN 150.

The flavor norm is based on Ocean Spray Cranberry Juice Cocktail,[2] the flavor of which can be described as between that of aqueous solutions of cherry and pomegranate, but having a light character of cranberry attributable to its aromatics. It is slightly more astringent than cherry and a little less so than pomegranate. One of its outstanding characteristics is its clear pomegranate-red color, probably due to its being produced from the black strains of cranberries.

A somewhat comparable beverage can be produced by filtered hot extract of juice from dark cranberries, with the addition of $1^1/_2$ to 2 parts of water and sufficient sugar to bring the total sugar content up to 15 to 20 per cent according to taste (Fellers and Esselen 1955). By such dilution the acidity may be reduced to the point where the addition of lemon juice or citric acid may be desirable.

As a diluent of coolers and other beverages, cranberry juice provides an almost brilliant pink color that should make it one of the most agreeable mixers.

For some of the pallid fruit salads and some canned fruits as desserts, addition of cranberry juice can serve as a bright pink dye.

Pomegranate Juice (115)

The expressed juice of the pomegranate (*Punica granatum*) is not to be confused with grenadine, which is pomegranate syrup with a pomegranate-juice base. The juice flavor is rated so high (115) because in the process of pressing some of the bitter elements of the seed are extracted.

It is one of the juices recommended as a mixer, not only for its flavor but its red color, and in cookery where a tangy sweet-sour flavor note is wanted.

[2] Ocean Spray Cranberries, Inc., Hanson, Mass.

Prune Juice (120)

The flavor norm is based on commercial prune juice. Really a concentrate of the decoction of prunes, prune juice is rated at 120 because of its high sweetness and bitterness. The sweet-sour balance of commercial prune juice varies with varieties and physical condition of the prunes that are available for processing.

The acidity usually being relatively low, a dash of lemon juice may improve it.

Tomato Juice (125)

The flavor norm of 125 is based on an average estimation of commercial packs of tomato juice, which are the products of elaborate processing as to selection, pre-preparation, preparation in cookery and usually involving some degree of concentration. Actually, the products of different packers will vary (and they may vary radically) as to varieties and conditions of the tomatoes that are used.

Being straight juices (packed without additives) the flavor profiles of the different packs vary according to the qualities and the techniques of processing of each specific product.

Juice expressed from a raw prime tomato doesn't at all taste like canned tomato juice. Raw juice is peculiar in its watery blandness. It is almost disagreeable. It certainly is unpleasant. Even the addition of salt doesn't make it agreeable for most experimenters. The answer is simple. The raw flavor components of tomatoes are largely chemically locked in the pulp and the skin; therefore, raw tomatoes, whole or sliced, are agreeable but the expressed juice is not. Further, the cooking processes cause physical and chemical changes that bring about the product we know as "tomato juice."

The techniques of processing tomatoes for juice vary from open-to-atmosphere crushing, cooking, seed removing and finishing to closed-line vacuum processing (Tressler and Joslyn 1954).

The superseded "cold-break" and open-to-atmosphere method of cooking degraded most of the flavor characters and especially the color. Contemporary techniques avoid exposure of whole or crushed vegetable matter to air from the moment of introduction into a processing system, primarily to inhibit enzymatic actions. Comparison of juices processed under vacuum with samples of the superseded packs will clearly demonstrate the newer products' superiority in the elements of basic tastes, aroma, and color.

Then, too, there are the considerations of tomato varieties, growing conditions and especially seasonal variations. The specific gravity of individual specimens will vary with their content of pulp and sugars, and the basic tastes will vary greatly as those solids are present in the pack.

Blends of Tomato and Vegetable Juices (140)

The flavor norm of 140 is based on an average of several commercial packs of vegetable juices, most of which contain more than 90 per cent tomato juice with the balance being the juices and pulp of some of the spice vegetables and herbs.

This is a good example of a small group of foreign flavors radically altering the strong inherent flavors of the main product. Here approximately 7 per cent of spice vegetable juices mixed with approximately 93 per cent of tomato juice results in a vegetable juice mixture with a flavor profile wherein no single flavor note may be dominant.

The formulas of other vegetable juice blends approximately follow this lead with individual differences of spice vegetable components with subsequent overall flavor differences.

Cola (Kola) (145)

The FN is based on the average of several commercial "cola" soft drinks. The presence of caffein in the prototype African beverage came from the caffein constituent in the kola nut. Incidentally the kola nut (Sterculiaceae) is rather light in flavor and low in aromatics, which accounts for its flavor norm of 40. (See Dry Botanicals Chart, pp. 360–361.)

In the beverage industry so-called "kola essences" extracts and syrups, both non-alcoholic and alcoholic, have long been produced. Kola essences and syrups were and still are composed of many flavor components beside ground kola nuts or kola extract for not only soft drinks but kola "beers," "wines," and "cordials." As with the "root beers" and kindred beverages the essences and extracts combined with different botanicals, sugar, and water were allowed at least partially to ferment. Consequently the stimulating effects of kola beverages might be the collateral results of kola nut derivatives and alcohol. Some of the kola bases (essences, extracts, and syrups) have dry or sweet wines as the liquid carriers of the constituent botanicals.

Guava Nectar (148)

Raw fresh guava is highly acid and slightly sweet with a dominant terpene flavor note. One or two of these small (1 to 2 in. in diameter) globular yellow fruits will satisfy most tastes; but the juice and pulp with additives produce a nectar which is much lower in flavor profile than the raw fruit. Guava nectar rates so high (148) because of the lingering spicy aftertaste. It is one of the most agreeable tropical beverages.

Wild Cherry Juice (150)

The juice of wild cherries may be not only one of the most flavorsome of all fruit juices but one which requires much care and labor for its acceptable production. (See Cherry, FN 105 this Column.) Incidentally, the juices of both cultivated and wild cherries can result in some of the best fruit wines and distilled liquors, but again, because of the laborious processes involved in their production, they are among the rarest of commercial offerings. Most commercial alcoholic cherry liquors are not "straight" productions but modified compounds.

CHAPTER 18

Alcoholic Beverages

COLUMN 15

Introduction

In no classification of man's food are there more physical and chemical similarities and more aesthetic differences than in wine.

As the world's peoples are more alike than they are different (which the racialists will dispute but the anatomists won't) many different wines are remarkably similar, their differences largely aesthetic. Here in America wines are more the expression of romantic concepts than they are the stimuli of experience. In most wine-producing countries wines are common beverages that are simply preferred over water. They are every-meal accompaniments, necessities of everyday food behavior as against our occasional usage. (See Fig. 32, p. 105.)

Perhaps the greatest difference in the over-all wine picture is social rather than physical, regional rather than typical. The family differentiation begins with wine diluted with water for infants. Through childhood into maturity the individual is accustomed to diluted wine as the common beverage. Enjoyment of qualitative differences is largely limited to occasions more or less festive and more metropolitan than rural.

In America, primarily due to the artifices of prohibition, the warped wills of food delinquents would prohibit the age-old beverages of temperance in their campaign against excesses and impose statutory restrictions on common tastes.

With such a false foundation, a phenomenon practically exclusive to our American social structure, and a contemporary development at that, we are faced with what amounts to the necessity for re-educating ourselves in a food liberty of which we were deprived. We have to learn anew about wine and its uses. We have to relearn about a food that other peoples grow up with, and so understand that it is one of the good things of everyday meals.

Appraisal of the subject should start with consideration of wine as a seasoning, a flavor component of a meal, then branch out into the study of wine as a beverage or accompaniment, and finally as an ingredient of a food. Start with analysis of the different types and varieties of wines: what to use as a beverage or seasoning additive, and when. The dimensions of the differences between wines are more imaginary than they are real. Physically and chemically wines vary little, the gap between the standard and the higher grades is narrow and within the range of varietal differences, minute, usually apparent only to an expert.

Many amusing tales are told of European connoisseurs' failures to distinguish between American standard wines and those of Europe, as between our fine wines and some of their best. They invariably failed in definitive appraisals.

Study of the composition of standard wines is a requisite for their comprehensive usage. Start with distinguishing between standard wines and the premium grades. Comparison of what in the different European languages is designated as *ordinary* wine, like the *vin ordinaire* of France and what our wine trade calls *standard* wine will reveal one radical difference: within the range of acidity many of the European wines are to us undrinkable. They are too sour. They would be practically unmarketable in the United States. So, while it is incontrovertible that Europe produces some of the world's finest wines, it also produces most of the worst. Many people abroad, by something of a reverse phase of education, accept what the wine trade considers "unsound" wine.

Responsible for the differences in standards are the advances of technical progress in enology (wine technology) in America, and the more or less static production methods and marketing in Europe. Underlying the production of poor wines abroad are two factors: first, so much unfavorable climatic and vinicultural conditions; second, failure of many vintners to progress technologically.

Actually, the service of wine, both here and abroad, is based on foreign customs and folklore. Most of the stuffy snobbery of those who pretend to be wine connoisseurs is based on hearsay; on ideas based on tradition and deeply rooted folk customs concerned with festivities and special occasions.

In perspective a study of wine behavior of the peoples of the different wine-producing countries will show that the people of each wine-producing area use their own locally produced wine in and with their own foods, and the majority do not distinguish between color or flavor intensity of the wine or its relationship to a food.

In the Chablis area only the light white native wine is used in and with their foods. In the red wine district of Burgundy (Chablis is in the white wine district of Burgundy) the bulk of the usage is the red wine of Burgundy. Here it should be noted that in those areas wine is stored at whatever the storage temperatures may be *at different times of the year.*

The service of chilled white wine is largely a recent metropolitan development. Refrigeration equipment is almost unknown in the wine-producing areas of some countries; so how can they "chill" white wine? How can they insist on chilled white wine as the only proper way to serve it? The wine trade's adherence to service of this or that wine at room temperature or chilled is at variance with the customs of the great majority of foreign wine-country people.

Here in the United States the majority of wine users have more or less blindly followed European leaders and their foibles in disregard of one of our basic food habits, our preference for chilled or iced beverages. In the author's opinion one of the outstanding reasons why wine is not more generally used in the United States is because of the wine trade's failure to recognize this preference for cool or cold drinks. If our overwhelming preference is for iced drinks, why make a blanket recommendation to serve red wine at room temperature? Before dissenting, try making blind acceptance trials for preference, after considering the physiology of taste. Virtually all of the red wines are relatively high in tannin and/or other astringent components, the registration of which is submerged when wine is cold, in contrast to being objectionably high (to some people) when served at room temperature. In other words, all of the evidence of organoleptic perception is in favor of cold service of all wines high in astringent components.

Almost every book about wine, almost every author who has written on the subject, and virtually all of the alleged wine connoisseurs have with what amounts to one voice, inveighed against diluting wine. The wine snobs (that is not the author's term, it is one long applied to superficial people who pretend to a knowledge of wines) withdraw in stiff-necked disdain from the idea of putting ice in wine because the melted ice would dilute it. They ignore the fact that most of the people in the wine-producing areas of Europe dilute their table wine. Further, they don't sip it, they drink it. To a person who uses wine only occasionally, it is almost impossible to drink the contents of a glass in a series of gulps, so to speak. He tends to gag. There is sound physiological basis for the rejection of straight wine. But let him dilute it, cut it by half, half water and half wine, and not alone can he drink it as he would water, but he may prefer it so diluted. Furthermore, he may like it still better with ice added. Here in California there is mounting recognition of popular preference for diluting wine by the sharply increasing popularity of "wine coolers"; wine with half or more water or soda and ice.

It must be granted that the average of man's acceptance varies with intensity of flavors, both metabolically and aesthetically. He can accept far more food and drink in the bland or low flavor rating, than he can food of a higher rating. So, it can logically be assumed that the average person will accept much more light wine, rated at 40, than he would a wine with an FN of 80. Even with an Italian dinner he would normally not take more than one-quarter as much red wine at 95 as he would white wine at 48. Fortified wines flavor scaling from about 150 to about 350 tend to be sipped over a longer period and used in much smaller quantities than wines served with foods. Distilled liquors, brandies, and the liqueurs are served, so to speak, in thimblefuls.

Here realize that the tastes, tolerance, and acceptance factors of all the liquors in the alcoholic column are based on educated or individually conditioned developments. Tastes for strong liquors as well as quantities greater than we think of as average must be granted to result from development of individual habits of food behavior.

Some Considerations of Color/Flavor Relationships Between Wines

The matching of wines according to the kind, lightness, or darkness of meats, is one of man's most persistent food errors. Almost altogether a custom which evolved within the past hundred years, it may present the outstanding error of status gastronomes to whom the custom is largely limited. Probably responsible for maintenance of such wine fashions are the romanticists among authors and some of the copy writers within the wine trade. In no other classification of food does so unreasoned a pattern have such a relatively long history of such incongruous mismatings.

Consider the decree: "Thou shall use white wine with fish and red wine with red meats!" Now think about the reasonableness of the application of that ukase: pairing white wine with *any kind of fish* regardless of how high in flavor some of the strong fish are, and particularly with complete disregard of accompanying sauces and condiments! Apply the same consideration to poultry and other animal meats. Certainly it is just as absurd to pair wines by color with reckless disregard for the kind and variety of animal meats, the kind of cookery and above all the kind of sauce and companion foods.

Wine service in or with other foods should be considered within a pattern of *seasoning*, as part of a composition, primarily of companionate flavors and secondarily of food aesthetics. And here the subject can be divided into two and only two elemental approaches, objective and subjective, what can be considered within the scope of a blindfold evaluation of flavor profiles as the objective phase followed by subjective facets of aesthetics. The principal consideration should be how the flavor of a given wine goes with the food it is to accompany. What is involved in flavor comes first; the romancing comes after.

Comparing the beverage and meat classifications of the Gustametric Chart presents fair flavor relationship. It must be clear that the flavor values of the different wines parallel the flavor values of the different meats: in the lower range of seafood, animal and poultry meat there are parallel wines; the medium range of meats level with the medium range of wines, and the high flavor rated meats have fair equals in the high flavor rated wines.

Here especially note that all of the substantially sour flavor component foods are above the range of the dry wines. Bear in mind that any perceptible acetic acid note in a wine classifies it as unsound. Likewise the presence of vinegar in an accompanying food precludes dry wine as an agreeable companion, except for some wines in the high acid and high bitterness range, FN over 100. None of the light or medium dry wines will be accepted by highly discriminating tastes as an accompaniment to a vinegary food.

Here the author emphasizes that his qualifications concern acetic acid, the sour component of the vinegars. Make allowance for inclusion of other acids such as citric and ascorbic, the presence of which to a modest degree won't conflict with the sourness of dry wines. Most of the natural fruit acids, particularly those of the fresh fruits, when properly compounded with basic foods go agreeably with dry wines.

Incidentally it should be realized that the fruit juices and fruit juice infusions in Column 14 in the higher flavor ratings accompany the higher flavor rated meats as well or better, more agreeably to some people than the heavy wines they parallel. Then, too, the beers will probably be more agreeable with strong meats.

With consideration of flavor alone a beverage accompanying a basic food should be considered relative to parallel, above, or below the rating of the food. If the wine rates below the basic food the flavor of the food will dominate; if it is parallel the flavors will be about equal. They can be thought of as on a par, at parity or co-ordinate. If the wine rates above the basic food the wine flavor will dominate it. If the chosen wine goes above the range that may be approximately complementary, it then becomes a contrast and if it is strong enough, it will overwhelm the flavor of the basic food.

Column 15 may provide the easiest set of measurements with which to gauge both flavors *and* quantities of the Gustametric Chart. Its classifications may provide the simplest approach to the idea of both simple and compound flavor scales as well as providing quantitative indices.

Assuming the flavor ladder to be evident and acceptable as representing averages, consider the different placements as approximate indications of *average acceptance* so far as *quantities* are concerned.

The columnar placements of alcoholic beverages are primarily according to kinds, secondarily to type, thirdly according to areas of origin or variety.

Kind.—The dry wines are a kind of alcoholic beverage.

Type.—Red wine is a type of dry wine.

Variety.—Pinot Noir is a variety of red wine.

Study of the different kinds, types, and varieties will prove that in few classifications of food is so much knowledge and experience required to distinguish the gradations of the many different alcoholic beverages. The difference between members of the same families may only be detectable through high connoisseurship. The cardinal taste differences that are the properties common to standard wines are easy to recognize. The flavor components of the premium wines may be measurable only in parts per million—so what we are willing to pay for it is a matter of aesthetics.

A fair knowledge of wine must include familiarity with areas and specific points of origin, as well as marketing practices. In none of our foods do we direct so much attention to origin: where a wine comes from, or who produced it. In no other food has marketing so markedly influenced our processes of selection. It was not until quite recently that publicity started to divert us from the misleading propaganda that only Europe produced fine wines.

Both the standard and the premium California and other American wines demonstrably surpass the bulk of European wines in the same classification. The exceptions are relatively few. Here it should be noted that much of the wine of the world is marketed in large containers; half-gallons, gallons, and larger. Some of the best American wines, marketed in inexpensive gallon jugs, meet the standards of our quality control conscious American wine industry.

Legal Classification and Regulation of Wine

The segment of the wine growing process from the crushing of the grapes to the delivery of the finished wine into the hands of the consumer is a permissive industry in the United States under strict Federal and state bureau controls. In a greater or lesser degree, this is true in all countries of the world.

The different regulations beside providing a system for taxing wine production and consumption are intended to insure compliance with Pure Food labeling standards and regulations. Beside national standards some of the states such as California impose regulations to maintain certain commercial standards. The major tax classifications of wine are:

1. Less than 14 per cent alcohol, popularly called "table" or "dry" wine.
2. 14 to 21 per cent alcohol content—properly called "dessert." (Fortified.)
3. 21 to 24 per cent alcohol content—these are not wines for general consumption and are used for blending only.

4. Wines over 24 per cent alcohol are considered to be distilled spirits and taxed as such.

5. Sparkling or effervescent wines, those containing an excess of CO_2 in the bottle which effervesce when opened; the champagnes, sparkling burgundy, carbonated wines. The tax on sparkling wines is particularly high and in a considerable measure accounts for the high price of those wines and their limited consumption.

6. Rectified wines. Wine cordials, flavored wine other than vermouth, traditionally flavored wines (wines from mixed fruits or those made by processes or containing materials other than those traditional to wine-making as defined in the Federal law).

Vermouth and other types of wine which have been customarily produced by flavoring a natural wine either as an inherent part of the traditional wine-making method or by addition of herb flavors are termed "natural herb-flavored wine" and are taxed according to their alcoholic content classification.

Note: The classifications which generally set the major wine type identities do not allow for other factors, such as sugar content (sweetness) or acidity, color, etc. The wines under 14 per cent which are sold as table wines and generally thought of—even among enologists—as *dry wines* may be dry and almost completely sugar free or they may be quite sweet. The sweetness of the effervescent wines varies more or less at the will of the producers.

The government agencies after insurance of normal food standards impose labeling restrictions to show:

1. The taxable alcoholic content classification.
2. Correct wine type, e.g., sherry, port, burgundy, etc. Varietal wines, for example pinot noir, must contain 51 per cent or more of pinot noir grape wine.
3. Certain processes must be indicated on the label like "bulk fermented" and "bottle fermented" champagne.

In California, in addition to complying with Federal laws, to be labeled California wine, the wine must:

1. Be produced 100 per cent from grapes grown in California.
2. Must contain only sugar or products from sugar produced from grapes. (Federal law permits wine to be produced with 25 per cent sugar addition, or the amount needed to make up natural deficiences of the grapes necessary to product the required fermentation.) California prohibits the addition of sugar other than pure grape concentrated juice on the basis that California grapes are normally high enough in sugar content when mature to make a high quality wine and the addition of sugar reduces the quality of the finished wine.

3. California sets minimum alcoholic content for the different types of wine on the basis that California is one of the few areas in the world where the grapes always ripen to a high enough sugar content to produce a satisfactory alcoholic content. This ability of the vineyards in the California climate always to produce ripe, fully matured grapes is the basis of the saying that "All years are vintage years in California." A *vintage year* in the European wine-growing areas is a year in which weather conditions permit full ripening of the grapes.

The regulatory factors in the reader's mind are simple: what is involved in blends is complex. Kinds, types, and varieties of wines, alcoholic content, and some other technical data may be shown on the label.

It is within the scope of mixtures and mixing processes that much specialized knowledge is required for any broad knowledge of the subject of wines. Starting with the varietals it should be clearly understood that the name of the grape variety on the label, e.g., pinot noir, does not mean that only wine from that grape is in the bottle. That is true in comparatively few instances. The remainder of the wine usually is from other varieties and may be from earlier years. So, the wine labeled pinot noir is in the majority of cases pinot noir blend, the quality of which is according to the ability of the vintner, the cellar master. The final product will vary according to the flavor judgment of the vintner.

There is no such thing as a burgundy grape. So the wine from which American burgundy is blended is usually composed of both red and white grape wines; and the qualities of a specific burgundy vary according to the vintner's stock and his blending ability, plus the not-to-be-overlooked directive of his sales organization in the direction of "what the public wants."

It may be of particular interest to know that the bulk of California white wines and our sherries are produced from Thompson seedless grapes; but so far as the author knows there is no varietal label specified as *Thompson*. Incidentally Thompson grapes are varieties non-existent in most of Europe because they won't ripen there.

Adjoining the dry wine types (white, rosé, and red) in Column 15 are the names of wine-producing countries or areas which produce the best known wines of a specific type. Incidentally, it should be known that virtually all of the wine-producing countries produce some wine of types other than those for which they are best known. Some districts of some areas produce only one type: e.g., white chablis in the Burgundy area of France. According to the kind of wine, panel appraisals of say, light white wines from different parts of the world would reveal remarkably little difference between wines of the same grade, particularly if they are produced from the same variety of grape. Comparison of light white wines from Australia, Cypress, France, and the United States would, by the majority of tasters, be voted indistinguishable. The same group of comments is applicable to most rosé wines.

It is only when comparisons are made between heavy red wines that determination of origin becomes relatively easy. But such distinctions are only easy when the wines of certain areas are compared. The distinction between the brownish and heavy red wines are easily made if some of the compared wines are industrially clarified and others are not. It is then a matter of judging the wines according to their non-soluble solids in suspension. Herein lies one of the most important differences between many European and American and British Com-

Factors Affecting Taste of Wine

1. Temperature
   Higher temperatures increase sourness or tartness
   Higher temperatures increase sweetness
   Higher temperatures increase bitterness
2. Alcohol
   Alcohol increases sourness or tartness
   Alcohol decreases sweetness but has a slight sweet taste itself
   Alcohol increases bitterness
3. Body
   The presence of substances which have a strong effect on the tactile receptors appear to increase sweetness and reduce the effect of sourness or bitterness
4. Sweetness
   Sweetness tends to reduce the effect of bitterness
   Sweetness tends to reduce the effect of sourness, but to a lesser degree than it affects bitterness
5. Acid
   Acid tends to increase the effect of bitterness and is often confused with bitterness in tasting
   Acid tends to reduce the effect of sweetness

monwealth wines. Most of the heavier European wines are made today much in the same way they have been made in some cases for hundreds of years; they are decanted from storage into bottles without being more than crudely filtered. With rare exceptions the wines of the United States and the Commonwealth are industrially clarified.

When comparing wines, it is important to remember that flavor of a beverage is a function of its solids in solution *and suspension.* Accordingly, the wine content of a given barrel will substantially vary in flavor if two different samples are compared, where one has been simply filtered and the other has been industrially clarified.

Thus a bottle of wine showing sediment or cake in the bottom or the side (according to how it has been stored) may be assumed to be more flavorous than another wine of the same grade that is free from perceptible solids. Sediment in a bottle of wine should not be taken as evidence of defectiveness. If deposits are encountered in a bottle of sound wine they generally are comprised of the following natural materials found in wine: cream of tartar, yeast cells, the natural grape coloring material and microscopic particles of the grape solids which were not removed by filtration or settling. Every book that fairly covers the subject of wine has more or less extensive treatment of the subject of wine solids ending with admonitions to allow bottled wines to rest (usually tilted sidewise) for several days or longer and then either decanting or carefully pouring wine from the bottle without disturbing the accumulated sediment. Decanting baskets, specially shaped, are widely used for table serving of sediment-containing wines.

One of the quirks of the American market is that many purchasers accept, perhaps seek, imported wines that show cake or sediment and reject American wines because they have sediment. Some of the best American wines, particularly the heavier varietals, will in time cast some of their solids as a sediment. This will indicate a desirable quality to those people who really know something about wine, but will militate against the purchase by people who are ignorant of qualitative factors.

Wine Bottle Closures

Cork stoppers were originally used to seal almost all bottles. Today the cork stopper has almost universally been displaced by the use of closures of various types composed of metal, plastic, rubber, or compound. In the case of wines where the traditional practices are generally equated with high quality, the use of cork stoppers has persisted. This, however, is diminishing and is restricted to the so-called quality or high priced wines. The majority of American wines are sealed with screw or crown cap closures and in the case of effervescent wines with flexible plastic stoppers.

The use of cork to seal wine bottles is sometimes promoted on the basis that this "allows a wine to breathe" for the full development of aroma and flavor. That is a fallacy. The entrance of air into bottled wine will result in oxidation, which will cause the darkening of white wines, precipitation of the color from red wines, the clouding of the wines and a flat flavor and aroma. All of the absorption of oxygen required to develop aroma and flavor occurs during the cellar life of the wine before bottling.

If it is allowed to dry, the cork will permit the entrance of oxygen and bacteria into the bottle, thus spoiling the wine. The growth of unsightly and unpleasant tasting molds sometimes occurs on the cork. Corks of quality for wine bottles are expensive, quite variable in quality and difficult to insert properly in a bottle. Modern closures permit the sealing of every bottle. The development of techniques of vacuum bottling or of bottling with the air space of the bottle filled with inert gas such as nitrogen protect the wine against changes. So sealed, bottles may be stored in any position without failure of the seal and when opened always present a clean surface for pouring of the wine.

In the production of sparkling wines, the selection of cork stoppers which would maintain the pressures developed in the bottle has always presented considerable difficulties to the champagne producer. In recent years, flexible plastic stoppers and crown cap closures have been introduced into champagne bottling with great success, thus maintaining the quality of the bottled champagne.

Columns 14 and 15 of the Gustametric Chart are considerable as scaling the entire range of natural and elaborated fruit flavors for seasoning purposes. Applications of the nomographic theory will indicate symbiotic complementary or contrasting non-alcoholic and alcoholic beverages as cookery components by kind or type. Each beverage should be considered for contribution of its specific properties to whatever it is to be combined with.

The use of only one fortified wine (usually sherry) and only one dry wine (usually some red) in cookery is one of the outstanding malpractices of unskilled cooks. They can be thought of as errors of *mis-taking* comparable to the usage of only one brand of worcestershire sauce and one brand of ketchup for sauce compositions.

White Dry Grape Wine (50)

The flavor norm is based on an average of the flavor levels of the different "white wines." There are no water-white (colorless) natural wines. There are some water-white *winelike* beverages, which some enologists call sophisticated wines. The colors of natural white wines vary from light lime-yellow, light yellow, yellow-gold through straw, and amber to light brown. Most of the yellowish white wines, being low in insoluble solids, are clear and remain free from sediment even in long storage.

Some of the amber and especially brownish white wines, being relatively high in solids will "throw" sediment in time.

The "low dry" white wines contain sugars in quantities ranging from 0.1 (in terms of grams of reducing sugars per 100 cc.) to about 2.5, with some that vintners consider best between 0.1 and 0.15. Incidentally, it should be realized that in the extremely low range (particularly between 0.1 and 0.15) sweetness in wines is subliminal, below the threshold of perception as sweetness.

The best known prototype white wines such as Rhine and Riesling (with sugars below 0.15) were and still are produced in different parts of Europe from grapes that did not develop enough sugar because of unfavorable climatic conditions. The best known of such wines are from the Chablis section of Burgundy in France, along the nothern Rhine in Germany, most of Switzerland, the mountainous sections of Austria and northern Italy.

The medium dry white wines of Europe which contain from $2^1/_2$ to 5 per cent sugar are produced in areas, the climatic conditions of which are favorable to almost but never complete maturation of their grapes. The outstanding prototypes of such wines are those produced contiguous to the Rhine in Alsace, the Moselle, southern Germany, some parts of Austria and Hungary and some areas in northern Italy.

The high dry (ranging from about 5 to $7^1/_2$ per cent sugar) white wines of Europe are produced in areas where growing conditions are usually favorable; Portugal, Spain, and Italy. What seems to be known only to the discriminating few is that some of the finest European white wines in the whole range of sweetness are produced in Portugal, Spain, and particularly Italy. Without any doubt there is a wider range of very good dry wines of all types produced in Italy than any other European country. Unfortunately, some of those wines are not only produced in quite small quantities but many of them do not travel well. Further, some of the best European white wines are at their best within one year of their production and are considered only fair when they are as old as two years. An outstanding example is the *heurigen* (colloquially "today's") white wines of Austria, principally around Vienna. Some of the Alpine wines of Austria are best liked in the state of incomplete fermentation within a month or two of their production in which state they are cloudy (the Austrians call them "stormy") and slightly effervescent, beside being medium sweet. Some of the *spumanti* of Italy are comparable; young, white, and slightly effervescent wines.

The amber and brownish white wines of Europe such as the tokays of Hungary and the raisiny wines of Portugal, Spain, and Italy come from those areas where grapes will not only fully mature but can become raisins. Likewise, they are the areas that produce the heavy, truly sweet wines such as port, some of the sherries, madeira, and malaga, most of which contain more than eight per cent sugar.

Most of the other well-known wine-producing areas of the world have favorable climatic conditions for growing and fully maturing grapes. Consequently wines of all types produced in those favorable areas are processed to meet marketing requirements. Practically all of those areas produce the different types of dry wines as well as some of the other kinds and types and varieties of alcoholic beverages.

Most of the dry white wines produced in the Jerez district of Spain convey a light flavor note of sherry. Some of the *stein* (stone) wines of northern Germany as well as most of the wines of Switzerland can be distinguished by their light flavor suggestion of rockiness.

Domestic white wines produced in the Eastern United States on labrusca root stocks convey what is known as a light foxy flavor which is particularly liked by many. Such wines are practically unknown outside the United States.

Rosé (or Pink) Dry Grape Wine (60)

The sugar content of rosé wines varies from a low of about 0.2 to a high of about 6 per cent. The FN is based on an average of rosé wines with about three percent sugar. The prototype rosés of France were produced from gamay and grenache varieties of grapes; grignolino, aleatico, and carignane in Italy. All of the prototype rosé wines were produced from those grapes because they were pink-fleshed: when such grapes are fermented they will vary in their characteristic pink color according to their state of maturation and particularly if the wine is fermented on the skins. If pink-fleshed grapes are fermented free of skins the wine will vary in color from pale pink to pale grayish pink. Some of the driest and lightest rosé wines are produced in the eastern United States and in California. Here again there is probably more variation in pink wines in Italy, particularly in the direction of slight effervescence than any other country.

Some of the darkest rosé wines (some being describable as very light claret in color) have their prototypes in Italy but are being produced on a larger scale in other countries, especially in the United States and the Commonwealth.

Nowadays with the market requirements fast favoring the rosé type of dry wine (one reason being that it is one of the most pleasingly colored wines) pink wines are a blend of white and red wines or they are fermented from a combination of white and red grapes.

Red Dry Grape Wine (80)

The sugar content of normal red wines varies from a low of about 0.2 per cent to a high of about seven per cent. The flavor norm is based on an average of California red wines.

An outstanding exception to the limitation of seven per cent (and still somehow trade classified as dry wine) is the American production of Jewish sacramental wine, the prototype of which contains about twenty-five per cent sugar. Such wine production seems to be peculiar to the United States. Wines produced for Jewish and other sacramental purposes in other countries conform to the average sugar contents of whatever wine is locally available.

The growing popularity of very sweet so-called dry wines, not only red but rosé and white, attests the incontrovertible fact that a large segment of people who like wine prefer it quite sweet.

From a consideration of sweetness, the driest red wines like the driest white wines are products of areas, the climate of which is not favorable to full maturation of grapes. Accordingly, the driest prototype red wines come from the mountainous and some of the coldest sections of Europe: Burgundy in France, northern Germany, Switzerland, Austria, the Pyrenees of Spain, and the Alpine areas of northern Italy. The prototype red wines highest in natural sweetness are produced in all the wine-producing areas of southern Europe, with some of the most tart ones made in Italy.

In all the other wine-producing areas where grapes fully mature, red wines having the different flavor characters of the various prototypes are produced, with some of the heaviest coming from California, North Africa, and the Commonwealth. Zinfandel, peculiar to California, and Barbera, produced both in California and Italy, may be the heaviest among red wines; and they are among the best.

Fruit Wine (105)

It is only for the production of fruit wines (other than grape) that the addition of sugar is permitted (in the United States) for two purposes: (1) in the fermentation processes because most fruits do not have enough natural sugar to promote satisfactory fermentation; (2) as a supplement for preservation. Familiarity with such requirements has militated against substantial production of fruit wines in almost all countries. Equally considerable is the probability that such elaborated fruit wines do not meet enough favor to justify their production.

Some berry and other fruit wines are so sweet that they are used more as cordials than as winelike beverages.

While most marketed fruit wines range in sweetness between $2^1/_2$ and 12 per cent, some of the citrus wines like orange are in the same low range as dry grape wines with as low as 0.1 per cent of sugars.

One of the best fruit wines is made from cherries which may be relatively low in sweetness and high in alcohol. It is produced and marketed only to a very limited extent because of both cost and technical difficulties of production.

Apple wine is the fruit wine more nearly commonly available; which is the fermented product of apple cider supplemented with sugar and processed for bottling according to procedures paralleling those of grape wines.

Effervescent Wine (120)

The flavor norm is based on an average of white to red champagne-type grape wines.

Effervescent wines, commonly called sparkling wines or champagnes, differ from still wines primarily because they have more CO_2 (carbon dioxide) in solution. All so-called still wines have more or less carbon dioxide in solution, most of them with not enough to be perceptible; but some that may not be completely fermented (which are sometimes called "sprightly wines") have enough CO_2 to be noticeable on uncorking and of course in drinking. The CO_2 in all partially fermented wines including natural champagne-type wines is due to the process of fermentation. The prototypes of effervescent wines were produced in all the wine-producing areas of the world but not until the craft of bottle-making achieved products that would withstand the internal pressures of natural carbonation were effervescent wines marketed in any considerable quantity. The prototype of champagne primarily involved a *dosage* of grape brandy to partially fermented white wine.

Today most champagne-type effervescent wines are produced in two ways: "fermented in the bottle" (it's really partially fermented in the bottle) and bulk fermented. The "fermented in the bottle" process starts with a blend of different wines (with rare exceptions, there are no "vintage" [of a given year] champagnes) to which sugar or syrup is added to promote secondary fermentation in the bottle. At the proper time the deposit that has accrued in the neck of the bottle is splurged, after which grape brandy and additional wine (to compensate for that which was discharged with the sediment) is added and the bottle is corked or plastic-sealed and wire-bound.

In the bulk process the selected blend of wines, with the proper supplements, is subjected to a secondary fermentation in a closed vessel (somewhat resembling a large stainless steel still) and fortified with brandy as the clarified effervescent wine is bottled. Here again, it is difficult and sometimes impossible for experts in a blindfold trial to distinguish between champagnes (of a given variety) fermented in the bottle, or bottled after the bulk process of fermentation. Preferences for specific champagne labels may constitute the outstanding example of a prejudice cultivated in café society.

Varying with several factors, the internal pressures of effervescent wines will vary between 4 and 6 atmospheres, roughly 60 to 85 lbs.

To compare the internal pressures of champagne-type effervescent wines with other carbonated beverages, here are several examples: soda water, about $4^1/_2$ atmospheres; bottled beer, about 3; cola drinks, about 3; citrus drinks, about $2^1/_2$.

The variation of effervescent wine flavor norms between 90 and 160 is attributable to (1) the flavor factors of the different wines, sugars, and brandies; (2) the amount of carbonation; (3) how long it is in the glass before being consumed; (4) the temperature at which it is drunk.

Accordingly, treating any wines by the champagne process will proportionately raise the flavor norm of a given wine on the Gustametric Chart. Thus the lightest of the white wine champagnes would flavor rate at about 75; the rosés as low as 90 and some of the reds as high as 160.

Incidentally under Federal Wine Regulations, effective July 1, 1959, the addition of up to 0.256 gram of carbon dioxide per 100 milliliters of wine is permitted. At long last, this makes it possible for American vintners to produce some lightly effervescent wines paralleling those of many other wine-producing countries.

Beer (150)

It is doubtful if there is any other alcoholic beverage produced in as many types and varieties as beer. Technically, beer is the liquor resulting from a mash of fermented cereals, as distinguished from the fermented product of fruits and vegetables. Corn is the cereal used for beer produced by the more or less primitive peoples in South America, Africa, and elsewhere. The beers that are familiar to most of us are largely based on barley, corn, and wheat, but there are other cereals also used in so-called "civilized" beers.

The early beers of Asia, Europe, and America were probably natural, somewhat cloudy, and unless spot-consumed, *not effervescent.* Much European beer, particularly that of England, is *still beer,* not effervescent, and certainly not carbonated. By far the bulk of American beer production is canned or bottled, which perforce requires pasteurization of the liquor before packaging, and carbonation in the process of bottling or canning. Because pasteurization dissipates carbon dioxide, the breweries process the carbonic acid discharged in fermentation and reintroduce it into the bottle or can at the moment of packing. American and some European tastes are for clear beer, which require brewers to polish-filter their products. Further, American tastes are for quite light, low-alcohol beers. By Federal regulations, for tax classification, the alcoholic content of beer is not to exceed four per cent by volume. Some of it is as low as 3.2 per cent; ale, porter, and stout, six per cent by volume. Bearing in mind that most beers produced abroad have very much higher alcoholic content than American beers, those beers when imported are watered down to meet United States Federal limitations on alcoholic content. It must be obvious that this lower alcoholic content accounts for imported beers not qualitatively equaling their prototypes in the countries of origin.

All of this is in marked contrast to the wide range of English beers. First, those beers are only rough-filtered so they are much higher in solids in solution and suspension. Second, they are darker in color, ranging from light brown to brown-black. Third, they are lower in carbonation. And fourth, their alcoholic content may be as high as nine per cent.

Another range of differences between American and foreign beer tastes is the temperature of service. American tastes are for cold to very-cold beers. Foreign tastes are from cool through room temperature to hot (mulled) beer.

Originally, possibly before the word "beer" came into the language, the product of malted and fermented barley (and sometimes oats) was called "ale." It was probably rather high in sugar and in alcohol, and was fermented partly or all the way and unless spot-consumed was not effervescent. It probably varied in color from light honey to dark brown. Somewhere along the line some bitter components were introduced, and found agreeable, and eventually hops got into the brew and someone called the new product "beer." Today some ales are produced with some hop inclusions, and some borderline beers are called "ale," and it is probable that some ales are called "beer." So today there is no sharp commercial distinction between ale and beer. It may be said that ales are low-bitterness beers.

Sherry (180)

The flavor norm is based on an average of California and eastern United States sherries. Technically sherry is a type of fortified dry wine varying from very dry (about 0.2 per cent) to medium sweet, sometimes labeled "creme" sherry with about 8 per cent sugars; and with 14 to 21 per cent alcohol content as produced in the United States and Canada. In the United States sherry is the most important aperitif or cocktail wine. Our tastes prefer clear sherries, light in color and light in flavor. The prototype sherries of Spain vary in color from amber to brown (with age all of them cast some sediment) and most of them range from medium sweet to very sweet. It is only comparatively recently that relatively dry sherries have been produced in Spain, but even so Spain produces no dry sherries so low in sugar as those produced in the United States.

In the ecology of beverages, the American adaptations from the progenitor sherries of Spain are made to conform to American tastes. In that process we have evolved what may be considered a new kind of wine, more or less distant from its sherry ancestor.

In the author's panel appraisals, American sherries were always preferred to those of Spain.

A pertinent historical note is sherry was and still is a meal accompaniment abroad, particularly in England. Serving sherry before meals as an aperitif or after meals as a dessert wine, are comparatively modern developments of custom. Here realize that serving sherries and other sweet wines with meals is a reasonable tendency to provide a sweet note with foods that may be low in sweetness.

Sake (210)

The flavor norm is 120 to 220.

Sake (here classified with the gins) is probably the lightest (16 per cent alcohol content) of the beverages in this classification. This rice beverage originated in Japan but is now being produced in the Hawaiian Islands and elsewhere in the United States. Sake is one of the few beverages that are customarily served warm (not hot) as an accompaniment with Japanese and other oriental foods.

Vodka (220)

Traditionally vodka was produced from potatoes that were culled after winter storage. According to the conditions of potato storage, usually subterranean or cellar, and the severity of winters, potatoes that were partly fermented or partly spoiled were used straight or in combination with rye or other cereal mash and the fermented product distilled. It is natural to assume that the producers would use for vodka only such potatoes as they couldn't or wouldn't eat—with some exceptions, of course, where they preferred the liquor to the potatoes!

Some such vodka is still available in Central and Eastern Europe, but it is rare. It is much too rough for what can be conservatively thought of as a civilized taste. Such vodka is the unrectified product of pot stills; so the liquor contains the fusel oils and other impurities that are removed in the processes of rectification by commercial distillers. Accordingly, anyone who would drink and like such vodka would drink and like anything; if alcoholics were forced to drink only that liquor, it might cure them of alcoholism. The over-all flavor rating would be extremely high, primarily because of the overpowering alcoholic bite in combination with an aftertaste that doesn't just linger—it hangs on. And the nasal twang is overpowering.

What the buyer is willing to pay for a bottle of vodka (and most gin) is practically concerned with the package and the label rather than the contents: the contents must meet government specifications of purity for alcohol and water.

Gin (230)

The norm is based on English and Holland gins made according to the traditional process in which crushed juniper berries were mixed with the fermented cereal mash (originally mostly rye) or by distilling vapors passing through baskets or trays of crushed juniper berries. To this liquor the term "gin" was applied, derived from the name *Geneva* or from the Dutch word for *juniper*.

Gin originally must have been ardent liquor. By strict interpretation of the word, it should only be applied to ardent spirits distilled with or through juniper berries.

On the basis of such strict interpretation there are very, very few straight gins produced today; and most of them come from Holland and England.

It should be distinctly understood that commercial gins are mixtures of water and neutral spirits (usually ethyl alcohol from grain) to which flavor has been added, essentially around 100 parts per million. While the term "gin" implies juniper, the word has long been applied to combinations of water, alcohol, and flavoring other than that of juniper berries: examples are sloe and *buchu*. Among the flavorings of European gins are angelica root, cassia, cardamom, and coriander.

Commercial gins are not aged or matured. They vary from water-white and wholly unsweetened to tawny and slightly sweet, and of course, with the kind and extent of flavor additives.

If crushed juniper berries are added to and allowed to steep in a bottle of gin, the product will have a higher flavor and an amber color, both flavor and color hinging upon the quantity of juniper berry addition. The aroma component of most commercial gins is subliminal, but the addition of the crushed juniper berries can make for a highly aromatic liquor; further, the addition of berries slightly raises the sweetness and bitterness components. The over-all result of steeping crushed juniper berries in plain gin is almost always preferred.

Incidentally, the commercial production of vodka exactly parallels that of gin, with only a difference of flavoring. Sake, tequila, and some arrack approximate gin and are almost as flavorless.

Tequila (235)

Tequila is the Mexican gin-like beverage which is distilled from pulque, which is the fermented sap water of one of the genus *Amaryllis,* which is better known as the century plant or the American aloe.

Tequila's disreputable name should be ascribed to crude productions of it. In Mexico tequila is marketed in a number of different grades, the best of which are produced in conformity with the highest standards of the distillation industry. They can be fairly compared with American gins but most of them are higher in alcohol.

Arrack (240)

The flavor norm is based on the protoype Levantine liquor which is the redistillation of fermented dates. Some arrack conveys only a subtle date flavor. Most contemporary productions carry an anise flavor. All true arracks have the peculiar characteristic of clouding when they are added to water.

Arrack, *arak and raki* are (in the Orient) terms applied to rice and coconut juice distilled products. In some Indonesian and South Pacific areas, the term *raki* has been twisted to *toddy* and indiscriminately applied to cereal home brew products as well as liquors from the juices of different kinds of palm fruits beside coconuts.

Aquavit (250)

The flavor norm of 250 is based on the prototype *akvavit,* the Scandinavian *aqua vitae,* a highly rectified, practically neutral and sometimes harsh, spirit distilled mostly from grain or potatoes and flavored with caraway seeds. It is not sweetened and it is not aged.

Fortified Sweet Wine (300)

The flavor norm is based on an average of the fortified sweet wines of both the United States and Europe, in which the sugars range from about 5 per cent to perhaps 25 per cent. Among the sweetest are the muscat wines of southern Europe and the Levantine countries and the ports of Portugal. Historically, sweet wines of the tawny to brown varieties were produced in what is now southern Italy, southern France, Spain, and of course Portugal, but bear in mind that Portugal was once a part of Spain. The progenitors came from the earlier Greek and Levantine civilizations.

Port.—Not until one has traveled around the Mediterranean countries and been exposed to the many varieties of the same kind of sweet wine does one realize that the sweet wines of Portugal are related to and of the same type as these wines. Perhaps these sweet wines could be geographically centralized in Southern Spain. Wine tasting in Portugal reveals a comparatively narrow range of sweet wines, natural and fortified, contrasted with a wider grouping in most of the other countries.

An expert exposed to a blindfold trial of interspersed malagas and the heavier sherries of Jerez (products of the provinces of Malaga and Cadiz in Spain) with parallel varieties of Portugal would be unable to positively distinguish between them. Adding some of the madeiras (of the Canary Islands) and the marsalas of Italy would really throw your expert into a taste dither.

Here in America, the ports commonly marketed are of one type, within a narrow flavor field of color, consistency, taste, and aroma. In Portugal, beside, the typical color and flavor characters that we know, there are variations from almost water white to muddy browns, and from quite light in body and flavor to syrupy and heavy in flavor. It is possible that the outstanding character of the prototype wines that has militated against their popularity in the United States is color: many of the malagas, madeiras, and the Italian wines of the marsala type are muddy brown.

In cookery an additive of sherry is most popularly advocated, which may be a quirk of copy writing. The author's experiments indicate that the sweeter and fruitier muscatels, tokays, and ports contribute more desirable components to food compositions. This is in line with European practices where malaga is preferred for cookery in Spain and wines like marsala in Italy.

Vermouth.—The prototype, probably originating in Italy, was a dry wine flavored with wormwood and other aromatic herbs, supplemented with sugar and fortified with alcohol. The typical vermouth of Italy (not exported to the United States) is relatively high in sugars and quite high in aromatic botanicals content. American productions of Italian type vermouths are lower in sugars and other botanical components. Wormwood (the objectionable component of absinthe) is not permitted here.

The development of dry vermouth (sometimes labeled French vermouth) is a recent evolution. It may have sprung up with cocktails.

Rum (350)

The flavor norm is based on an average of rums distilled from sugar cane juice and those distilled from molasses. By definition, rum is a spirit distilled from various products of the sugar cane.

Other names are "rhum," "rom," and "ron."

Commercially, rums are divided into three categories: (1) the very dry, light-bodied rums like most of those of Cuba and Puerto Rico; (2) the full-bodied rums such as those of Jamaica and some New England rums; (3) the more aromatic rums such as are made in the Dutch East Indies and some of the Caribbean islands like Demarrera.

The majority of the rums in the third category owe their aromatic properties to their being produced from sugar cane juice, not molasses.

It should be noted that high grade rums in the three categories are produced in Mexico in quite large volume.

Brandy (400)

By common interpretation, brandy is a spiritous liquor distilled from grape wine. Technically, it is the distilled product of the fermented juice of any fruit or combination of fruits. Like all other alcoholic spirits, brandy is practically water-white as it flows from the still. Coloration of brandy is assumed to result from aging in charred casks, but is frequently artificial.

Cognac is brandy supposed to be made from *St. Emilion,* and *La Folle Blanche* grapes, restricted to the Cognac district of France. The names of *Grande Champagne, Petit Champagne,* and *Fine Champagne* are geographical references within the Cognac district. The stars on cognac labels are supposed to refer to their age, not their quality: one star, not less than three years old; two stars, not less than four years old; three stars, not less than five years old.

V.O., V.S.O., V. S. O. P., and V.V.S.O.P.: *V* stands for "very," *O* for "old," *S* for "superior," and *P* for "pale."

Label phrases such as "Fine Champagne," and "Napoleon" can usually be brushed aside as a hawker's gobbledygook. Imagine liquor surviving from the time of Napoleon! And the use of the word on a label has about the same implications as the word "old" or "ancient" by some whiskey distillers.

In France the phrase *Fine de la Maison* simply means "bar brandy"; and that, like our bar whiskey, can be almost anything.

One of the distilled spirits, a brandy is a highly complex *manufactured* product. Competence in judging brandies requires knowledge of wines and wine-making, and of distillation.

Flavor Factors in Judging Brandies

To rate a brandy for flavor profile, keep in mind these factors of taste: (1) the viscosity ("body") of the liquor, the water, the alcohol and the solids in suspension or solution; (2) alcoholic bite and burn sensations in oral and nasal cavities; (3) the group of aromas present (the chemical elements will dominate the floral elements present); and (4) the final psychosomatic judgment.

The flavor and aroma of an individual brandy come from the impurities it contains: they are congeners which pass through the distillation process along with the alcohol which is collected in the condenser. It is the amount and kind of these impurities which determine the brandy preferred by various judges. There is more room for purely subjective personal preference in judging brandies than in perhaps any other food experience. A brandy that is, technically speaking, defective because it contains the right kind of "impurities," may be preferable to one that is purified and polished to the point of blandness.

Variation (other than concentration) in brandy flavor is caused by first, the ingredients: (1) the country or area in which the grapes are grown; (2) the variety or blend of varieties of grapes (meaning the wines from those varieties); (3) the conditions of growing and harvesting in the specific season or seasons.

The second influence on flavor is the method of distillation: the kind of still and how it is operated. It is not simply a matter of pot stills *versus* tubular or columnar stills. The products of both can be practically identical. Nor is it a matter of still size. A general impression is that pot stills are small and more or less home- or country-made. The fact is that the bulk of the world's brandies (as well as many whiskies) are made in pot stills which vary in capacity from a few hundred gallons to thousands of gallons. The fact that many of the small and some of the largest brandy distillers use tubular stills does not by itself render the product either superior or inferior; neither does single versus multiple stage distillation, nor the use or lack of accessory rectification.

Following distillation (and rectification, if any) the liquor is blended and then matured (aged in barrels or casks for several years). The methods used in these steps are more influential than any other on the final flavor. Here is where the product of small or medium and sometimes obscure distillers may produce a brandy superior to those of the big name organizations; an outstanding example of the failure of price as an index to quality in food. The foibles of the label-buyer show up here. For example, without detracting from the merits of some French brandies, it is incontrovertible that some of the best brandies have been and are being produced in other countries, where technology has progressed further. In France, you should know, all material, equipment, and processes are government-frozen so that it is illegal to improve them! Because of refinements in processes of rectification and slow percolation through activated charcoal, many brandies of more advanced countries contain fewer of the acrid fusel oils which spoil flavor, and leave an off-flavor hangover. Furthermore, not only do grapes ripen more uniformly in non-European wine producing areas of the world, but some of those areas produce types of wines which make for superior brandies. The grapes of the desert around the Mediterranean, heat-ripened and high in sugar, would become raisins if not harvested for wine. Distilled in pot stills and matured in wooden casks, they make the best brandy. An example is that produced by the Trappist monastery in Jordan. Brandies of outstanding merits in flavor profiles (such as mellowness, smoothness, and particularly the aromatics) are also produced in Portugal, Spain, Greece, and Turkey.

What is not generally recognized is that some American brandies are the smoothest, the lowest in fusel oils, of all brandies. Advances in distillation, rectification, and maturation processes have resulted in brandies bordering on the bland. Our American tastes incline toward bland liquors, so American distillers use processes for those tastes—going far beyond the practices of foreign distillers.

The brandy connoisseur may brush off American brandies as "lacking in authority." The fact is that what he calls "authority" the American enologist would call undesirable congeners which are mistakenly allowed to condense with the alcohol and are not rectified out.

On the other hand, many Europeans prefer the brandies of France, Armagnacs and Cognacs, because of their high content of such impurities, and may even disdain the smoother, less harsh brandies of Portugal and Spain.

A notable example of personal preference is the occasional insistance on *grappa*, either straight or as a supplement to black coffee. Plain *grappa*, one-step pot-distilled is the crudest, harshest, and roughest grape brandy. It flavor rates highest on the flavor scale, because of its content of native, definitely chemical-tasting impurities.

Whiskey (500)

Whisky—short for whiskybae (Gaelic, *uisgebeatha*, literally "water of life"). In modern trade usage, it is Irish whisk*ey* and Scotch whisk*y*.

In the British Isles whiskey or whisky is chiefly made from malted barley while North American distillers mainly use corn with other cereals in mash mixtures. Rye accounts for some of the flavors of Canadian and some American whiskies.

Adams (1960) suggests seven classifications of whiskey.

Bourbon.—Rich, faintly sweetish, faintly vanilla-like, with the suggestion of charred oak barrels. The best straight (usually Bottled in Bond) bourbons may be considered as the best American whiskey.

Rye.—Its component of rye aromatics conveys an impression of harshness which may be somewhat balanced by its barrel aging impression.

Corn.—Some of the more acceptable corn whiskies are lightly yellowish and convey a slight suggestion of corn but most of the corn whiskey is water-white and sharp in taste.

Blends.—The dominant flavor of most blends is bourbon and they are watered down to make them more bland. From $^3/_5$ to $^4/_5$ of blends are alcohol and water: a 90 proof blend has 55 per cent water with 45 per cent "whiskey and neutral spirits." Some blends contain beside pure alcohol and water, sherry or other coloring matter.

Canadian Whiskey.—Some whiskies made in Canada for Canadian tastes are higher in rye aromatics than the Canadian whiskies exported to the United States for American tastes. Canadian neutral spirits used in whiskies are reported as having to be aged.

Scotch Whisky.—Its characteristic smoky taste is due to the peat-fire drying of barley malt used for its mash. By far the bulk of marketed Scotch whisky, is a blend of whisky and neutral spirit. Much of that marketed in the United States is 80 to 86 proof, as most of that marketed in England and Scotland is 90 proof. Pot distilled straight Scotch whisky, which is available to researchers of the subject is, even at the high proof of 90, possibly the smoothest of all whiskies and so bland as to be unacceptable to most Scotch fanciers.

Irish Whiskey.—It may be compared to Scotch without the burnt taste. Its flavors are due to congeners distinctly different from those of other malt whiskies.

Other Whiskies.—The author adds an eighth classification to cover whiskies made in different parts of the world from combinations of cereal mashes and some botanicals. An outstanding example is *ng ka py*. While some productions of *ng ka py* are gin-like, most of them may properly be classified as whiskies. It is one of many Chinese liquors, made from different cereals such as rice or millet, that flavor rate from 400 to 700 according to their components which beside cereals may include some botanicals. The alcohol content may range from 90 to 110 proof, and the sugars about five per cent. The weakest example of this beverage can be likened to grappa brandy (FN 400–450) and the strongest rather close to concentrated burnt Scotch whisky.

Liqueur (600) and **Cordial** (200–800)

The flavor norm is based on liqueurs distilled from a base of natural botanicals.

Several dictionaries, O.E.D. and Webster, similarly define liqueur and cordial as an aromatic and sweetened spirit used as a beverage. Under United States Federal regulations they are "products obtained by mixing or redistilling neutral spirits, brandy, gin, or other spirits, with or over fruits, flowers, plants . . . or other flavoring materials derived from infusions, percolations, or macerations . . . and to which sugar or dextose . . . have been added in an amount not less than two and one half per cent of the weight of the finished product." Cordials and liqueurs are produced in a wider range of color (seemingly covering the whole spectrum, including violet) and flavor than any other kind of beverage. Only in sweetness are they somewhat comparable, but even so they range from a low of about $2^1/_2$ per cent sugars to more than 25 per cent. Here a pertinent note is that the syrupy consistency of many liqueurs is due to the presence of glycerin.

Examples in the low flavor ratings are some of the low sweetness, low alcohol (glycerin-free) fruit cordials. In general, people think of cordials as sweet, fruity liqueurs that are relatively low in alcohol as against thinking of true liqueurs as being sweet, fruity or flowery beverages high in alcohol. Examples of the latter are liqueur Holland gin and liqueur Scotch whisky. Among the highest sweetness and lowest alcohol liqueurs are Yugoslavian maraschino (cherry) liqueur and a rather large number of Italian aromatic and fruity liqueurs. Examples of liqueurs in the high alcohol range (from 50 to 110 proof) are: apricot liqueur, Bénédictine, blackberry liqueur, Cointreau, crême de cassis, crême de cacao, crême de menthe, Chartreuse, Grand Marnier, prunelle, strawberry liqueur, Triple Sec, and many others.

Many, if not most, of the creme liqueurs made in the United States and abroad are flavored by natural or imitation extracts, not with crude botanicals. The difference can be radical. Compare liqueur produced with fresh peppermint leaves with creme de menthe.

Bitters (800)

The flavor norm is based on Italian bitters; which are properly classifiable under cordials. They provide an outstanding example of the survival of a type of wine. It is the progenitor of most of what we know as cordials and liqueurs. Contemporary production of bitters are developments of renaissance compositions of elixirs and medicaments, fortified with the crude alcohol derived from the then newly invented still.

Some of the Italian bitters are made with more than 30 botanicals and the strongest of them taste like what they are—medicine. Some of the monastery productions of liqueurs are reported to contain between 100 and 230 components. The light bitters produced in different parts of Europe are relatively low in sweetness and alcohol and are popular as aperitifs, appetizers.

Among the most popular bitters used in the United States are the complex botanical bases with a dominant burnt orange flavor note. Orange bitters, of which there are several varieties, are the most popular. While each producer follows his own botanical formulation, they all have a more or less dominant flavor note of "burnt" orange peel and angostura bark.

In cookery, a drop or two of orange bitters is desirable where a touch of bitterness and some of the flavor notes peculiar to orange bitters are indicated. Virtually all chefs have orange bitters as one of their "within reach wines" for admixing, particularly with sauces and dressings.

Proof.—The term refers to the standard of strength of alcoholic liquors (or of vinegar); the strength of a mixture of alcohol and water having a specific gravity of 0.91984 and containing 0.495 of its weight, or 0.5727 of its volume, of absolute alcohol.

A *proof gallon* is a gallon, the proof spirit of which equals 49.28 per cent alcohol by weight. In the United States, proof spirit contains 50 per cent of alcohol by volume at a temperature of 60°F. which is an arbitrary measurement. Each degree of proof is approximately equal to half of one per cent of alcohol.

Example: Brandy labeled 80 proof should contain slightly less than 40 per cent by weight of alcohol.

Footnote to Column 15—Flavor Trends in Aperitif and Appetizer Cocktails

Over a period of the last few years there has been a steady trend in the United States to develop drier and blander fortified wines for cocktails such as martinis.

This has been particularly noticeable in vermouth. In the last five years vermouths with almost no flavor, in comparison with the older vermouths, have been developed and are popular. For example, one brand of vermouth is produced from an almost flavorless, colorless base wine. That wine is made from Thompson grapes grown in selected vineyards and picked considerably before maturity to give the blandest, lightest colored wine possible. It is then infused with only enough herb extract to give it a light suggestion of vermouth flavor.

This and similar types of vermouth on the market were for several years the object of considerable activity of the government agencies who questioned their identity as vermouth and filed charges against the producers. As a result the product was held off the market for a long time. The government also feared that the products were being used by bars to increase the amount of vermouth and reduce the amount of gin in the martinis, thereby substituting a lower cost for a higher cost material and defrauding the customer.

Gins have become progressively lighter. In the case of one gin, the herb formula used was steadily reduced until it was approximately half its former strength.

Cocktail sherries are continually being made paler and drier.

In many quarters these trends are thought to be the result of our normal outgrowth of whiskey and hard liquor drinkers' transferring to more sophisticated mixed drinks and wines, and to the search by a nervous and high-strung people for appetite stimulants, perhaps on a similar basis to the mechanism which causes dry wines to prevent satisfaction of appetite. Another explanation sometimes advanced is that the modern generation does not appreciate the simple flavors that their forebears did, and that the prohibition generation lost its taste for traditional beverages.

CHAPTER 19

Herbs, Raw

COLUMN 16

When there is a choice, most foods are selected for their nutritional and intrinsic flavor values. Second choice in the order of selection are foods that are chosen as supplements: they "go with" other foods, thus forming a pattern of what we may call the food behavior of culture. If we take the basic foods as the foods of necessity and the more highly flavor rated foods as the seasonings of choice, we may get a clearer perspective of the whole food picture.

We must start by defining *season.* Literally, it denotes a time of year, a season during which flavors peculiar to it are more readily available. The mechanical processes of civilization have changed most of the seasonality of foods so that now, in one form or another, we have most of the seasonings of the world within the grasp of our supermarket hands.

The bulk of our food is chosen for nutritional value. Most of the rest centers about that which by broadest interpretation, we cover by the word "flavor." Man does not live by bread alone. He certainly does not live by the basic foods alone. The spice of his food life is concerned with what goes with his bread; not just what he puts on it but what foods accompany it, and with whom he eats it.

Consideration of seasoning starts off in two directions: what kind and how much. While the bulk of this section is concerned with "what kind," it is in the "how much" that most seasoning errors lie.

Disregarding for the time being the use of seasoning to disguise off-flavors, one of our most common food preparational faults is over-seasoning, starting with the commonest of all, just too much salt. Next is too much pepper; then too much sugar, then too much vinegar. Here it must be apparent that our excessive use of seasoning starts with components of the cardinal tastes.

Next come the herbs, spices, and condiments, the uses of which are just as vague and mysterious in kind as in quantity to the majority of domestic and commercial cooks alike. If they know what kind, they are not certain about how much. The traditional pinch of this and handful of that is not a logical procedure. But by far the worst of errors common to careless cooks is the assumption that if a little of some particular kind of seasoning is good, a lot of it will be much better. A little basil in the tomato sauce becomes so much basil that all that is tasted is basil. Instead of using just enough mint to make a delicate flavor in lamb gravy, the unreasoning cook commonly adds so much mint to the gravy that the mint is tasted more than the meat.

A primary objective in the construction of the Gustametric Chart is the provision of a practicable system of seasoning. The qualification of the chart's usefulness is the student's willingness to assimilate its *modus operandi*, the theories and principles upon which it is constructed. The introduction to this section outlines the fundamental procedures. In the discussion of each column as a specific classification, different elements are successively introduced and, to some extent, discussed in detail. Under the subject of herbs and spices are to be considered the basic principles of flavor harmony for which the chart, Fig. 16 serves as a circular comparator.

There is a close analogy with the harmonics of color and music. The language of color and sound, graphic art, and music can readily be applied to many of our treatments of flavor.

Like color and music, the different seasonings in the different classifications may properly be thought of as in close harmony or in discord, complementary, contrasting, or discordant. If several seasoning materials are to be used, they may be considered as having relationships that are agreeable in color as in painting, chordal as in music, but always according to a definite scheme of production. The composition must be good, the final effects agreeable, whether it is a sketch or a finished painting, an improvisation in music or a concert piece. Therein will lie the difference between the trained artist and the untrained who does not plan and produce according to standards.

One of the advantages of the nomographic system is its indication of an establishable series of flavor harmonies within the orbit of any given zone. An example could start with mutton and the common accompaniment of mint sauce. The line projected on Fig. 28 from mutton to mint intersects and passes through an arbitrary profile of what, on the average, will be acceptable flavors as accompaniments or inclusions.

Table 8 (Mint Chart) shows first the extreme variations in a single herb family and, for discussion in these few paragraphs, the options inherent in the flavoring matter of just *one* of the hundreds of herbs and spices.

For purposes of common usage, the Gustametric Chart shows placement of only a few of the mint family. Where the curve passes through the herb and spice columns, the other herbs and spices within a radius of plus or minus five units may be considered analogous flavoring materials. The nomographic theories can be applied to the circular comparator charts to provide complementary as well as contrasting options.

If the Gustametric Chart is folded horizontally along the "100" line, and vertically between Columns 8 and 9, a number of things become apparent: (1) Most of the basic foods of necessity and choice are in the left lower corner. (2) Most of the seasonings are to the right of Column 8 and above the 100th parallel.

Starting with Raw Salad Vegetables (Column 9) and Fruits (Column 10), the common seasoning profiles radiate through Columns 9 through 24, each component modifying the flavor of a basic food in Columns 1 through 8.

In flavor rating seasonings, starting with Column 9, which applies to the basic foods as well, the components involving the cardinal tastes come first. According to their intensity, they will scale in each classification. Foods that are low in sourness, sweetness, or bitterness are in the lower part of the scale. That the mildly sweet are rated under 50 is apparent; those that are mildly sour stretch between 50 and 100; but it takes study to see that intensity of sweetness and sourness rapidly raises most ratings up to and above 100; that bitterness as a substantial factor rates most foods above 100; and that pepperiness and saltiness likewise ascend the scale above 100. These facts regarding the cardinal tastes are comparatively easy to judge and to use.

Not so easy is the ability to comprehend and to use the aromatics, with which seasoning is primarily concerned. It is the aromatics, the esters, the volatiles for which most seasonings are selected and used. It is what we pay for in herbs and spices. After the visual factors, it is the floral and fruity aroma by which we judge fruits and wines. Thus the selection of foods for flavor is principally concerned with food aesthetics, the most expensive part of our food behavior.

Dipping briefly into this area of aesthetics, we find that the strongest of our flavor memories is in the field of smell, within the scope of our nose tastes. Recalling the memories of mouth tastes involves mental labor that is rarely satisfactory. Such mouth tastes are vaguely remembered after visual suggestions of comparable foods, but nose tastes materialize from the wraith of a food smell that revivifies and embodies a food experience.

Obviously herbs and spices most frequently stimulate both the nose and mouth senses. Such herb and spice smells may be divided into two groups: objective and subjective.

Objective indirect herb and spice smells arising from memory include those commonly associated with things and places. They bring forth pictures of specific peoples and foods: the curries of India, the chilies of Mexico, the coffees of Java, the smells of eating places and kitchens, spice stalls and stores in foreign market places, the by-ways and bazaars of the Orient.

Subjective smells which are personal, direct, and present include the fragrances of green vegetation, the light herbs of spring and summer, the stronger greens and more fragrant floral harvest herbiage of late summer and autumn. Here, too, are herbiages associated with literature, customs, and folklore: the medicine man and the witches' brew, supposedly containing potent herbs of terrifying power.

In the foregoing, herbs and spices have been discussed as if they were in a single column. In discussing individual seasonings, it will be necessary to distinguish first between herbs and spices, and further between raw herbs and dried herbs.

In trying to differentiate between herbs and spices, we must draw a theoretical line—a wide swath and a wobbly one—through a botanical jungle that includes examples of every class of vegetable matter from subterranean to arboreal; subsurface and surface; from light to very strong; and from low in the scale to the very top of it. Much of the confusion, the wandering of the dividing path through the field of herbs and spices is partially explained by the word "spice" being a variant of *specie*. The spice trade itself seems to avoid distinguishing between herbs and spices.

As the roughest kind of generality, for our purposes we may think of herbs as *relatively low* in oils, and spices as *relatively high,* but this distinction is limited as a comparison between Columns 16 and 18 will show. One of the reasons for erecting three columns of what can be classified as spice matter is to provide classifications of usage according to the part or condition of the kind of vegetable matter used. However, the majority of the herbs consist of what is commonly called leafage, and the majority of the spices are processed seeds, flowers, or fruits. The confusing items in both broad classifications are the roots and fruits in the herbs, and the roots, leaves, and bark in the spices. Garlic is commonly listed as an herb, but if it isn't a spice, what is? And bay *leaves* are universally listed under spices.

As in all other classifications, the listings in the herb and spice columns are based on relative flavor values, primarily considerations of intensity according to the way those foods are commonly used. Spearmint is flavor rated lower than peppermint. In application of similar quantities of the two herbs, peppermint dominates spearmint.

Responsible for the dominance of peppermint are its esters, stronger than the esters of spearmint. Peppermint has some components that spearmint does not have. The lasting quality of those esters can be compared to the resonance of musical notes. Those with longer wave lengths continue to reverberate. Here our gustometry is in inverse ratio to the musical scale: the short wave notes start at the bottom and the long wave, more persistent notes are at the top. All other flavor notes are in between. There is a growing belief that the physiological phenomena of taste may be measurable as electronic wave impulses, the intensities varying with the nature and quantity of stimuli, paralleling what has long been confirmed in our perception of sound waves.

Within the class of herbs, two columns have been erected. Column 16 is Herbs, Raw, and Column 17 is Herbs, Dry. This has been done for two reasons: First, there is a substantial difference in flavor rating between the raw and the preserved herb. Second, the majority of herbs are available to most people only in their dry or otherwise processed conditions, in which they usually flavor rate *lower* than the true flavor of the raw vegetable matter. Much and sometimes all of the fidelity of the original is lost through the effects of dehydration, transportation, and age.

The flavor norm of raw onion is 375, whereas dehydrated onion is flavor rated at 60. The point of emphasis in this instance is that the Gustametric Chart shows a vertical differentiation of 315 points between two adjoining columns. Also implied by this juxtaposition is that a change of condition of a food suggests a change of level of its flavor. That change may take several different directions.

In general, foods deteriorate as they age. Some of the flavor components become stronger and others weaker. It is an incontrovertible fact that individual flavors, as they change in the majority of food because of chemical action, in time develop some characters that may be foreign to the original flavor, whatever that may have been. Raw onions, as their flavors change, may be thought of as metamorphosing into a flavor placement foreign to the original. Some dehydrated onions don't taste at all like onions.

We can picture the flavor of onions moving toward the placement of sugars in Column 19, but the other flavor components that they develop in dehydration may be thought of as sliding up or down into the depth of the different chemical tastes.

Again using a musical analogy, everything Bach wrote was black and white on paper, presented in two dimensions: up-down and sidewise; but the player and the auditor must appreciate Bach to explore and to feel his liturgical depths. Again we emphasize the kinship of art in food as in music. Their appreciation is concerned with emotional factors which may or may not be measurable.

The flavor intensity of raw green herbs is higher than that of dried ones. If both raw and dry herb or other spice vegetable matter are to be combined, the differences in their flavor values should be recognized.

Starting with the original idea of a mint sauce, several options immediately below and above mint are possible. The flavor of mint can still be dominant but by combining it with one or the other of its neighbors, a subtle but definitely agreeable compound flavor will result. To get away from the same old mutton and mint combination, try some of the herbs a few degrees below or above the position of mint. Some of the spices and other suggested seasonings on a line from mutton to mint may provide options for trial.

Instead of projecting the flavor curve through mint, center it about some other herb and work up or down from it. Here a knowledge of some of the flavor preferences of other peoples will make for interesting trials; such as the Levantine preference for mint and the Italian for oregano. Here you will note that marjoram is the cultivated variety of oregano and milder in flavor. However, comparing the two, marjoram and dried oregano can provide us with a basis for consideration of what is involved in a congeneric flavoring matter that is easily distinguishable despite its very close botanical family relationship. The flavor can be said to be analogous but like all other family relationships, have some differences. Colloquially they might be termed "the same only different." Wild oregano like wild sage has a penetrating aroma that is present to a subdued degree in its cultivated relations. The experienced taster will readily detect the difference between commercially ground herbs and the use of whole unground ones. There is a radical difference between stored ground black pepper and freshly mulled pepper berries. There is a very great difference between fresh coriander leaves (which resemble parsley and have quite a delicate light, sweet taste and aroma) and ground coriander seed. The seed, while more pungent, more penetrating than the coriander leaf is only distantly suggestive of its raw leaf flavor.

Several of the raw herbs such as thyme, basil, and chervil may be judged analogous in flavor but each has its own properties, each just a little different from the others. Combine any two of the close-together herbs with some judgment of proportions for interestingly different flavor effects. But be warned that compounding of more than two herbs or spices requires judgment for flavor harmony: but they are workable with consideration of the delineation possible with our nomographic system. Use of a single herb or a single spice is a simple and perhaps epicurean approach to cookery.

In the spice classification cumin and caraway are neighbors. Their flavors will probably be judged analogous, one supplementing, perhaps reinforcing the other. Kuminost, the Scandinavian cheese, is flavored with ground cumin *and* whole caraway seed. For a flavor trial and an after-dinner conversation piece, one might call for opinions as to which flavor and to what extent each contributes or dominates that cheese. Here the judgment may be that the cumin provides the agreeable flavor background and the caraway seed a combination of penetrating spot analogous flavor and an agreeable kinesthetic factor.

Within the column headed Raw Herbs, there is a subheading of Spice

Vegetables. This has been done to draw attention to a few of the many vegetables commonly used in cookery but infrequently used as seasonings, especially the greens of root vegetables such as carrots and radishes and the onion-like group. Indenting is here a device for differentiating between the vegetables used as "raw herbs" and those that are uncommon in this usage—ammunition for foraging cooks.

Here contemplation of some of our customs must be judged ludicrous. We use celery hearts and stalks and discard the leaves; but we use celeriac leaves and discard the heart and the stalks.

Attention is further directed to the possibilities inherent in the use of the greens of both salad and leaf vegetables for seasoning purposes.[1] As an example, celeriac greens are much higher in celery flavor than celery. Conversely, celery root is lower in flavor than celeriac root.

Virtually all the green vegetables in Column 9 are common ingredients most cooks overlook. The heart greens of both carrots and parsnips discreetly used yield agreeable flavors as well as desirable nutrients.

The crowns of leeks and onions are wasted by most of us. Foreign usage starts with raw service of the heart greens of many of the root vegetables: beets, carrots, kohlrabi, parsnips, radishes and turnips; while some of the tender crown leaves are cooked, usually with other vegetables or meats or for seasoning soups. The traditional *pot-au-feu* has a few sprigs of carrot greens. Many of the Oriental pottages use bits of the many different kinds of radish greens. The place of those more or less bitter or sour vegetable tastes is part of the sweet-sour-bitter balance set of factors. The greens of our spice vegetables which we almost universally discard are one of the most commonly available and the cheapest sources of the bitter and sour components.

Besides the root vegetables which are too often marketed shorn of their greens, there are a number of vegetable greens which most people never see, or if they see them, they take no notice. They never think of using the tip leaves of sweet potato and yam vines and the tender leaves of some kinds of pimiento plants. In the discussion of wild foods, there are a number of common plants we consider weeds that are staples of other peoples, particularly some of the marsh and woodland greens. While it is true that some of them are too sour or too bitter for our tastes, there are others most of us would accept, and like, providing we weren't told from where they came! An example would be skunk cabbage prized by many Europeans, and early bracken (fern) tips.

A large number of herb seeds that have no general use here in Amer-

---

[1] *Caution:* The greens of most of the nightshade family (tomatoes and white potatoes) must never be used. *They are poisonous;* they contain solanine, tomatine, etc., which are steroid alkaloids.

ica are widely used abroad, some of them of different botanical families but surprisingly analogous in flavor relationships with those we know. For instance, while celery seed may be the only one extensively used by us, trial of carrot, parsley, dill, and fennel seed will be judged to be analogous. They, and some of the weed seeds are among the roadside and field garnerings of the European herb gatherers. In the chart on Dry Botanicals (Fig. 34, Appendix II), most of the make-ups for the tisanes (teas) of Old World usage are from the fields.

Only within the past few years have some of the spice vegetables transmigrated from the Orient to our American markets. Returning servicemen, like the Crusaders, returned with vices and spices and some literally outlandish tastes—a fair number of them quite good!

Woodruff (45)

The herb flavor rated lowest in the classification of herbs is the most delicate of those in common usage. Woodruff (*Asperula odorata*) is best known for the flavor it imparts to Germany's "May wine." Its German name is *waltmeister:* "master of the woods." Without any doubt there are many, many herbs of lighter rating, but they are comparatively unknown.

In a classification of flowers as food rose petals would seem to be lighter than woodruff but on trial they contribute a bitter component from which woodruff is free. Many of the lighter herbs and especially flowers can be used in food assemblies to yield flavor contributions that will rate lower and lighter than woodruff, but only as the result of skillful composition. Flavor norms of most of those other herbs will be found to be higher when they are considered by themselves.

Angelica (74)

Angelica (*Angelica archangelica* or *Archangelica officinalis*) is widely cultivated in Europe for the large ribs of its leaves and is used as a vegetable (somewhat like rhubarb), and the aromatic carrot-like root is used in cookery.

In the United States it seems to be available only packed in syrup or as glacéed stalks.

(See the Dry Botanicals Chart, Roots.)

Marigold (75)

Both flowers and buds are used. It is one of the Old World herbs long used for flavor as well as appearance. Marigold petals (*Calendula officinalis*) were probably used in Europe long before saffron (crocus) stigmas were introduced. The inherent bitterness of marigold petals accounts for its flavor rating above saffron.

Lovage (78)

A member of the carrot family, lovage (*Levisticum officinale*) is one of the *Umbelliferae* the leaves of which are used for salads and in some more or less sweet cookery. The aromatic seeds are used in cakes and pastries. (See Dry Botanicals Chart, Leaves, FN 60; also see Column 17, FN 46.)

Savory (Winter) (80); **Summer Savory** (78)

Winter savory (*Satureia montana*), a perennial, and summer savory, (*S. hortensis*) an annual, are herbs of the mint family (see Mint Chart, Table 8), the flavors of which are practically inseparable when the plants have grown alongside each other. Flavorwise it may be the lightest of the mint family, the aromatics faintly suggesting marjoram and spearmint.

Balm (Mint family–*Melissa officinalis*) (82)

See Dry Botanicals Chart (Shrubs); and also the Mint Chart.

Burnett (83)

The spikey pinnate leaves of burnett (*Sanguisorba canadensis*) are favored for raw salad inclusions, particularly with cucumbers. It is one of the herb garden favorites for food garnishing instead of parsley. It is a lush grower, and, if the flower stalks are kept trimmed, under favorable conditions it is perennial.

Celery (85) (*Apium graveolens*)

See Green Cooked Vegetables Column 8, FN 85.

Kari (88)

Kari or kara (*Murraya koenigii*) are colloquial East Indian terms (which in English usage were twisted to "curry") for the leaves of an Asiatic shrub. Bunches of kari leaves are more widely encountered in the markets of Asia and the Orient than green parsley is in American shops. Kari leaves convey the basic floral components of mild curry powders but are devoid of any pungency. They have the aromatic flavors of many curry powders but no pepper bite. Kari leaves are so widely used in the Far East because they convey a lightly floral flavor of curry to fruit, vegetable, fish, and other dishes where curry without pungency is wanted. So for the seasoning of light vegetable and animal concoctions kari leaves are used instead of curry powder or paste.

The "curry-leaf tree" may be the most important stranger to European and American herb gardens. Probably because it loses most of its flavor values in dehydration curry leaves are not commercially available in a dried form.

Marjoram (90)

Also see Mint Chart and notes relative to oregano (*Origanum majorum*).

Fennel (90)

Commonly, only the hearts of fennel (*Foeniculum vulgare*) are used, celery-like, in salads and cookery. Why the lacy greens are commonly ignored by American cooks is puzzling. The threadlike tips are almost as light in flavor characters as woodruff, and combine agreeably in light flavor profiles of delicate basic food concoctions. This is another instance of the green leafy matter having a radically lower flavor rating than the commonly used part–in this case, the heart matter.

The over-all flavor of fennel can be likened to that of basil, but it is lighter. Like basil, it goes particularly well with tomato preparations.

(See Column 9, FN 90, Column 8, FN 85.)

Pimiento (95)

The flavor level of 95 is assigned to the members of the varieties of this family[2] that colloquially are called "bell peppers." The flesh of all immature sweet bell peppers are practically free of pepper bite, but the seeds of all of them are more or less peppery, which implies that for ordinary cookery they should in pre-preparation be deseeded. The flesh of some of the so-called sweet bell peppers, when mature (most of them are red when mature) are more or less pungent. Some hybrids are white through yellow and orange to purple-black.

Sage (96)

It is not generally realized that this quite common grayish-green leaved garden border shrub (*Salvia officinalis*) is the sage of commerce. Fresh sage leaves are much to be preferred to the dry imports for poultry stuffings. This border sage is not to be confused with *scarlet sage* (*S. splendens*) which has no desirable flavor value. (Refer to Mint Chart and Dry Botanicals Chart.)

Oregano (98)

Both oregano (*Origanum vulgaris*) and marjoram are easily grown from seed, and their cultivation is rewarding for those who relish Italian sauces. In salads and cookery, the two plants are practically indistinguishable in appearance and flavor.

(See Mint Chart, Dry Botanicals Chart.)

Celeriac (100)

Celeriac (*Apium graveolens,* var. *rapacium*) is a turnip-rooted variety of the garden celery. The flavor norm of 100 is based on the root. Heart and stalks have higher flavor values. The leaves, because of their high bitterness, should be sparingly used in cookery. Use the leaves of stalk celery (*Apium graveolens*) which are much less bitter. (See Column 7, FN 100.)

Dill Weed (105)

The thready greens classify as an herb, the seed as a spice. Dill weed (*Peucedanum graveolens*) is the herb most commonly used for seasoning pickles. Note that as a raw herb dill weed flavor rates at 105 and that the mature dill seed (in Column 18) flavor rates 160 as a spice (see Dry Botanicals Chart; see Column 18, FN 160.)

Chervil (110)

Chervil (*Anthriscus cerefolium*) looks like small and smooth-leaved parsley but in flavor is lighter, with a faint suggestion of licorice. In European cookery it is more popular than parsley.

Chervil is one of the four herbs (parsley, tarragon, and chives are the other three) referred to in classic French cuisine as *fines herbes:* the term *fines* in this usage implies small or light.

Parsnip (116)

The seasoning possibilities of parsnips are commonly overlooked, especially the heart greens (see also Column 9).

---

[2] See Column 9, Capsicum, FN 800.

Consider the use of parsnip shreds in place of herbs in some cookery compositions. Shred the roots and sparingly use the heart greens. Both the roots and the heart greens provide desirable flavor components to some marinades. (See Carrot Tops, FN 145, this Column.)

Basil (120)

Basil (*Ocimum bacilicum*) is one of the "sweet herbs" of romance, now principally known in combination with tomato concoctions. It, together with the other sweet herbs easily home-grown, should be more frequently used for sweet-fragrant condiments. (See Mint Chart; Dry Botanicals Chart; Shrubs.)

Thyme (125)

Of three common varieties of thyme (*Thymus vulgaris*) the yellow-green variegated may be the lightest: the creeping and bush types are stronger. (See Mint Chart; Dry Botanicals Chart; Shrubs, FN 82; and also Column 17, FN 80, Sage.)

Radish (30–400, av. 125)

The mildest varieties are Oriental; some of which are bland, almost devoid of pepperiness. Some of the small, black, woody European radishes may flavor rate as high as 400. The well-known white, yellow, green, pink, and red are commonly used raw. Overlooked are the possibilities of their usage in cookery; not only the roots but the heart greens (see Carrot Tops, FN 145, this Column).

Marination of some kinds of radishes, particularly the long white Oriental *daikon* which is starting to make an appearance in American markets, can be rewarding with just fair processing. Those radishes, sliced or cut into strips remain crisp and crunchy, where many other kinds of pickled radishes become soft. Note the tendency of some varieties when pickled to develop disagreeable fungal or sulfurous odors.

Foreign, especially Oriental, usages of raw radishes include accompaniments of mixed seasonings for dip and dunk.

Rosemary (130)

There are two common varieties of rosemary (Mint famliy, *Rosmarinus*), bush and creeping. It is one of the classic herbs most favored for animal meat seasoning. (See Column 17, FN 97, and Dry Botanicals Chart.)

Tarragon (135)

Known to most of us as a vinegar herb it should be more generally used not only in cookery but in salads as a condiment and garnish for its pleasing aroma. Tarragon (*Artemisia dracunculus*) is one of the most favored herb components of fish sauces. (See Column 17, FN 110, and Dry Botanicals Chart.)

Parsley (140)

There are many varieties. A smooth-leaved type of parsley (*Petroselinum hortense*) is commonly used in Italian cookery and is probably the best eating kind, both cooked and raw. It can be as mild as celery, and it is more aromatic. We use parsley almost exclusively as decoration. Europeans fry it, cook it, eat it raw and decorate with it last. Most crinkly varieties of parsley are too high in bitterness to be agreeable when fried or cooked. (See Column 9, FN 99, Roots, and also Column 7, FN 98.)

Carrot Tops, and other "green tops" (145)

Like parsnip greens and radish greens, they are included in this classification to point exploratory cooks to foreign usages of these and other root vegetable heartgreens as herb seasonings, particularly in cookery, as well as salads (see Celery Leaves, FN 160).

The greens of root vegetables almost always flavor rate higher than the roots (exception: the onion-garlic group). Accordingly they should be used with discretion.

Celery Leaves (150)

See Carrot Tops, FN 145, this Column.

Coriander (160)

One of the classic sweet herbs, coriander *Coriandrum sativum* is sometimes confused with sweet cecily of England and other herbs which resemble it.

Coriander is sometimes carelessly mislabeled in American sectional markets: examples—Chinese parsley, Greek parsley, etc.

The leaves closely resemble chervil—like a smooth-leaved light green parsley, but of higher flavor rating and more aromatic, like the other *Umbelliferae*. The mature seed is the coriander of commerce. The greens, both raw and dry, have much more applicability than the seeds (see Column 9, FN 160).

Leek (180)

The Gustametric Chart shows arrows indicating that the greens of the genus *Allium* including onion, garlic, etc. all rate lower than the bulbs.[3] However, it is emphasized that the bitterness in the greens tends to persist in cookery.

Chiso (185)

Chiso or *siso* is the Japanese name of this red herb of the mint family (*Perilla nankinensis*). The Chinese name is tō-sū.

Hardly known in the United States outside of Oriental markets in California, this herb will sooner or later be one of the most popular condiments because of its visual and flavor characters. In appearance and growth habits it resembles a mulberry-red peppermint, even to the leaves. Under soil conditions it likes, and it seems to be quite catholic about this, it grows rank and luxuriant. The flavor can be likened to a combination of parsley, coriander, and cumin, with the fragrance of celery and an overtone of spices. It goes equally well with or on cold foods and in cookery.

Chiso is frequently used in Oriental cookery because of its property of coloring liquors; the red color runs free and remains fairly stable. It leaches out of the herb as it is infused. Obviously if the color is to be retained, chiso must not be blanched.

Spearmint (190)

Because so many members of the *Mentha* are used as herbs, a separate chart of the mint group is given on pp. 308 and 309.

Spearmint is the variety of *Mentha* (*Mentha spicata*) generally grown for

[3] For Leek, Chive, Scallion, Shallot and Garlic, see FN 375 in Column 9, Raw Salad Vegetables.

commercial and domestic usage. Study of the Mint Chart, Table 8, will show that there are other "true mints" that flavor rate both lower and higher than spearmint, but they are comparatively little grown. What may not be generally realized is (1) that most of the popular herbs (in the United States) are members of the mint family (*Labiatae*); (2) most of the sub-varieties of *Mentha* do not taste like mints; they have no constituent of menthol; (3) the essential oils (responsible for the aromatics of each member of the mint family) are *volatile*. The volatility of the essential oils of the various members of the mint family accounts for the lower flavor rating of the different plants when they are dried or subjected to heat exchange in the production of foods. An illustration of a perceptible difference between closely related mints is spearmint oil which "does not give a sensation of cooling as peppermint does" (Youngkens 1951). A cookery note is that most members of the mint family can meet and agreeably mix, what might be termed an agreeable congeneric marriage of seasoning. The exceptions are when some of the coarse and harshly flavored family members add their harsh, commonly rejected influences (see the Mint Chart for catnip, horehound, hyssop, etc.),

Spice—Vegetable Greens (190–700)

The onion-like group of spice vegetables, starting with leek hearts at 190 and cresting with rampion at 700, is arranged in an ascending order of pungency, in order to suggest the use of the greens of all of them. Incidentally, take notice that the flower clusters and the immature seeds as well as the mature seeds have herb and spice characters as well as garnsh values.

The green spikes of the onions, garlics, and the crosses between them appear in Oriental food presentations far more perceptibly than in their cookery. Here is a paradox between the food behavior of the east compared with that of the west. Certainly they use the bulbs for flavoring, but the observant traveler will be amazed at the frequency of appearance of sectioned onion tubes and garlicky grass-like spears, from thin rings in broths and salads to varying lengths in and on basic dishes. The greens of the onion family may be the most nearly universal food embellishment and seasoning ingredient in the Orient. As onion bulbs are unquestionably the most nearly universally used spice vegetable, it is stressed that the western world has largely ignored the use of onion family greens as condiments.

The indentation in Column 16 distinguishes the greens from the bulbs as much to direct attention to the separate use of greens as to show that the greens generally flavor rate lower than the bulbs. But they have one trait in common: a grassy character of the different flavors. Example: scallion greens impart a green flavor, not too grassy, as an additive either raw or cooked. The bitterness tends to disappear in cookery.

Blanch onion family greens if they are to be used with cold salads or spices—to reduce both grassy and bitter notes. Incidentally, blanched leek spears are among the most popular for greens decoration in chaud-froids, in which they are elaborated, formed to meet the dictates of fancy, primarily because they are so easy to work with and so very bland when blanched. (See other discussions of the onion family in Columns 7, 8, 9, and 17.)

Nasturtium (210)

Flowers, immature seed pods (the fruits) and the leaves are frequently used abroad, especially in salads. Both the green seed pods and the leaves are

TABLE 8

HERBS OF THE MINT FAMILY[1]

Flavor Level (Rated Raw)	Mentha (True Mints)	Other Species of Labiatae	Vernacular Names
	(Mintha, name of a Greek Nymph)		
400		*Hyssopus officinalis*, 2 varieties	Hyssop
350		*Marrubium vulgare* (name refers to bitter qualities)	Horehound Hoarhound
300		*Nepeta cataria*, about 8 varieties	Catnip Catmint Catnep
...		*Nepeta hederacea*	Ground Ivy
...		*Lavandula vera*	Lavender
240	*Mentha piperita* var. *officinalis* var. *vulgaris*		Peppermint White Mint Black Mint
195	*Mentha spicata* (or *viridis*)		Spearmint
...	*M. citrata*		Bergamot Mint Lemon Mint
185		*Perilla nankinensis*	Red Mint Chiso (Japanese) To-Su (Chinese)
...		*Salvia sclarea*	Clary Clary Sage
150		*Monarda didyma* *M. fistulosa* *M. odorata* is the Bergamot o the Old World	Bergamot Wild Bergamot Bee Balm Horse Mint
140	*Mentha rotundifolia*	*M. gentilis variegata*	Round-leaf Mint Lamb Mint Apple Mint Pineapple Mint
130		*Rosmarinus officinalis* (Sea Dew, Latin name for Rosemary)	Rosemary
125		*Thymus vulgaris*, 3 varieties; NB: About 100 species. Many kinds possess characteristic scents when bruised: lemon, camphor, turpentine, caraway, etc.	Thyme
...		*T. citriodorus*	Lemon Thyme
...		*T. serpyllum*	Creeping Thyme Mother-of-Thyme
120	*M. pulegium*		Pennyroyal
120		*Ocimum basilicum* *O. minimum*	Basil, common Dwarf Basil
100		*Origanum dictamnus*	Dittany
98		*Origanum vulgare*	Oregano Wild Marjoram

96	*Salvia officinalis* (Latin name refers to healing) Over 500 species	Sage, common or garden Gray Sage
90	*Origanum majorana*	Marjoram, sweet or annual, garden or knotted
82	*Melissa officinalis*	Balm Lemon Balm Bee Balm
80	*Satureia* or *Calamintha montana* (Ancients grew it near beehives, used it as we do mint in mint-sauce)	Savory Winter (perennial)
78	*Satureia* or *Calamintha hortensis*	Savory Summer (annual) Basil Thyme

[1]In botany mints are said to belong to the Labiatae family; there are about 2800 species.

lightly peppery but quite sour. Nasturtium leaves have long been used to substitute for fruit verjuice (literally the green juice of underripe fruit). (See Column 9 and Column 10, FN 210.)

Abroad, immature (small and tender) nasturtium seeds are marinated as substitutes for capers. The seeds lose most if not all their pepperiness and most of their acidity in pickling.

Chrysanthemum (Leaves) (220)

The Oriental usage of the young greens of some varieties of chrysanthemum has only recently been introduced to America. For particularization refer to Japanese cookbooks. Chrysanthemum leaves are rated much higher than the flower petals because of their pungency. This is an example of one part of a plant rating much higher than another part.

Watercress (Peppergrass) (225)

Watercress is of more use in cookery than in salads and garnishes. (See Column 8, FN 95; Column 9, FN 225.)

Peppermint (240)

Peppermint (*Mentha piperita*) is frequently grown in domestic gardens where it may be confused with spearmint. The taste of raw peppermint leaves is more pungent than that of spearmint. Biting the leaf of raw peppermint conveys a feeling of cooling (an example of pseudo-cooling-sense-perception) whereas spearmint leaf will not convey a pseudo-impression of cooling (see Mint Chart, Table 8; see also Spearmint, FN 190 in this column).

Lemon Verbena (250)

There is no relationship between lemon grass and lemon verbena (*Lippia citriodora*); the former flavor rates just below the latter. The leaf of lemon verbena is one of the Old World herbs favored for its light but quite penetrating lemon floral flavor note (somewhat comparable to lemon grass usage in India) where *fragrance* is valued as a component of a made dish; (see FN 140 in Column 17, Dry Herbs).

Oxalis (Oxalidaceae) (250)

"Sourgrass" and some of the other woodsy sour herbs are among the herbs of longest usage as part of the sour-sweet balance.

There are a large number of varieties of this family of bulbous, tuberous herbs, the leaves of which are quite sour. The roots or tubers of most varieties are edible but for one reason or another unpopular except in South America. All of the varieties seem to have weed habits of growth, and with few exceptions the usage of the leaves has been ignored, like those of nasturtiums. Refer to notes on the sweet-sour balance, Column 19.

Garlic Chives (475)

The dense grasslike flat leaves of garlic chives look like garlic sprouts rather than onion chives. Their flavor is slightly lighter than that of ordinary garlic greens. They seem to be a recent introduction from China. They may be discreetly used where "a little garlic" is wanted.

Ginger (600)

Ginger is here listed because the raw rhizome is now available in Oriental shops. In Oriental cookery it places within the four or five most favored spice vegetables, perhaps second only to the onion group, but its range of applications is broader. Raw ginger may have a wider range of usage than any spice vegetable; it has compound applications within every classification of the Gustametric Chart. One of the qualities of raw ginger (far more than dry ground ginger powder) besides its particular flavor note is its property of subduing or masking off-flavors of other foods, especially those of fish.

In Oriental seafood compositions raw ginger is almost as commonly used as salt. Refer to flavor masks in the first section and to Column 18.

Rampion (700)

The colloquial names of rampion (*Campanula rapunculus*) are "ramp" and "bellflower." The tuberous root and the leaves are used both raw and in cookery. The taste is mild, but the flavor can be described as more penetratingly garlicky than garlic. As garlic goes, rampion is stronger than garlic. Its lasting qualities are far beyond the tolerance of all but those with the grossest tastes.

Horseradish (800)

If hybridizers would develop a smoother and milder strain, horseradish would be far more commonly used as a raw vegetable. Its bite and bitterness are so easily dissipated in cookery that considerable skill is required to maintain its desirable characters. Most acids seem to submerge and to dominate whatever we like in horseradish, and most cookery flattens it. There seems to be nothing worthwhile left. Maintenance of the desirable qualities requires patient experimentation via the try-and-try-again method.

Red Pepper (900)

The flavor level of 900 applies to raw, ripe capsicums of the cayenne and related varieties; detailed under cayenne pods in Column 18.

Caution: If in doubt whether a specimen of red pepper is mild or hot (red or any other color regardless of form) first smell the bruised pulp. If in doubt, gingerly taste it—at your own risk! If a small chunk of a hot variety is squeezed between the fingers, a pepper-hot vapor is produced. If the flesh of the pepper is hot the crushed seed is much hotter!

Here it is emphasized that pepper hotness is kinesthetic; it is much more closely related to pain than it is to what we think of as taste. Tasting raw cayennes can really hurt the tongue.

CHAPTER 20

Herbs, Dry

COLUMN 17

One of the purposes of this column is to reveal the effects of drying processes in flavor appraisal, by showing the influence of *condition* upon a class of food, by contrasting the flavor ratings of dehydrated herbs in Column 17 with the same herbs in fresh, raw condition in companion Column 16.

Elemental considerations are the physical and chemical effects of *change of condition* of any food substance. Columns 16 and 17 list only the herbs and spice vegetables but the same considerations apply to all other foods. Change the condition of a food substance by either physical or chemical modification of its components and the flavor is changed. Incidentally, always allow for extraneous influences on the food ingredient.

Malted barley dried over smoldering peat possesses an inherent flavor which imparts the smoky component which is the characteristic of Scotch whisky. This is a clear example of modification of inherent flavor of a grain by industrial processing. The process of malting barley is one which involves conversion of a simple grain, altering the starch and some of the other components. The result is a change of state. Therein lies the key to comprehension of what can, and usually does, happen when preservational processes are applied to herbs. They are altered. It will not do for us to brush the subject aside by saying that dried herbs are the same as raw herbs only less so or more so, as our opinions may be. We might just as well say they are the same only they are different. They are not the same; they are different.

All the basic factors involved in food judgment are present in appraisal of dry herbs. All the factors of organoleptic perception are involved. No one would claim that dry herbs look the same as raw herbs. No one would say they smell the same, taste the same, or feel the same. They certainly don't have the same effects flavorwise as raw herbs.

The primary flavor value of herbs resides in their volatiles, a large percentage of which is lost in most processes of dehydration. Dehydration modifies most vegetable aromatics, primarily by oxidation. The essential oils oxidize, but the bitter components, most of which are non-volatile—that is, fixed—seem to concentrate. Bitterness becomes dominant when companion flavors depart. The sugars are so low in most of the herbs as to be imperceptible. The sweet odors of some herbs are *floral*. They are attributable to components that are measurable in parts per million.

As a generality, the raw herbs are much to be preferred to dry herbs, but allow for important exceptions and some overall qualifications. Do not think of all dry herbs as a retrogression from the green growing state. Many herbs have flavor components of such nature and strength in the live herb as to militate against their use in the fresh state, but are acceptable and welcome when the herb is dried. This observation applies more to spices and the spice herbs than it does to the common herbs. Some herbs are actually toxic in the raw condition but lose their toxicity in the process of dehydration. Raw camomile, so very strong and difficult to use in cookery, is quite bland, quite light, and pleasingly aromatic in its dried condition. When freshly plucked, it has a somewhat unpleasant odor which evanesces as it dries.

Most city dwellers, unfortunately, find comparatively few live herbs available. With very few exceptions those available are limited in variety and restricted to conditions that lend themselves to broad marketing practices. The city dwellers' choice is thus largely limited to dry herbs. But here a technological note enters. Our American spice industry has advanced far beyond most of those abroad. The majority of foreign markets sell herbs as they do spices, in bulk, and it is a lamentable but incontrovertible fact that the proportion of foreign matter (including infestation and filth!) present in many importations is nothing short of appalling. Foreign herb market offerings are rarely even superficially cleaned. Most are not graded, and good packaging is only beginning to make its appearance in foreign markets. This suggests a paradox: some European countries import more packaged herbs and spices from California than they do from the countries of origin, which means that some of the people in those countries are as fastidious about herbs as we are.

Another point is that the American spice industry has transplanted herbs and developed strains superior to those produced in the areas of origin. Like our canners, our spice producers are thus able not only to produce superior strains of the product but to exercise quality control over every stage of growth and harvesting. They eliminate the seasonal variations and the unfavorable bulk handling and transportation which account for many of the highly variable conditions and qualities of those herb offerings abroad. This is one of the many reasons for acknowledging as fallacious the generalization that if it is imported it is good.

The only herbs specifically discussed in the classification of Column 17 are those that are ordinarily available only in dehydrated condition. All the other herbs, the majority in this column, are specifically discussed as classified in Column 16.

Fig. 34 headed Dry Botanicals for Beverages (Appendix II) should be considered here because so many of its listings are dried herbs and while the principal function of that chart is referred to beverage compositions many of the herbs usually thought of only in connection with beverages provide flavoring options for solid foods. Here a point of emphasis is that many of the botanicals listed in that chart which in the United States and some European countries are used only for beverages, are in the areas of their origin used for seasoning foods just as we use herbs and spices.

Woodruff (30)

Woodruff (*Asperula odorata*) may be best known as the herb used in German "May Wine." As the lightest of the common floral herbs it is compounded in many beverages, especially in mulled hot drinks. It may also be used in bakery and confectionery products and in light fruit sauces. Its aromatics are light and highly volatile. (See Column 16, FN 35.)

Saffron (40)

While the saffron of commerce is the yellow-orange-red stigmas of this species of purple-flowered crocus (*Crocus sativus*) the color and flavor of different packs of saffron markedly vary. Light yellow-orange saffron is rather light in flavor, the orange saffron is of medium flavor, and the distinctly reddish-orange saffron (of Iran) is highest in flavor. In southern Europe and the Near East, saffron is much used and appreciated for its flavor and only secondly for its yellow dyeing property. In the United States it is almost exclusively used as a dye. In Canada, Europe, and the Middle East it is relatively inexpensive, so cooks are more prodigal in its use. Very few American cooks (because of its cost) use enough saffron to impart its distinct flavor.

In early days of the spice trade it was considered a spice. Technically it is a spice herb.

Melilot (41)

The vernacular names of melilot (*Melilotus officinalis* or *M. vulgaris*) are sweet clover, white clover, yellow clover; sometimes called "hayflower" probably because of the constituent coumarin. It is one of the fragrant Old World herbs, used in bakery, confectionery, and desserts.

Safflower (43)

The petals of the orange-red colored flower petals of this thistle-like herb (*Carthamus tinctorius*) have long been used in the Orient for dyeing and cookery. Abroad it is frequently marketed as saffron, which it closely resembles, but the color is more reddish. However safflower in cookery yields a golden-yellow color: the red tinge of the petals does not leach.

Its flavor is in the same field as saffron but slightly higher, and it is much lower in cost.

Marigold (45)

The dried flower petals have long been used in Old World cookery, like safflower and saffron, primarily for the color component, secondarily for the flavor.

Much lighter in color than either safflower or saffron, marigold (Genus *Tagetes*) is flavor rated at 45 because of its higher bitterness.

The use of herbs to color foods goes in three directions: (1) as accompaniment, embellishments, or garnishes; (2) inclusion of the herb; and (3) decoction of the herb. The use of the three yellow- or orange-petaled flower herbs here mentioned is objected to by some purists because the cooked petals and stamens appear as flecks and wisps, perhaps giving the impression of foreign matter in the foods of which they are made a part. The use of muslin bags or metal "tea balls" as infusion devices avoids offending the fastidious.

Here a very strong reminder is enjoined: that one of the oldest and most tenacious of the Old World usages for herbs was and still is as coloring matter. Many of the herb greens and petals of some flowers that are not usually thought of as herbs are still widely used abroad for their color contributions, particularly in bakery and confectionery products.

Borage (58)

The bright blue borage flowers are one of four English cordial flowers used in some beverages and pastries.

Onion (60)

The flavor norm is based on commercially dehydrated "onion flakes." Toasted onion flakes flavor rate higher. Dehydrated onion greens will flavor rate *lower* when rehydrated. (See p. 318.)

The pungent constituents of onions[1] being volatile accounts for most dehydrated onion products being devoid of onion bite. When rehydrated they taste lightly "herby" with a delicate onion character, which is quickly lost in cookery.

Mushroom (72)

Only by liberal interpretation are mushrooms and some of the spice vegetables considered herbs but because in dried form they are used as herbs they are included in the Dry Herbs, Column 17. Incidental to this point is the fact that most of the spice vegetables are commercially dehydrated for seasonings in cookery.

The flavor ratings of dried mushrooms vary according to variety and their physical condition which in turn depends on point of origin, how they were dried, how long and under what conditions they were packed, transported, and marketed. This implies that a given variety of mushroom may and frequently does have anything from slight to radical differences in flavor; perhaps more so as they are more often marketed dehydrated than they are fresh.

Some mushrooms readily dehydrate: e.g., *Marasmius oreades* (fairy ring mushroom, Chinese grass mushroom) which under ordinary field conditions will dry *in situ*. Other varieties, e.g., all the boleti will deliquesce before they mature, which requires gathering them in states up to half grown, reducing them to thin slices and rapidly drying them. Not only will boleti and some of the other high moisture mushrooms spoil before they naturally dry or before they can be dried at relatively low heat (and over fairly long periods) but *seem to* spontaneously generate animal infestation. Actually animal organisms, insects, and other pests inhabit the soils that spawn mushrooms, establish residence in and with their hosts in infancy and as parasites remain with them until what-

[1] See also Columns 7, 8, 9, and 16.

ever the end is. Accordingly, magnifying glass examination of dried mushrooms is suggested for detection of evidence of infestation or contamination.

All mushrooms will rehydrate if soaked in water at room temperature: it is not necessary to simmer or cook them. All good mushrooms are edible when raw. (Refer to Column 9.) When dry mushrooms are cooked by dry or wet cookery processes their flavors vary greatly from what they were when fresh. The point here is that after mushrooms have been dried (by any ordinary processes) and subsequently cooked, the flavor of such cooked *dry* mushrooms is markedly different from cooked fresh mushrooms.

Parenthetically the same processes applied to most other foods will have approximately the same results: most if not all animal and vegetable foods that are dehydrated and subsequently rehydrated and then cooked will have markedly different flavors from the original foods that were cooked in the same way starting with fresh or raw foods. Here the very important point is that simple rehydration of foods is *not reconstitution.* In the processes of dehydration most if not all foods as they lose their moisture under conditions of heat exchange are chemically altered with more or less loss of aromatics. Whatever rehydration process is invoked all it can materially contribute is what is in the water. This latter factor suggests the use of seasonings and supplements to make an acceptable broth of the water in which dried foods are rehydrated to contribute components that will either compensate, correct, or modify the composition in which the dried food is used.

Sage (80)

The genus of sages (*Salvia*) is very large and widely distributed, and varies greatly, particularly in size and color of the flowers. Scarlet sage is primarily cultivated for color. Some of the salvia blues have high saturation values.

The sage or sagebrush of the American West and Southwest is not related. The most common one, *Artimisia tridentata,* is a shrub with a bitter juice and a sage-like odor. But note that with a cautious hand it has fair usage in cookery, particularly for sprinkle-seasoning in barbecue practices where, under rough and ready circumstances most people will eat anything anyway.

Sage (*Salvia officinalis*) as an additive to cheddar and other cheeses has very old European usage. Here, again, note the use of an herb not alone for the flavor but the soft green color it provides. (See Table 8, Mint Chart.)

Dittany (100)

(*Origanum dictamnus*)

One of the lightest and most aromatic members of the mint family. (See Mint Chart, Table 8.) It is also called pepperwort: its light pepperiness volatilizes in cookery.

Lemon Verbena (140)

Like all of the herbs, lemon verbena (*Verbena citriodora*) loses many of its values in dehydration. (See Lemon Verbena in Raw Herbs, Column 16, FN 250.)

Wintergreen (Leaves) (180)

Vernacular names of wintergreen (*Gaultheria procumbens*) are "checkerberry," "box berry," "partridge berry," "tea-berry." The leaves are used for seasoning, but the berries of some species are edible (see Tea-berry, Column 14, FN 60).

Costmary (250)

Costmary (*Chrysanthemum balsamita* or *Balsamita vulgaris*) is one of the most agreeable and highly aromatic herbs which would be more frequently used if it were better known. However, it is one of the herbs, the bitterness of which is not much altered in cookery.

In England it is often called *alecost* because it is sometimes used to flavor beer. In Germany it is *frauwenmintz* because it is pungent and slightly bitter.

Balm of Gilead (380)

While the buds have long been used in beverages for their balsamic constituent, they are of considerable use in cookery as a pine aromatic. Incidentally, they may be preferable to pine needles, because the flavor note of balm of gilead[2] (*Abies balsamea*) buds is less penetrating than that of pine needles.

(See Dry Botanicals Chart.)

Yarrow (500)

Milfoil or yarrow (*Achillea millefolium*) is one of the Old World bitter herbs used for beverages and cookery. (See Dry Botanicals Chart.)

Pine Needle (750)

Used in beverages for a flavor note, it can be compared with balm of Gilead (balsam fir) buds, but pine needles (*Pinus sylvestris*) have fixed bitter components that are more persistent than those of balsam buds.

Rue (850)

A colloquial name is "herb of grace." Rue (*Graveolens,* Linnaeus) is the bitterest of the Old World "bitter herbs." It is much used as a component of bitters and European liqueurs but less often used in cookery because of a combination of its bitterness and the medicinal (actually chemical) smelling aromatics. Those people who like the smell of chrysanthemums may like the flavor rue imparts. It has a very strong odor.

Hop (950)

Hops (*Humulus lupulus*) are the mature catkins; oblong or ovoid, loose and papery, straw yellow and up to two inches long. Toward maturity and when dried or cured they develop a surprisingly strong aroma peculiar to hops. It is almost as strong and penetrating as (and somewhat parallel to) drying geranium florets. While the sum of a flavor appraisal of hops must be peculiar to hops it should be known that in usage, the floral esters being volatile, evanesce and only the bitterness remains; unless exceptional care is taken in compounding and processing beverages and other foods where hops are used for flavoring.

In general hops are best known for their association with beer but experience with their use will demonstrate their applicability particularly to many other beverages where the addition of a bitter note would be desirable (e.g., many of the bland, simply sweet fruit juice compositions) and some made dishes.

The common hop is a perennial *native* herb; native along rivers and thickets in our eastern states and some areas of the Rockies as far south as Arizona and in Florida. Some of the gatherers of wild foods know and appreciate the young hop shoots, which are used like asparagus. Like the curled shoot tips of some kinds of ferns, hop shoots are often no more bitter than asparagus.

---

[2] The vernacular name is "balsam fir."

APPENDIX TO COLUMN 17

The indented line in Column 17 with the single listing, Onion-60, is intended to cue placements of the spice vegetables of Column 16 when they are dehydrated. They are not flavor rated in Column 17 because their flavors differ so much due to either variety or processing.

Commercial dehydrated mixtures of herbs are omitted from coverage in Column 17 because each mix would have its own flavor rating according to its composition, e.g.: herbs compounded and labeled "Italian Seasoning" by two different producers would have two different flavor ratings.

"Soup vegetables," dehydrated spice vegetables, are omitted from Column 17 because their flavor ratings would vary with their compositions and other factors. Dehydrated pimientos from two different producers, labeled "Sweet Bell Peppers" red or green, would have different flavor ratings.

Some parallels may be made with some of the discussions of Flavor Bases in Column 19 in that the products of each processor are according to his taste and his ideas of what the public wants, and they are subject to change without notice. Some of the herb processors pack mixtures of herbs which, for example, are labeled "Bouquet Garni for Soup" and "Bouquet Garni for Beef," the compositions of which can only be according to individual ideas.

Here the point is: (1) there are no fixed compositions of mixed herbs; and (2) the flavor rating of any mixture would hinge on the qualities of the components and the proportions. Also, the important factor of time must not be overlooked. The time between harvesting, processing, packing and *using* of herbs is critical, because the aromatic values of most herbs are highly volatile.

Developments in the technology of food dehydration have resulted in the marketing of such vegetable and herb assemblages as soup, salad dressing and sauce mixes and herb compounds that are in the forefront of convenience foods. To the cook in a hurry they are frequently the shortest cut for some kinds of seasoning requirements.

CHAPTER 21

Spices

COLUMN 18

Sesame Seeds (25)

Sesame seeds (*Sesamum indicum*) contain approximately 51 per cent oil, 20 per cent protein, no starch. The seeds are used as is or toasted in cookery and in bakery products.

Sesame paste consists of the decorticated kernels mulled to a buttery consistency; it is one of the Middle East's earliest bases for dips and spreads. *Tahini* (Egypt), made up of sesame paste, garbanzos, garlic, olive oil and salt mulled, is an example of such a product.

Toasted Sesame Seeds (45)

Black Sesame Seeds (90)

Available in the Chinese herb shops, sesame seed that has been roasted to a state where it is brown-black, is used primarily both for its charred and for its slightly bitter secondary taste values, in cooked foods, both in the Near East and in the Orient.

Paprika (50)

The name paprika (*Capsicum tetragonium*) is derived from the Magyar term that suggested pepper. In the Teutonic countries the term "paprika" is alike applied to raw paprikas (what we call green or red bell peppers or pimientos) as well as paprika powder, and is generic for a kind of cookery: meat paprikas, vegetable paprikas, etc. Here in America we think of paprika as limited to the specific spice and a specific color. Allow for *green* paprikas produced in Hungary and Austria. The bulk of Hungarian paprika and the "Hungarian type" paprika produced in the United States comes from only the pulp of what we call pimientos, from sub-varieties propagated for their almost total absence of pepperiness in the pulp.

The seeds of paprikas and pimientos, which are pungent, are excluded in the production of commercial paprika. Commercial paprika is bland and paprika-floral, almost free of pepper hotness.

Sloe (50)

The vernacular name is "black sloe." The small sloe trees (*Prunus umbellata*, Bailey 1943) are native in our southeastern states, South Carolina to Florida. The small globular pure yellow to orange-yellow and red-blotched seedless cherry-like fruits are lightly sour and bitter. They are sometimes used in conserves, but more widely favored for their pink coloring in flavoring of beverages, e.g., sloe gin.

Elder (58)

The fruits of the three species (*Sambus* or *Sabus nigra, S. canadensis* and *S. caerulea*), all called "elderberries," are used in cookery and for beverages, e.g., elderberry wine.

Refer to the Dry Botanicals Chart for comparison with other dried berries for flavoring services.

Hawthorn (62)

FN is based on dried hawthorn berries (*Crataegus aestivalis, C. mexicana*).

Bailey (1943) reports between 800 and 900 species of *Crataegus* have been described, and that the fruits of the two given above are made into preserves and jellies. The fruits of two other groups, Molles and Favae, are reported as making for jellies similar in quality and taste to guava jelly.

Refer to the Dry Botanicals Chart for Comparison with other dried berries for seasoning services.

Aniseed (68)

One of the many floral-flavored spice seeds. The seeds of most of the other Umbelliferae are much higher in flavor rating.

In Chinese cookery aniseed (*Pimpinella anisum*) is one of the most favored spices for seasoning poultry sauces.

Sumac (70)

FN is based on the small, one-seeded dry smooth or hairy drupe (Bailey 1943). There are about 150 species in the temperate and sub-tropical regions of both hemispheres. The leaf may be used in beverages but usually it is the berry which is used for its tartness (Nickell 1911). The dried berries of a few varieties of edible sumac (*Rhus glabrum*) are one of the oldest spices in Levantine usage. It is one of the best spices for services where its slightly sour, faintly saffron-like, bitter and peculiar floral aromatics may be desirable.

Caution.—It may be advisable to restrict usage of sumac to reliable commercial offerings. Gathering the attractive, brilliant red wild sumac berries, is fraught with extreme hazard. Many varieties are *poisonous.* It may be more dangerous to gather wild sumac for berries than wild mushrooms.

Poison oak, poison ivy, and poison elder are all in the *Rhus* genus.

Corn (75)

Dehydrated corn kernels (*Zea mays*) flavor rate from 30 to 90 according to variety and strain and condition, from some of the very bland whites to the reds and blues to black Mexican. Corn as a spice seed may provide the class with the widest varietal spread, and accordingly the greatest range of cookery applications.

Huckleberry (85)

The FN is based on dry huckleberry (Genus *Gaylussacia*), placed in this column for its usage as a spice. (See Dry Botanicals Chart.)

There are about 50 species in eastern North America and South America which are closely allied to *Vaccinium* (Bailey 1943), commonly called "blueberries" the fruits having a berry-like drupe with ten nutlets (Bailey 1943). Huckleberries are blue or black, and most of them are edible, but a few are not. While the many different varieties of huckleberries are among the native fruits of earliest usage for conserves, jams, and pie fruit, in their dried form they are not thought of as a spice; but should be considered so in either a raw or dried condition. (See Blueberry, FN 58 in Column 10.)

Wild Cherry (90)

FN is based on dried wild cherries (see Dry Botanicals Chart). In dried form, it is suggested that wild cherries be considered as a spice. When crushed, the product yields pulp and seedy flavors, (see Column 10, FN 70 and Column 14, FN 150).

Poppy (95)

A number of different varieties of poppies (Genus *Papaver*) are abroad propagated both for seasoning and for the production of oil. Some of the tiny poppy seeds are favored for bakery purposes in the Middle East and some of the coarser varieties for their nutty bitterness and probably their crunch appeal.

In some areas poppy seed is the only source of vegetable oil. It is one of the row crops of country gardens for home production of vegetable oil, particularly in Germany.

Juniper Berries (98)

Juniper berries (*Juniperus communis*) have long been used in some liquors, particularly gin. They convey a floral flavor of pine that seems to go naturally with meat dishes, especially in outdoor cookery. When freshly gathered and roasted they are highly aromatic. Juniper berries, like California tree pepper and western laurel, have been commonly ignored as a spice where they are frequently available for the taking.

Rye (100)

While we associate rye (*Secale cereale*) almost exclusively with bread and whiskey it is widely used in Germany as a spice in cookery.

Cocoa (110)

Our acquaintanceship is largely limited to "ground cocoa" and cocoa products, mainly chocolate in different forms. In the countries of origin, the whole cacao bean (*Theobroma cacao*) is cracked and, as *cocoa nibs* (that is the trade term for the fragmented cocoa seed) is used in cookery, both for its flavor and its color. We use browned flour for thickening and color, but in the countries where cocoa is grown, ground cocoa nibs are used for thickening and the browning effect in cookery. The use of cocoa to darken sauces is a field of exploration for the experimentally inclined cook. It provides body and texture factors somewhat different from those of starch and the final color can be quite agreeable. The over-all flavor composition suggests what may be entirely new compositions to most cooks. If cocoa is discreetly used it may be impossible to identify its presence in a blindfold trial: there will be no chocolate taste if sweetness in the product is subliminal.

Rose Hips (115)

The fruit of the wild rose (*Rosa canina*), but more commonly, especially in Europe, the mature fruits of any wild rose that may be obtainable, is used primarily for conserves, secondarily in bakery and a little in cookery. Mildly sweet and slightly tangy, its bitterness is dissipated in cookery. Its floral notes evanesce with prolonged or high-temperature cookery. Accordingly, rose hip jelly, while it has a characteristic taste, has no jar aroma. The light rose aroma is only perceptible in eating. Incidentally, our common garden rose fruits are edible if picked mature. The fruits of some varieties are higher in acid than others. None of them seems to be as floral as those of the wild roses, especially the Western wild "Rose of Castile" briar. Rose hips have the highest vitamin C values of any known fruit.

Cardamom (125)

Cardamom (*Elettaria cardamomum*) is one of the basic ingredients of curry powder mixtures. In Europe it is widely used for flavoring cakes and liquors.

Dill Seed (160)

Dill seed is the fruit of *Peucedanum graveolens*, an annual herb of the order Umbelliferae. This seed, like most of the other umbelliferae florets, does not acquire its characteristic flavor until maturity and after proper conditioning. Raw, and particularly immature, its normal flavor is barely perceptible, and is more woody than spicy. In common usage, it is almost entirely restricted to pickling marinades. Nomographically projected on the Gustametric Chart, it will be found to be an agreeable inclusion in the composition of many dishes.

Pepper Anise (170)

Vernacular names are Chinese anise, Japanese anise, and in the United States, prickly ashberry. Pepper anise is probably so called because in some conditions it somewhat resembles pepper berries. Pepper anise (*Xanthoxylum fraxineum,* Nickell) has no peppery component, no piperine. Its aromatics suggest a combination of cardamom, coriander, and allspice, with a touch of caraway. If it weren't for the slight bitterness, which is not volatile, its flavor level would be much lower. As one of the common spices of China, the flavor of pepper anise can be detected in many Chinese dishes. It is one of the best of all spices, and one of the spices usually compounded in the offerings of Chinese herb shops of "Five spice powder" which powder varies in composition according to the ideas of individual producers.

Angelica (Seed) (175)

In Old World bakery products, it is particularly favored in biscuits and cookies for its high floral aromatics, e.g., angelica-seed cookies. (See Column 16, FN 74 for the root and leaves.)

Vanilla (190)

Vanilla is the fruit of a climbing orchid (*Vanilla planifolia*). It is most often used in a liquid form, as an extract or flavor. Caution must be exercised in using the whole bean or particles of the whole bean in cookery because of its penetrating bitterness.

Coumarin (from *coumarou,* the tonka-bean tree) is a widely used commercial substitute. Coumarin flavor rates higher than true vanilla.

Fenugreek (210)

One of the basic components of curry powders, fenugreek (*Trigonella foenumgraecum*) has wide application in cookery, especially with salad and salad dressings. It amalgamates particularly well with the flavors of herbs.

Turmeric (225)

The root of turmeric (*Curcuma longa*) is the only root that the American spice trade considers as a spice. The root is heat-processed, dehydrated, and ground, in which form it is commonly marketed. In commercial curry powders it is the component responsible for their yellow coloration. In foreign markets many curry compounds are marketed without turmeric. Turmeric has applications for the flavor peculiar to it, as well as imparting its agreeable yellow color.

Coriander Seed (230)

Abroad and particularly in Asia, the whole coriander seed (*Coriandrum sativum*) is more frequently used than the pulverized form, both in bakery products and in cooked foods. While it has some pepperiness, it is liked for its floral characters. In India the whole seed is fried with the other curry spices and served in the finished dishes.

Mustard Seed (240)

Black mustard is *Brassica nigra;* brown mustard is *B. juncea,* and white mustard either *B. hirta* or *B. Alba.*

In domestic cookery the different mustard seeds are ordinarly used whole or roughly crushed in marinades and for pickle seasoning.

For mustard pastes and compounds refer to Column 21, Volume II.

Fitches (250) (*Nigella sativa,* Linnaeus)

A member of the family Ranunculaceae with the vernacular names "Black Caraway," "Black Cumin," "*Kizha*" (Egypt), etc.[1] This spice seed is second in popularity only to sesame in the Levantine countries, where it is most frequently used simply compounded with soft cheeses and dips and as a substitute for pepper (even though it has no piperine, no pepper bite) in sauces and sprinkle seasoning. In North Africa and in the Near Eastern countries it is far more frequently used than caraway or any of the other umbelliferous seeds. For cheese dip and spread combinations as well as many dish compositions, it has more agreeable placement potentialities than either caraway or cumin. One of the most important spices, it has been overlooked by the spice trade. It is usually available in some of the food specialty shops.

Allspice (260)

Allspice is the unripe berry of *Pimenta officinalis.* The name allspice comes from the idea that it combines the flavors of clove, cinnamon, and nutmeg.

Curry Powder (275)

The word "curry" in the Tamil dialect of India means "cookery," but throughout the country the term is generic for *sauces,* the compositions of which vary from North to South and East to West, and there are as many different arrangements of the components as there are of dishes. This means that to an Indian family curry[2] is not a powder taken out of a jar but a composition of spices especially assembled for a single dish. Such curry spice assemblies differ not only for vegetable and meat dishes, but are varied according to the kinds of vegetables, the kinds of fish, poultry, or red-blooded meats. The Indian cook would no more use the same "curry" spices for the different basic foods than we would mix country gravy with everything that is cooked in the kitchen.

[1] Habet el Barouka, the seed of blessing, Arabia.
[2] See kari, Column 16.

TABLE 9

SPICES AND HERBS, FRESH, DRIED OR PRESERVED, USED IN INDIAN CURRY POWDERS OR PASTES

Bay leaves	Coriander	Lemon grass[1]
Black pepper	Cumin	Mace
Cardamom	Fennel	Mustard
Cassia	Fenugreek	Nutmeg
Cayenne	Ginger, Dry	Poppy seed
Celery seed	Ginger, white, or galangal (wild ginger)	Star anise seed
Cinnamon		Turmeric
Cloves	Kari leaves	White pepper

TABLE 10

SUPPLEMENTAL SEASONINGS INCLUDING SOME FLUID CARRIERS

(In the order in which they are most frequently used)

Garlic	Ghee or fat
Onion	Thick coconut milk (scraped or ground coconut pulp in water)
Green and ripe mango pulp	
Tamarind pulp	Thin coconut milk (second extraction from ground cocoanut with water)
Lime juice or other citrus juice	
Lime chutney or preserved lime (made from dried limes)	Yogurt or sour milk curd

1. *Lemon Grass.*—Flavorwise the raw lemon grass (*Andropogen citratum*) may rate around 125 (below lemon verbena). In India it is used as a component of curries where lemons are not available and a lemon peel flavor is desired. Incidentally, in the absence of lemon grass, lemon or orange leaves are used which can impart quite delicate citrus leaf esters.

Curries in India, like chilies along our United States Southern Border and in Mexico, vary from mild and what may be called subtle in flavor to varying degrees of pepperiness.

Superiority of flavor in local Indian cuisine is attributable in part to purists' spot-preparation of curry pastes from whole spices which are subsequently agglomerated with *raw* vegetable pulp and then sautéed or fried. As liquid carriers, fruit or vegetable pulp, coconut milk or coconut cream and sometimes ghee, milk curd, or yogurt are used. In basic Indian cookery curry sauces are *never* thickened with flour. Most American commercial curry powders are relatively mild compositions of the different curry herbs and spices.

As a compound of spices, a touch of curry powder is applicable to many sauce compositions. If a small enough quantity of curry powder is added to a sauce so that its presence cannot be detected as curry it will raise the spice flavor level of a sauce.

Most curry powders made for American and European markets are light yellow to yellow-orange in color. Most curry powders compounded for use in countries with a high Indian population vary from deep yellow to orange-red in color; and pastes will vary from light brown to prune brown. With rare exceptions commercial curry powders and pastes made for Indian tastes are more pungent that those made for Americans.

Curry powders or pastes for red meat and dark vegetables tend to be dark in color.

Curry powders for some poultry, fowl, and for certain fish are dark yellow in color. Curry powders or pastes for fruits, light vegetables, and light fish are light (not necessarily yellow) in color.

Fennel (280)

Fennel (*Foeniculum vulgare*) is one of several Umbelliferae seeds, the flavor of which rate within a narrow band: the others are cumin—290; celery seed—300; and caraway seed—320.

Cumin (290)

FN is based on cumin seeds (*Cuminum cyminium*) of the Asiastic varieties (not caraway, with which it is frequently confused). Cumin is one of the favored components of East Indian curry compounds. In the Levantine countries, it is widely used for sprinkle-seasoning of broiled meats. It is among a number of spices that amalgamate well with shish kebab marinades.

Celery Seed (300)

The seeds of celery, like some of the Umbelliferae vegetables, are considered to be spices for the flavors peculiar to each of them. Their applications may be considered paralleling those of carrot, caraway, dill, and cumin.

Caraway (320)

Caraway seeds (*Carum carvi*) are among the best known spice seeds because of their usage in rye bread and cheese. Abroad, caraway is favored for inclusion in heavy game and beef stews and sauces, and in meat puddings and some of the stronger sausages. In beverages, caraway is known for flavoring German *kümmel* and some Scandinavian *aquavit.*

Coffee Seeds (325)

Coffee seeds (*Coffea arabica, C. liberca, C. robusta,* etc.) (refer to Column 14) is listed among the spices because it agrees with most chemical interpretations of the word spice and it is used as a spice in cookery in the areas of origin. In dry or liquid form coffee is usable as a seasoning additive in many compositions, some of which can be nomographically determined on the Gustametric Chart.

Trial of left-over coffee for darkening some broths and sauces as well as bakery products will yield shades of brown much more clear than most other procedures and combinations. So used, coffee is actually a vegetable dye. When judiciously used, the combination of liquid coffee provides flavor and color characteristics that are particularly agreeable *in* cookery.

Mace (340) **and**

Nutmeg (350)

The nutmeg of commerce is the seed and mace is the ruminated aril which surrounds nutmeg (*Myristica fragrans*).

In the countries of origin, principally the East and West Indies, the husk of the nutmeg fruit is used for seasoning and in fruit preserves. When raw and fresh, mace is one of the most delicate floral spices, but it is only commercially available in dried and usually pulverized condition, the flavor of which is notably different from its raw state.

The fruit of the native American nutmeg pine (which is not even distantly related to the true nutmeg) has a flavor surprisingly close to true nutmeg.

Star Anise (360)

Star anise is the star-shaped fruit of the tree *Illicium verum.* It is also known as Chinese and Japanese anise. It is not related to the common anise or to pepper anise.

It is one of the five ingredients of the "five spice powder" referred to in Chinese cookery. It is one of the warm floral spices most favored in Asia and the Orient, and why it has never been generally recognized by the spice trade is puzzling. The flavor of star anise may be described as between cinnamon and clove; warmly aromatic but devoid of the pungent characters of cinnamon and clove.

Grains of Paradise (375)

Grains of Paradise (*Melegueta*) are the aromatic pungent seeds of one or more species of the genus *Amomun,* of the *Scitaminea,* a native of West Africa. The flavor is close to pepper but is not so pungent; it is more floral. In the countries of origin it is used instead of black pepper.

Penner, White (390) (*Piper nigrum*) and

Pepper, Black (450) (*P. nigrum*)

All true peppers belong to genus *Piper,* in the *Piperaceae.* Cayenne or red pepper is from a plant not a true pepper, but a member of genus *Capsicum.* Other spices called "pepper" are Jamaica Pepper (allspice), and Melegueta pepper (grains of paradise).

The most important species is *P. nigrum,* black pepper; next are *P. officinarum* and *P. longum,* the long peppers; *P. clusii,* African pepper, has some use; and *P. cubeba,* cubeb, a drug; *P. miniatum* and *P. betle* used for chewing by Asians; *P. methysticum,* is kava, used by Polynesians.

The process of bleaching and sometimes partially decorticating pepper to what is marketed as "white" pepper results in removing the flavor components contained in the hull.

Cinnamon Group (400)

Cassia (440)

The cinnamon of commerce is the bark of trees, *Cinnamomum zelanicum* (Breyn).

Cassia is the bark of *Cinnamomum cassia* (Bl.) which is one of several species of *Cinnamomum.*

The flavors of the best cinnamon and the best cassia are practically indistinguishable; but ordinarily commercial offerings of cinnamon are a little lighter and more delicate in flavor than that of cassia. Cassia is usually cheaper than cinnamon but for some purposes because it is stronger in flavor, perhaps coarser, it may be preferred to cinnamon. Cassia is frequently marketed, especially abroad, as cinnamon.

In quill form cinnamon and cassia are easily distinguished from one another: cinnamon bark is quite thin, being fairly uniform between $^{1}/_{32}$ and $^{3}/_{64}$ inch in thickness whereas cassia bark is not uniform in thickness and it is usually more than $^{1}/_{16}$ inch thick.

Cinnamon Buds (380)

Cassia Buds (400)

Refer to Dry Botanicals Chart.

Both cassia and cinnamon buds flavor rate about 20 points lower than their companion barks. Both cassia and cinnamon buds are favored in beverages and bakery goods (over barks) because the buds beside conveying the basic cinnamon flavor have additional floral esters.

Gardening hobbyists should know that in areas and under conditions where the cinnamon shrub can be shielded from frosts it will do fairly well here in the United States. Fresh cinnamon leaves underlain cake batter will suffuse their aroma in the process of bakery, thus providing a cinnamon note from the volatiles alone. Incidentally, this same procedure is applicable to many other leaves, particularly peach, apricot, and almond. It provides a subtle and most elusive fragrance to teas, while other flavor factors contributed are so minute as to be below the threshold of perception. This is one more demonstration of the importance of aroma, which in turn proves that our sense of smell is far more acute than our senses of taste.

While cinnamon and cassia buds are more aromatic than the barks and may be preferred in beverages, bakery products, and light desserts, the barks may go better in sauces, particularly the heavier ones.

Ginger (475)

The FN is based on dehydrated and pulverized ginger. Refer to Column 16, Raw Herbs, where the FN of *raw* ginger is set at 600.

Pepper (Tree) (500)

What should interest residents of California and other states where the two varieties of *Chinus molle* (California pepper) trees will grow, is that while those trees are not botanically related to the black vine-peppers, the berries are remarkably close in appearance and flavor characters, with some factors much in favor of our own trees' products. In pepperiness it just about parallels that of black peppers, but in aromatics it is much higher, with a pine component that in some combinations, particularly for barbecue sprinkle-seasoning of meats, can be distinctive and agreeable. In other words, the berries of our California pepper trees are not only edible but they provide one of the very few true spices growable over any wide area in America. A good part of the time they are free for the picking, at least until the owners of the trees become aware of the value of their crop!

Bay Leaves (525)

Vernacular names: bay laurel, western laurel, myrtle.

The FN is based on *Laurus nobilis,* the bay leaf of the Mediterranean area. The leaves of the laurels of our western states are slightly higher in flavor rating than the Mediterranean varieties. The different myrtles grow wild along the Pacific Coast, and some of them become enormous trees, but what is not generally known is that the Mediterranean laurel, the leaf of which is prickly along the edges resembling a softer holly leaf, does well wherever myrtle will grow. Again, here is a wild food that is ignored, perhaps because there is so much of it, and it is usually free for the gathering.

Incidentally, bay laurel berries are edible. They may be considered as a true spice.

Clove (560)

Cloves are the dried flower buds of a tree of the myrtle family. The flavor rating is based on whole cloves. Powdered cloves would flavor rate much lower. In the process of pulverizing clove buds lose much of their pungency and aromatic qualities.

Pickling Spices (700)

Like some of the specialty spice packs (pumpkin spice, poultry seasoning, Italian seasoning, and there are many others) different packers create and market mixtures of herbs and spices that vary according to purpose and the ideas of their blenders. Pickling spices and some of the herb-spice compositions are most easily used and would be used much more frequently if, as a pre-preparational process, a decoction (either aqueous or acid, vinegary) is made, so the liquor rather than the whole spices is used. A two-ounce package of pickling spices, simmered, not boiled, in a quart of water or with vinegar, will provide a mother-liquor, a little of which added in cookery as well as salad dressings, provides a spice lift to needy compositions.

Mustard (Powder)[3] (800)

The FN is based on commercially processed mustard seed powder, the very high pungency of which sets it at 800. Some mustard powders would flavor rate lower, depending upon proportionate constituents of less pungent brown and black mustard seed. Especially note that the pungency and aromatics of mustard seed are not liberated until crushed.

Cayenne Pods (900)

The principal species are *Capsicum minimum* (Roxb.), also called bird pepper, bird's eye pepper, mad pepper, Guinea pepper. The oblong fruit, $^1/_2$ inch to $^3/_4$ inch long is orange-scarlet in color. They are cultivated in the East Indies, Zanzibar, and Japan and are the source of most cayenne of commerce.

A second species, *C. annuum* narrow, pointed, 2 to 3 inches long, is colorwise the most variable of the capsicums, ranging from different yellows through orange, red, violet, and purple to nearly black. Their vernacular names are most frequently applied according to their colors. Whatever they are called, they are very, very hot. Nepal pepper, marketed in the United States, is a ground orange-colored variety of *C. annuum*.

A third species is *C. grossum* which includes a pungent form.

While the different varieties and species and sub-species of cayenne peppers are widely available in the form of dried pods (infrequently raw) they are commonly marketed by commercial processers who blend them as ground chili pepper.

[3] See Mustard Seed, FN 240 in this column.

Ground cayenne pods have been and by some producers are still labeled "red pepper"; but the term "red" as applied to pepper is ambiguous. As a practical adjective it is worthless; as a specific term of color it is inaccurate. "Red" pepper is rarely really red. The term "red pepper" originally meant ground cayenne or equal. Today the term "peppers" is indiscriminately applied to the whole capsicum family, from the bland pimientos to the pepper-hot capsicums.

CHAPTER 22

Bases

COLUMN 19[1]

It is probably safe to assume that more than 95 per cent of the production of the flavor industries goes to the food packing industries. It may be that only 1 or 2 per cent goes into domestic trade channels. The reason for the negligible domestic usage of liquid and powdered flavor essences and extracts is probably that:

(1) Outside the food industry, very few people know that such concentrated flavoring substances are produced and available.

(2) Comparatively few domestic cooks know how to use those concentrates.

(3) Equipment and utensils for accurately weighing and dispensing concentrates are lacking.

It may be that concentrates of vegetable flavoring comprise the convenience food additive most generally overlooked by domestic cooks. No special equipment or unusual skill is required to use most meat bases, but liquid and powdered extracts and essences may require a gram scale and an eye dropper. Skill comes quickly with a little experience and with care, especially toward restraint. Such small quantities are involved in use of some of those substances that they should be dispensed according to apothecaries' measurements. The average woman knows that the amount of liquid perfume remaining on the end of a glass applicator meets a certain requirement; she knows that the size of the tip of the applicator is a critical factor.

Domestic cooks should know that all common and many uncommon herbs and spices are available in the form of liquid essences or extracts and many animal and vegetable concentrates are available in powder form. Further, within the past few years the flavoring industry has developed animal and vegetable liquid and powder concentrates within wide ranges of specific flavor or seasoning profiles. For example, there are more than 20 large flavoring houses, some of which produce ten or more compounds under the headings of "sausage seasonings," seasonings

[1] Columns 19, 20, and 21 are intended to cover manufactured (with a few exceptions) basic flavoring substances.

Column 19 lists (1) primary flavor bases, appealing to the cardinal tastes (sour, sweet, saline, and bitter); and (2) tertiary flavor bases, which are a combination of primary and aromatic taste substances. The secondary tastes are kinesthetic, none of which come into the scope of Column 19.

for ham and other smoked meats, catsups or pickles. All the true fruit flavors are produced not only as natural essences and oils, but also as imitations. All of them are produced in different concentrations.

The purpose of pointing out the availability of such flavorings is that seasoning concentrates have obvious advantages over natural forms and conditions. An applicator touch or drop of garlic or pepper essence or Italian herb flavor can lend itself better to flavor profile control than the crude or natural seasoning.

The four primary flavors can be discussed as classes to indicate the broad boundaries of the flavor balance of sweet, sour, saline, and bitter.

Sweet

The sweet bases generally include the following:

(1) The different sugars, (see Cane and Beet Sugar, FN 100 in this column.)

(2) Syrups, including (a) refined sugar syrups—refined sugars dissolved in water flavor rate (because of dilution) lower than in their solid state; and (b) fruit syrups—they may rate either above or below their sugar constituents, according to the flavors contributed by their fruit components.

(3) Beverage bases, including fruit extracts and flavors. They flavor rate far above the simple sugars because of relatively high contributions of fruit, floral essences and alcohol.

(4) Although not strictly bases, preserves of sweetened fruits are often used as cookery additives in a basic stock sauce or baste. (See Volume II, Preserves, Column 21.)

Sour

The sour bases generally include the following: (1) Commercial vinegar. (See Vinegar, FN 600 in this column.) (2) Sour fruit extracts, such as lemon and lime. (3) Citric and ascorbic acids, which are usually marketed in a crystalline form. (See Citric Acid, FN 500 in this column.)

Saline

Refined table salt (NaCl) is refined rock or sea salt the flavor level of which is 300. (See Salt, FN 300 on the Gustametric Chart.)

Salt compounded with other food substances is separately discussed. (See Smoke Bases, FN 425 in this column.)

Sea water will flavor rate higher than 300.

Some other salts, notably monosodium glutamate (MSG) contribute saline tastes, but most of them are much lower in the flavor scale than refined table salt.

Saline Compounds

Salt in combination with other more or less high flavor rated food matter, is very old. Fish pastes may be the oldest. Anchovy paste is a contemporary offering of a prehistoric food preparation.

Here again it is pointed out that there are far more compositional options for liquorous saline bases than is possible for dry combinations. To achieve an anchovy-flavored, free-flowing salt is difficult, if not impossible. It would probably just taste fishy. To produce an anchovy paste is easy, depending on how fussy you are; but there is little or no problem to producing an anchovy salt-brine, which should probably be called an anchovy-salt purée.

Here, acquaintance with essential compounds, bases, extracts, and flavors can open up a whole new field of experimentation for the exploratory cook.

Salt Compounds

Monosodium Glutamate (40)

Monosodium glutamate is the neutral sodium salt of glutamic acid. When tasted alone, MSG "is slightly salty and when first put on the tongue has a lightly sweet taste." It also "mildly stimulates the sour and the bitter taste buds. . . ." It is said that when it is used in seasoning foods, MSG adds no flavor of its own. However, *like other salts,* taste perception of the presence of MSG in a food composition depends on (1) the quantity used, whether it is below or above the threshold of perception; and (2) individual sensitivity to the presence of MSG. Some people can detect MSG in quantities substantially below the threshold of average perception.

MSG is widely used in the packing industries to enhance flavors, and in general the presence of MSG is not noticeable. Excepting for the relatively few people who are particularly sensitive to MSG, it is a seasoning supplement which, discretely used, is recommended for much domestic cookery.

Bitter

There is no *common* bitter basic food substance. Though quinine is the substance commonly used for panel testing bitterness perception, and tannin is the most frequent bitter component in foods it should be noted that beside hops and rue in Column 17, many of the herbs and spices which rate over 100 have relatively high bitter components. Examples are the herbs, costmary and chrysanthemum and the spice fitches. Incidental to the subject of bitterness, it may be pointed out that some of the bitter vegetables of the Orient (not shown on the Gustametric Chart) even though they appear in American-Oriental shops, are too bitter for American tastes. Several of them are melon-like, but taste as if they had been seasoned with gall. (See Chincona, FN 800 in this column.)

---

* Griffith Laboratories, Inc., Chicago. Wm. J. Stange Co., Chicago.

Sugar (25 and up)

Not all sugars are sweet, just as not all sweet substances are sugars. Saccharine, one of our most common sweetstuffs, is a coal-tar by-product. Some metallic sugars such as "sugar of lead" or lead acetate are used in weighting fabrics but not in food; they are poisonous. All food sugars are members of the saccharose or glucose groups of carbohydrates, "all of which are soluble in water, more or less sweet to the taste, and either directly or indirectly fermentable" (Oxford English Dictionary 1933).

"Sweet" as explained in Part I of this work, means the quality of stimulating the organoleptic recordance of the cardinal taste of sweetness. It is important to realize where sweetness (as well as sourness or bitterness or salinity) begins, and what are the steps involved in sensory perception after the threshold has been passed. There are some differences between races in the capacity to perceive some kinds of sweetness.

Milk Sugar (Lactose U.S.P.) (25)

Lactose is usually available in four granulations: one coarse granular, one regular, and two impalpable; usually from drug stores but sometimes stocked by health food shops.

Corn Sugar (50)

The FN is based on the solid substances obtained by dehydrating liquid corn syrup. Commercial corn syrup and sugars are of four types:

(1) *Corn Syrups.*—Clear, colorless, noncrystallizable, viscous liquids consisting of mixtures of dextrose, maltose, and higher saccharides.

(2) *Corn Syrup Solids.*—The solid substance obtained by dehydrating liquid corn syrup.

(3) *Crude Corn Sugar.*—A solidified corn sugar "liquor," consisting essentially of dextrose.

(4) *Dextrose.*—A pure, crystalline solid, which is the major dry corn sweetener.

Corn Syrups.—Most of the commonly marketed *white* corn syrups have (beside corn sugars) about 20 per cent refined beet or cane sugar. The various shades of *brown* corn syrups have about 20 per cent of *raw* beet or cane sugar, the different shades of brown being attributable to the amount of molasses present in the raw sugar components. If there are any flavor notes in corn syrups (other than simple sweetness) they are due to their raw beet or cane sugar components.

Cane and Beet Sugar (Sucrose) (100)

Most marketed white sugar comes from sugar cane. Around 25 per cent is derived from sugar beets. Chemically and organoleptically, beet and cane sugar are the same. Both beet and cane sugars are marketed in the same conditions or forms from loose white or cubed crystals, to the different brown sugars and the different liquid or syrup states; in all of which conditions they are indistinguishable from one another. They look the same, taste the same, and chemically they are the same.

At 98.6°F. refined sugars are odorless. The more or less crude sugars are more or less aromatic. Volatiles are removed in the processes of refinement, along with some of the desirable flavor components. Cane sugar, beside the white crystalline refined products, is marketed in different grades of partial refinement, through light brown, brown, and dark brown. All brown sugars have more or less molasses coating the sugar crystals. All brown sugars flavor rate higher than white sugars. White sugars are simply sweet; they contribute no aromatics to a made dish, whereas brown sugars contribute flavor components according to the nature and amount of their molasses constituents.

Maple sugar, because it is marketed usually unrefined has a flavor other than simple sweetness. Different batches of maple sugar will have more or less maple (and other) flavors, depending on point and conditions of origin, processes of production, and storage factors. If maple sugar were to be refined, it would be indistinguishable from any other refined sucrose.

The flavor ratings of unrefined beet or cane sugars would be subject to the same qualifications as directed at maple sugar. In the different areas of origin, crude beet and cane sugars are domestically produced, though not much marketed.

Shops that carry Mexican and Caribbean foods usually stock sugar cakes that may vary in color from light to deep brown; they are the products of simply boiling down sugar cane juice which in some cases is only roughly sieved before cooking it. The flavors of those crude sugars vary from crude brown-sugar-sweet to something that can be described as an earthy fruitiness with occasional vanilla notes. Incidentally, some Mexican sugar-like offerings which can be mistaken for slabs of light brown sugar are actually glacéed or caramelized cactus pulp. Such products, like many boiled-down fruit syrups produced in many parts of the world, should be considered as preserves. The caramelized quince pulp of Spain is another example. Some of the Levantine progenitors of "Turkish jellies" are relations of the sugar producing process. Long before the manufacture of refined sugar, those people were producing sugar in the only way they knew how, boiling down sieved fruit juices, some of which were so high in pectin that instead of a crystalline mass, a sweet gelatinous state was evolved.

Usage of Sugar

The following sugars are recommended for the uses indicated:

(1) White sugars for simple sweetness. Granulated or powdered white sugars lend themselves to icing and coating. Granulated white sugar is suggested for use in cooking most green vegetables and most aquatic foods.

(2) Crude or brown sugars for added aromatics of molasses components. The under-refined brown sugars and some syrups may be better than white sugar in cookery of dry beans, peas, and some of the animal meats.

(3) Sugar syrups for solubility. Liquid forms allow more exact proportioning and are easier to use, and thus are often preferred in beverages. Crystal sugar is insoluble in alcohol, so liquid forms are preferable in alcoholic beverages.

(4) Caramelized sugar for flavor or color *without* much sweetness. The different sugars as they are subjected to temperatures which cause loss of moisture of crystallization, darken and alter in flavor according to their kind and condition. When roasted or toasted short of complete moisture evaporation, they have different caramel flavors. If the process is carried on to what is commonly designated as "burnt," where all the moisture of crystallization has been driven off, no sweetness is left, only ash, of the peculiar color that is used for darkening made foods, including beverages. In this condition it can be said

that sugar can be added to other foods without contributing sweetness.

As a footnote on the use of sugars (and other sweeteners) a general observation is that foreign cookery employs far more sweetening substances and sweet foods than that of the United States. Scanning the cookbooks of the world will reveal universal tendencies toward the sweet-sour balance in food composition. Study of commercial catering and industrial packing practices, and a reading of labels on canned and packed foods, will indicate adherence to formulations that show awareness of the sweet-sour balance. Probably because of dietary objections, many of which are not clinically justifiable, *domestic* uses of sugars and other sweetening substances in the United States are restrained. A clinical note that is here in order is that it is probable that not more than 20 per cent of Americans are overweight or have substantial concern with caloric considerations. Only about five per cent are clinically obese, and those should be under medically supervised dietary regimens.

Sugar and some of the salts can be said to be symbiotic, acting as companionate supports of flavor in food matter without their presence being recognized by the average person. The great majority of dishes (especially green leafy vegetables) are improved with a little of either, usually both, sugar and salt. Only so much should be used as will raise the flavor of a dish without the individual seasoning being identifiable That is the almost universal practice of the food processing industry. A trace of sugar will allow cutting down the amount of salt used, and the over-all flavor level will be raised. Bearing in mind that taste perception varies with temperature, it should be understood that more sugar may be required for low temperatures and less for higher temperature consumption. In the addition of sugar to sour, as in saline, combinations, correction of the sweet-sour-saline balance will be necessary. Addition of more of one may require addition of the others.

Sugar Compounds

Only recently has one such compound appeared on any widely marketed scale: sugar and cinnamon. The idea is ancient, what the English call "caster" sugar refers to what we now call confectioner's sugar (about 175-mesh) that can be shaken from a caster, the English term for what looks like an oversized salt shaker. The early American term for the pewter and silver shakers was "muffineer."

Many different kinds of herb and spice matter were and still are combined with pulverized sugar for hand sprinkling. Many kinds of pulverized sweet herbs and spices can be combined and shaken from a caster. Sugar compounds are one kind of sprinkle-seasoning; one phase of the infinitely wide range of seasoning that, as powders or meals, can be showered on top of foods. It is a field that has been barely developed, and will in the near future be expanded primarily because of our inclination toward outdoor open-fire cookery.

Commercially available are Griffith "Basilroyal" and "Sageroyal," "Gingeroyal" and "Pepperoyal," etc., Stange "Peppercreme," etc.[2]; a wide range of herb and spice extractives on dextrose or salt carriers. Such compounds may provide the handiest spice additives in everyday cookery; they are particularly amenable to seasoning accuracy.

The variability of herb and spice composition with salt and sugar is infinite: varying from say much sugar and a little mustard to much mustard and a little sugar. Incidentally, the combination of sugar and/or salt with herbs and spices as seasoning compounds is ancient.

Honey (125)

Honey is really a syrup, a concentrated solution of sugar with floral esters, which latter account for its higher flavor rating than refined sugar. Obviously, wild sage honey will flavor rate higher than orange blossom honey. Most honey is the product of the bee's metabolic conversion of floral nectars plus comb curing.

MEAT BASES

Chicken Base (180)

Meat Extract (250)

Within the past few years a group of flavor substances have been evolved which are commercially called "flavor bases": chicken base, beef base, etc. Primarily they are intended for flavoring broths and soups, sauces, and stocks, starting with products like Leibig's beef extract and "bouillon cubes"; the latter is composed of cereal products (as the dry carrier) and liquid extract. Most of the prototype meat bases were either liquid essences or compounds of cereals and essences or extracts.

The new meat bases are compounds of fats and meat essences and seasoning additives which are marketed in cubes, small to medium jars and small to large cans. Within the very few years in which the new fat-base meat flavor compounds have been marketed, they have become one of the mainstays of restaurant food production They are certainly among the best and easiest to use convenience foods.

FRUIT FLAVOR SUBSTANCES

Fruit Flavors (290)

Beverage Bases (350)

Fruit Extracts (400)

Essential Oils (700)

(Refer to the Dry Botanicals Chart in the Appendix to this volume.)

Until the turn of the century, essences of fruit and what may be described as botanical compounds were the simple products of cookery, infusion, or brewing, and comparatively simple distillation. Today, such products may be listed in two groups: (1) domestic or non-industrialized fruit bases, such as syrups and flavor compounds and some kinds of preserves; (2) commercial production of simple and compound fruit essences, extracts and flavors.

While the flavor industry started with the introduction of essences and extracts for beverage purposes it has expanded to the production of flavoring matter for virtually all foods.

Production of *Wine Concentrates* is one of the newer developments of the beverage industry, the evolution of which is along the lines of the production of fruit juice concentrates which aim at removal of water (and sometimes of alcohol) and return of the aromatics to the finished product. Now being made are concentrates of burgundy, sauterne, sherry, and port. Where wine is to be used for flavoring (as well as a fluid carrier) natural wine is preferable. But if fluid dilution is to be minimized, then wine concentrates are an option instead of wine extracts or wine "flavors."

Smoke Bases (425)

Smoke bases are available in two forms:

(1) Where smoke concentrate is combined with granular salt, of which there are several kinds. Some are "straight," like hickory smoke and salt, and others are "seasoned" smoke and salt.

(2) The other form is liquid smoke extract, which is also available both as a simple and a seasoned smoke extract. Incidentally, one of the common Chinese do-it-yourself seasonings is ground pepper dry-roasted in a frying pan with salt, yielding a smoky pepper-salt that is particularly agreeable.

Black Pepper (450)

While individual peppers are covered in Column 18, it is pointed out that commercial pepper is available in different conditions and forms, not only the standard grinds but as extracts and compounded with other seasonings. Those peppers range in flavor levels from around 50 for the several kinds of paprikas to essential pepper oils the flavor levels of which would center around 700.

Citric Acid (500)

Citric acid is one of several acids widely used in the food packing industry as a sour component in achieving a sweet-sour balance. Ascorbic acid may be next in popularity. Both are easy to use in everyday cookery.

Asafoetida (550)

The gum of various Asiatic plants of the genus *Ferula* with an offensive alliaceous (between onion and garlic) odor; it is one of the oldest base flavoring substances of Asia, the Near East, and southern Europe. Fortunately the disagreeable esters evaporate in cookery. The smell is volatile but the taste is durable. If trials are made with minute amounts it may be favored as one of the best seasonings. If it weren't for its revolting odor it would be in more nearly common usage.

Vinegar (600)

The sourness of vinegar comes from acetic acid, which is not ordinarily used in pure form in made dishes. Commercial vinegar contains from 5 to 8 per cent acetic acid. The flavor rating of vinegar at 600 is based on five per cent acetic acid in distilled white vinegar, where it contributes only simple sourness. Grain vinegars such as malt vinegar, and fruit vinegars such as apple, pear, and wine vinegars, contribute fruit and floral flavor components in addition to simple sourness and they accordingly flavor rate higher.

Cinchona (800)

Cinchona (*Rubiaceae; Cinchona ledgeriana,* yellow cinchona; *C. rubra,* red cinchoma) is listed to provide a single and probably what is most nearly commonly used bitter substance (quinine) in commercial beverage formulation. Here note that two of the dry herbs in Column 17, hops and rue, are primarily used for their bitter components. Quinine is most frequently used in panel flavor determinations for sensitivity to bitterness. Two or three parts per million of quinine in an aqueous solution is about the threshold of average bitterness perception.

Cayenne (850)

Cayenne and red pepper are commonly thought of as being synonymous, but the fact is that red pepper is commercially produced in pungencies rating from paprika lows of around 50 to highs of over 800, but the latter only when they have cayenne components. Cayenne *per se* generally applies to the hottest of the capsicum peppers. Here is an instance where cayenne liquid extracts are more reliable than pulverized cayenne pepper. The extract lends itself to dilution as a seasoning, but a minute flake of cayenne pepper may be traumatic on the tongue, hot enough to actually hurt.

CHAPTER 23

Dried Fruits and Nuts

COLUMN 22

Dried Fruits and Nuts Compared

These are in the chart in Column 22 as a group of foods that fit into a natural order. While all nuts and seeds are fruits, all fruits are not nuts; but in common both nuts and dehydrated fruits are dried fruits. While most fruits are commonly used while they are immature or just short of maturity, nuts, with few exceptions, are used after they mature.

Another factor common to both dried fruits and nuts is that of time or period of processing or time-maturity equilibrium. In the processes of dehydration, the starches in fruits are converted to sugars, and the acids and tannins in both fruits and nuts are chemically submerged or altered to where, under proper conditions and over the required time, those components of taste are more or less in equilibrium and are at a stage where the overall flavor is agreeable. For example, some prune-plums are distinctly sour when first split and exposed to a dehydration process, which sourness largely disappears in the process of drying. Most nuts are definitely bitter when harvested, but lose much of their bitterness over varying periods of storage. Many nuts are milky when harvested but that milk gradually stabilizes and firms as the nut matures in storage.

Dried Fruits

For dried fruits, most fruits are gathered when they are fully mature and then heat processed; while some fruits like plums and grapes, by either a natural or manufactured step, become what are termed "prunes" and "raisins."

As ordinarily marketed the dried fruits are (1) naturally sun dried in which condition they are usually lowest in moisture and may not be particularly agreeable in appearance; (2) industrially dehydrated, frequently sulfured (to avoid severe discoloration); (3) partially dehydrated and paper, plastic, or otherwise packaged to retain moisture and avoid contamination.

Glacéed or candied dried fruits are classified as confections in Column 24, discussed in Volume II.

In the United States most dried fruits are commercially dehydrated. They are subjected to a number of preliminary steps according to the varieties, grades, and conditions of the fruits.

The first step is to remove the spoiled or infested fruits; then, cleaning and grading; only after this are the fruits dehydrated under controlled conditions. After dehydration, the fruits are again graded and packed in bulk or for the consumer.

The term "dry" applied to fruits can be a misleading word. Practically none of the dried fruits is dry—dry in the technical sense of under one per cent moisture. Production of dried fruit with under one percent moisture necessitates the reduction of the fruit to a purée, and then dehydrating it in a vacuum; and packing in practically air-tight containers under special conditions.

In the past the only dried fruits that were marketed were those that had sufficient sugar and acid to shrivel and dry at atmosphere without spoiling. Most natural fruits have more than 85 per cent moisture. In the not so distant past, only those fruits were dried which in the round, or when halved, or portioned, would sun dry to not more than about 25 per cent moisture and at that moisture content have sufficient sugars and acids to "keep."

Naturally dried prunes and raisins average between 20 per cent and 25 per cent moisture. They may naturally lose their water of constitution through the skin, but they are never naturally anhydrous—completely free of water. Further, the are seldom uniformly dry.

Recent commercial developments have resulted in production of dried fruits of kinds and varieties unknown and not practicably possible in the past. The modern packing of dried fruits has resulted, not only in substantial upgrading, but introduction of many kinds of fruits in dehydrated form. New techniques have yielded what amounts to new dried fruit products by new packaging methods. Many of the newer forms of dried fruits are, in the processes of production, preconditioned ahead of dehydration by blanching or humidifying; and the final product may be coated or gas packed to retain some moisture and avoid contamination.

The alteration of flavor from what is inherent in the different fruits to the end result of all dried fruits is due to two phases involved in the processes of dehydration. They are: *Physical* and *Chemical.*

Physical.—The physical phase is primarily concerned with heat exchange, which may be simple drying or controlled-atmosphere dehydration; and, of course, time and length of dehydration. Also what is involved in the packaging techniques is within the physical phases.

Chemical.—The chemical phase starts with alteration of the carbohydrates, primarily the starches, to sugar; the acids and the bitter components. Equally important are the phenomena of fermentation. Consequently, a dried prune only remotely resembles the flavor of the tree-ripe plum; and the flavor of a raisin is different from the natural grape.

They have not only been physically changed, they have been chemically altered.

Nuts

A nut is a fruit which consists of a hard or leathery shell enclosing an edible kernel; also some nut-like seeds, such as the seeds in a pine cone, pumpkin seeds, peanuts and lotus seeds.

Perhaps no single class of food can be so visually deceptive as nuts. As a rule the appearance of the shell is no index of the quality of the kernel.

No kind of nut has any shell aroma in its dehydrated mature condition, so the sense of smell cannot serve in selecting nuts. A squirrel will not even pick up a bad nut; it needs only to sniff the nut to know it is bad. But a squirrel's smell receptors are far more acute than those of man.

Normal color and form of a nut's shell provides no index of the qualities of a nut's kernel.

In very few classes of food is so little discrimination used by average people as when they buy nuts. They almost invariably purchase by "kind," by appearance of the shell. Only in a few nuts, like almonds and pecans (and rarely, walnuts) is a distinction made between hard shells and paper shells.

Like all other fruits, the quality of nut kernels and seed meats will vary substantially between individual varieties and sub-varieties; in growing conditions, which may vary from year to year. Nuts from a single tree may be good one year and not so good another year. According to variety and growing conditions, nut meats will vary in how they fill the shell.

What will come as a surprise to most people is how many different sub-varieties or strains there are. While many of those strain differences are perceptible by the appearance of the shell, only cracking a number of nuts in the same lot and appraising the quality of the kernels can demonstrate the eating qualities of the nut.

Only persistent vigilance while eating nuts can avoid the occasional rancid kernel with which all nuts seem to be plagued. Nut meats should not be eaten in the dark. One can get hold of shriveled nut meats, and particularly infested or chemically decomposed nut meats; and it takes only one such experience to shy the participant away from nuts for a long time. Without exception anyone would be revolted by unexpectedly biting into a live crawling or wriggling thing.

Usage of Nuts.—Pecans, while perhaps known by most people for use in pralines and bakery goods and in candies such as chocolates, have wide application in a chopped condition sprinkled over green leaf and fruit salads. The same applies to walnuts: most people eat walnuts out-of-hand or they eat them in candy but only a knowing cook chops nuts and includes them in salads or in sandwiches; particularly where the composition is soft the nut provides a kinesthetic factor.

Many items in the Dried Fruits and Nuts classification, Column 22, are options for kinesthetic effects: with fluid foods like some of the soups, chowders, or stews, or with the more substantial animal and vegetable foods, such as roasts and the salads for the desirable factor of crunch and kinesthetic variation. The nuts may be added for crunch and the dried fruits for a chewing component.

The three last classifications of the Gustametric Chart are the "Supplements" which cover ordinary usage. While many of the foods are used for out-of-hand eating or accompanying a food service, it is particularly emphasized that many foods in the three groups should be considered as components of made dishes.

Sesame (25)

See Column 18, FN 25.

Macadamia Nut (30)

Vernacular names are "Queensland nut," and "Australian hazelnut."

The macadamia (*Macadamia turnifolia*) is an Australian emigré to the Hawaiian Islands where it is now being propagated on a large scale. The kernel of the nut is round, creamy white in color, tender in texture and in flavor can be compared to a delicate filbert.

Lotus Seed (35)

Vernacular names for American lotus (*Nelumba nucifera*) seeds are "water chinquapin," "water nut," and "rattle nut."

It is one of the prized nut-like seeds in the Near East, Asia, and the Orient, where it is particularly favored for inclusion in animal and vegetable dishes and in confections.

Raw lotus seed is rarely commercially available in its natural condition in the United States, but canned or dried (from the Orient) it is occasionally stocked by food specialty or "gourmet" shops.

Dried cracked lotus seed can be rehydrated by blanching (like dried chestnuts). Repeated change of water will carry off most of the tannin in the paper-thin skins, but scraping them is laborious. When properly rehydrated they have good texture but most of the delicate flavor is lost. In their best condition they are slightly firmer but less delicate in flavor than macadamia nuts.

Coconut (38)

Coconut is the friut of the coconut palm which in North America and in Europe is generally thought of as a "nut." In the United States the nut-like meat is largely marketed in shredded, chipped, or ground conditions. In the areas where they flourish, coconut meat, cream and "milk" are commonly used as components of animal and vegetable dishes as well as in bakery and confectionary.

Liquefying shredded, scraped or chunked dry, or raw coconut in a blender is recommendable not only for curry compounds but many sauce compositions. It has more applications in cookery than any other nut-like fruit. (See Coconut Milk in Column 14, FN 13.)

Peanut (Raw) (40)

Some vernacular names are "groundnut," "pinder groundnut," "monkey nut" (Bailey 1943); also "goober" and "goober pea."

While popularly called a "nut" it is really a *pod,* the plant of which is related to beans and peas. The two common varieties are the small, round Spanish peanut (*Arachis hypogaea*) and the oblong Virginia peanut. While commonly used for out-of-hand eating and in confectionery, it should be appreciated for its application to cookery. In the condition of butter it is widely used abroad as a component of brown sauces.

Raw peanuts, free of the paper skin should be more widely used as components in the *cookery* of vegetables, not only for their flavor but for their contribution of agreeable kinesthetic values. For Levantine dishes (e.g. rice or wheat pilaf with pine nuts) chopped peanuts may be an acceptable substitute for pine nuts.

Pistachio (42)

The pistachio seed (*Pistacia vera*) is one of the very few greenish "nuts"; its color is called "pistachio green." In the United States it is used almost exclusively as a nut but in Europe it is favored for pistachio paste, both for its agreeable color and its delicate pistachio flavor. In the countries of origin (largely southern Europe and Asia Minor) it is most frequently used in praline-like confections.

Almond (Sweet) (44)

Simon (1956) lists five common varieties of almonds (*Prunus amygdalus,* var. *dulcis*) but in American markets they are labeled "hard shell' or "soft (paper) shell." It may be the most popular nut for both out-of-hand eating and cookery, bakery, and confectionery. In the immature form with undeveloped vestigial kernel and fairly soft but firm fruit pulp, it is occasionally glacéed. (See Bitter Almond, FN 270 this Column.)

Chestnut (48)

There are several species of European and Asiatic chestnut. *Castanea dentata* is the wild American chestnut which is said to be richer in quality than any foreign kind, but the size is less than half that of the introduced nuts. A superior (and larger) seedling variation is Rochester. The old world chestnut is *C. sativa.* The Japanese species of chestnuts are relatively small; the nuts ranging in size from small to larger than the old world chestnuts. In quality, the Japanese chestnut meats are not so high in sweetness or nuttiness as the European and American kinds. Incidentally, horse chestnuts (*Aesculus hippocastanum*) are inedible.

Chinquapin, *C. pumila* (Bailey 1943) is a native chestnut of good quality, the smallest of the chestnut family in the size of both nut and tree, which usually is more of a bush than a tree. The nuts are only occasionally available in local markets.

Next to the coconut, the chestnut is the most generally used nut, particularly in Southern Europe. Both fresh and dehydrated, it is used in cookery, usually chopped but also mashed or puréed, both as a starch and for its agreeable kinesthetic values. In bakery and confectionery (French *marrons glacés*) its use is secondary. In American markets, chestnuts are generally available dried.

They readily rehydrate. Trial of chestnuts, particularly in cookery, should demonstrate usability in many kinds of cookery.

Brazil Nut (50)

Some vernacular names are "butternut," "nigger-toe," "cream nut," and "pear nut" (Bailey 1943).

Qualitatively Brazil nuts (*Bertholletia incisa* or *Treculia africana*) are one of the most unstable of all nuts; their shelf life is comparatively short, and even among new shipments they are highly variable. They seem to become rancid quickly regardless of how they are packed or stored.

Pear (55)

See Column 10, FN 45 for main discussion.

Cashew (62)

Ordinarily eaten out-of-hand, the cashew nut (*Anacardium occidentale*) is adaptable to many kinds of cookery, bakery, and confectionery. It is occasionally available in paste or butter form in cans or jars, in which condition it looks like pale peanut butter but retains its peculiar delicate cashew flavor.

Carob (66)

The large bean-like pod of the carob tree (*Ceratonia siliqua*) is colloquially called St. John's bread. If used shortly after harvesting when the pods are not too dry they are rather agreeable eaten out-of-hand but when long stored they become brittle and woody; they lose some of their sweetness and light acidity. Kibbled or ground (freed from the hard seeds) carob is extensively used abroad as a substitute for coffee and cocoa. In domestic and commercial bakery and pastry production, fine or coarsely milled carob is used not only for its intrinsic flavor qualities but as a filler, for its spongelike body. (Refer to Dry Botanicals Chart.)

Filbert (70)

The prototypes of filbert nuts (*Corylus*) were oblong in shape, but some of those now being commercially propagated in the Pacific Northwest are nearly round, like their smaller wild relations, the hazel nuts. They are almost exclusively used for out-of-hand eating.

Peach (73)

See Column 10, FN 64 for main discussion.

Apricot (78)

See Column 10, FN 65 for main discussion.

Hickory Nut (82)

There are about 18 species of hickory (*Juglandacea carya*) in eastern North America, with globular to oblong fruits, the nuts of which are hard-shelled and four-celled.

Vernacular names are nutmeg hickory, water hickory, swamp hickory, pig nut, shagbark, mocker nut, king nut, shellbark, etc.

Fig (84)

Imported dried figs (*Ficus carica*) are almost exclusively of the Smyrna variety and come from Turkey and Greece, either pressed or on strings. American production of dried figs are primarily of the Calimyrna variety, loose, pressed, and paste. The marketing of several varieties of brown and black figs is secondary. It should be noted that the flavors of dried figs are quite different from fresh or partially dehydrated figs. Fresh figs are very low in acid and high in flavors peculiar to the different varieties of figs, but in different states of dryness, the sour and bitter notes noticeably rise. (See Fresh Fig, FN 62, Column 10).

Prune (86)

Not so long ago, only one variety of plum (*Prunus domestica*) the so-called French purple prune, a small variety, was marketed. By hybridizing, several purple and "white" varieties were developed, which are now available in different packs. Both the large purple and white varieties are superior to the prototypes. (See Plum Fruits, Table 6 in Column 10, FN 72.)

Pecan (90)

The pecan (*Carya pecan,* Engler and Graeb; *Carya olivaeformis,* Nutt.; *Hicoria pecan,* Brit.) is probably the most popular *native* nut. While there are many varieties and sub-varieties, hybrids and strains, they may be roughly classified as either hard-shell or soft- (or paper-) shell; small, medium, or large, and round to oblong. The qualities of the nut meats vary not only with different varieties of nuts but according to growing conditions during specific seasons and the conditions under which the nuts are harvested, stored, and held from the time of harvest to the time of consumption.

The character of the paper skin that envelops pecan meats seems to be more variable than that of any other nut, not only between varieties but according to growing conditions in different areas at different times. In most name brand offerings of pecans the nuts are fairly uniform in superficial factors. The nut meats may average the same degree of plumpness, moisture, and flavor; which are the effects of maintenance of quality control by the industry, but as with other nuts, occasional shriveled or spoiled nut meats seem to be unavoidable.

Pine nut (92)

Other American vernacular names are "Indian nut," "piñon," "Pignolia."

The nut-like seeds of many different pine varieties (species of *Pinus*), are used as food, but what are marketed as pine nuts are the large-seed varieties. Most market offerings are imports from southern Europe, with a relatively small quantity coming from our southwestern states and Mexico. Historically pine nuts have been one of the preferred nut-meat components of Levantine *pilafs* and other made dishes. Because of its quite delicate pine flavor it can be an agreeable component of many barbecue dishes, particularly where an element of smokiness can be introduced. Introduction of crushed fresh or dried pine needle in other kinds of chopped, crushed, or mulled nuts could with care effect an imitation pine nut flavor. Only some of the larger squash and seeds have texture characters somewhat comparable to pine nuts.

Walnut (English) (96)

The commonly marketed white walnut (*Juglans regia*) also called "English walnut," is of Persian origin. The qualities of walnuts are highly variable, differing between varieties and particularly growing conditions, and most important the time elapsing between harvesting and consumption. They range in form from round to slightly elongated, small to very large, and medium light to hard shell. Commercially graded fresh nuts are usually good if consumed within a few months of harvesting, but in time they deteriorate. Halves or broken nut meats and chopped nuts rapidly become rancid. The nut meats being high in oil, they rapidly oxidize on exposure to atmosphere. (See Black Walnut, FN 135 this Column.)

Currant (Dried) (98)

The dried currants of commerce are grapes (*Vitis vinifera,* variety *Black Corinth*), not *Ribes.* (See Currant, Column 10, FN 74.)

"The fruit of this variety of grape is entirely seedless and the berries remain very small. Their size is owing to the fact that they set by the stimulative parthenocarpy. This type of set also accounts for the seedlessness. This is an old variety which has been grown in Greece for centuries. Greece is still the principal country for the production of this type of dried grape. California produces about 3000 tons annually of the variety called Zante currants."[1]

Dried currants were favored in bakery and made dishes because they were seedless; but today unless very small berries are desired, seedless Thompson grapes have points of superiority.

Date (100)

Until comparatively recently the most commonly marketed variety was *Deglet Noor* (*Phoenix dactylifera,* Linnaeus), mostly pressed, some more or less loose, which was imported from the Levantine countries. Since the development of the date industry in Southern California, a number of other varieties and hybrids have become available in both natural loose, and pulp conditions. The best dates are "dead ripe" and usually available only where they are grown. In that condition they ferment rapidly, so they are not transported to any substantial extent. Dates chopped or minced make an agreeable component not only in bakery and confectionery but in salads and some cookery.

Litchi (Dried) (110)

While it is ordinarily thought of as a nut (called lichee or lichi nut [*Litchi chinensis*] in the United States, because it is marketed in a dry, somewhat nut-like condition) it is not a nut: it should rather be considered a fruit. The prune-like pulp surrounds a hard, inedible seed is enclosed in a brown colored, knobby, and brittle shell. (See Litchi, FN 68, Column 10.)

Raisin (110)

Historically, muscats produced in the Mediterranean countries (usually called "Sultanas" in the English-speaking countries) were the only commonly

[1] From a letter from Dr. A. J. Winkler, Professor of Viticulture, University of California at Davis.

marketed raisins. With the development of the raisin industry in California and the hybridization of some varieties, the American market has veered toward a preference for seedless raisins which are principally the "white" Thompson and secondarily Black Monucca (a strain of Thompson). While Americans eat raisins largely out-of-hand, European usage may be largely in cookery.

Walnut (Black) (135)

The black walnut (*Juglans nigra*) is also called the American walnut. *J. cinerea* is the butternut (Bailey 1943). Other American walnuts are *J. rupestris* and *J. regia* (Texas and South Central States), *J. californica* (Pacific States). All *native* American black walnuts have very hard shells, are internally dense, and the nut meats tightly encased. Because of their resistance to cracking and extraction of the nut meats, they are unpopular with all but the very patient; they who are willing put in a lot of work to get some of the most savory of all nut meats. Hybridization has developed some black walnuts having shells that are just as hard as those of the parent stock but thinner and more brittle and differing from the parents in having cellular dry pulp between a thin and very hard nut-meat casing and the shell. Further, some of the new hybrids have larger nut meats and it is possible to extract the meats in quarters and halves, which is almost impossible with native nuts.

Citrus Peels

Orange Peel (250)

Citron (300)

Lemon Peel (575)

The flavor ratings of the citrus peels listed in this column are based on such peels as are ordinarily marketed, which are relatively high in moisture. This is an important qualification, because when comparing the flavor ratings of some of the citrus peels in the Dry Botanicals Chart it will be seen that they are at higher flavor levels. The reason is that most of the citrus peels marketed as dry botanicals are much lower in moisture than those marketed in average food shops. Citrus peels are far more generally used in cookery in southern Asia and the Orient than in the Occident. Examination of Asiatic and Oriental cook books will reveal many specifications of different citrus peels in their made dishes. Peels of certain varieties of mandarins and oranges are favored in China where such peel, ground, is as much an ingredient of their "spice powders" as turmeric is in Indian curries.

Almond (Bitter) (270)

The bitter almond (*Prunus amygdalys*, var. *amara*), because of its relatively high content of hydrocyanic acid (HCN) is frequently used as a flavoring for beverages or in extract form for desserts, bakery, and confectionery. In extract or essence form its careful use raises the flavor level of congeneric fruit dishes such as apricots, peaches, and plums. (See Sweet Almond, FN 44 this Column.)

Tamarind (400)

The FN of 400 is based on the prune-brown pulp surrounding from 1 to 12 seeds in the brittle-shelled brown pods of tamarind fruit (*Tamarindus indica*).

The pulp tastes like prune pulp that has been soaked in concentrated lemon juice. While it is high in sweetness, it is notable for its high sourness. In the countries where it is available tamarind pulp is the favored sour-sweet additive in cookery. It is one of the favored sour components of curry compositions in India.

Tamarind pulp is considerable as an option instead of lemon and lime juice in many different highly seasoned made dishes, particularly strong stews.

Partially dehydrated tamarinds are available in food specialty shops, herb shops, and Italian and Mexican food stores.

Refer to Column 14, FN 83 for notes on Tamarind in beverages.

Bibliography for Part II

ADAMS, L. D. 1960. The Commonsense Book of Drinking. David McKay Co., Inc. New York. Column 15.

ALPERT, PHIL. 1958. Cheeses Of All Nations (A price list, copyrighted), Phil Alpert, 235 Fulton St., New York. Column 4.

AMERINE, M. A., and CRUESS, W. V. 1960. The Technology of Wine Making. Avi Publ. Co., Westport, Conn. Column 15.

AMERINE, M. A., and JOSLYN, M. A. 1951. Table Wines. The Technology of Their Production in California. Univ. of Calif. Press, Berkeley, Calif. Column 15.

ANDERSON, A. W., and POWER, E. A. 1956. Fishery Statistics of the U. S., 1954. Statistical Digest. *39*. U. S. Dept. of the Interior, Fish and Wildlife Service. Column 1.

ANON. 1958. Corn Syrups and Sugars. Corn Industries Research Foundation, Inc., Washington, D. C. Column 19.

BAILEY, L. H. 1943. The Standard Cyclopedia of Horticulture. The Macmillan Co., New York. Columns 8, 16, 17 and 18.

BAILEY, L. H., and BAILEY, E. Z. 1941. Hortus Second. The Macmillan Co., New York. Columns 7, 8, and 9.

BODENHEIMER, F. S. 1951. Insects As Human Food. Dr. W. Jun, The Hague, Netherlands.

BUCHANAN, B. F. 1954. Basic Facts about Ac'cent. International Minerals and Chemical Corp., San Jose, Calif. Column 19.

CHAPMAN, V. J. 1950. Seaweeds and Their Uses. Methuen and Co., Ltd., London. Column 1.

COFFEE BREWING INSTITUTE. 1956. A Survey of World Literature on Coffee for 1953. Publication No. 7, March, 1956, Coffee Brewing Inst., Inc., New York.

COFFEE BREWING INSTITUTE. 1956. A Survey of World Literature on Coffee for 1954. Publication No. 13, June, 1956. Coffee Brewing Inst., Inc., New York.

COFFEE BREWING INSTITUTE. 1957. A Survey of World Literature on Coffee for 1955. Publication No. 23, June, 1957. Coffee Brewing Inst., Inc., New York.

COFFEE BREWING INSTITUTE. 1957. Chemical Study of Coffee Flavor. Publication No. 26, October, 1957. Coffee Brewing Inst., Inc., New York.

COFFEE BREWING INSTITUTE. 1957. Coffee Solubles and Beverage Acceptance. Publication No. 27, November, 1957. Coffee Brewing Inst., Inc., New York.

DODGE and OLCOTT, INC. 1956. Reference Book and Catalog of Flavors and Seasonings. Dodge and Olcott, Inc., New York. Column 19.

DOVE, W. F. *et al.* 1948. Flavor and Acceptability of Monosodium Glutamate. QM. Food and Container Institute, Chicago. Column 19.

FELLERS, C. B., and ESSELEN, W. B. 1955. Cranberries and Cranberry Products. Mass. Agr. Expt. Sta. Bull. *481*. Columns 10 and 14.

FISH AND WILDLIFE SERVICE. U. S. Dept. of Interior. 1959. Fish and Seafood Parade. Commercial Fisheries Rev. *21*, No. 8. Column 1.

FITCH, J. E. 1953. Common Marine Bivalves of California. Calif. Dept. of Fish and Game. Fish Bull. *90*. Column 1.

FLOOD, W. D., and WEST, M. 1953. An Explaining and Pronouncing Dictionary of Scientific and Technical Words. Second Ed. Longmans, Green and Co., London. General.

FLOWER, B., and ROSENBAUM, E. 1958. Apicius, the Roman Cookery Book. George G. Harrap and Co., Ltd., London.

FOOD, DRUG AND COSMETIC ADMINISTRATION. U. S. Dept. of Health, Education and Welfare. Definitions and Standards under the Federal Food, Drug and Cosmetic Act.

1952. Bakery Products. No. 2, Part 17.
1952. Cheeses and Cheese Products. No. 2, Part 19.
1952. Canned Fruit. No. 2, Part 27.
1953. Wheat and Corn Flour and Related Products. No. 2, Part 15.
1954. Fruit Butters—Jellies—Preserves. No. 2, Part 29.
1955. Oleomargarine and Margarine. No. 2, Part 45.
1956. Canned Vegetables and Vegetable Products. No. 2, Parts 51 and 53.
1957. Dressings for Foods: Mayonnaise, French Dressing, and Salad Dressing. No. 2, Part 25.
1958. Chocolate and Cocoa Products. No. 2, Part 14.
1958. Eggs and Egg Products. No. 2, Part 42.
1958. Macaroni and Noodle Products. Part 16.
1958. Milk and Cream. Part 18.
1958. Shellfish. No. 2, Part 36. General.

FOOTE, F. N. 1925. Coffee, The Beverage. The Spice Mill Publishing Co., New York. Column 14.

FOSTER, E. M., NELSON, F. E., SPECK, M. L., DOETSCH, R. N., and OLSON, J. C., JR. 1957. Dairy Microbiology. Prentice-Hall, Englewood Cliffs, N. J. Column 4.

GARDNER, D. G. 1958. Water Composition and Coffee Brewing. Publ. No. 31, Mar. 1958. The Coffee Brewing Institute, Inc., New York. Column 14.

GILL, THEODORE. 1888. Apodes. Riverside Natural History. Vol. III, pp. 100–108. Houghton Mifflin and Co., New York. Column 1.

GROSSMAN, H. J. 1943. Grossman's Guide to Wines, Spirits, and Beers. Charles Scribner's Sons, New York. Column 15.

HALL, SIR A. D., and CRANE, M. B. 1933. The Apple. Martin Hopkinson, Ltd., London. Column 10.

HALSTEAD, B. W. 1959. Dangerous Marine Animals. Cornell Maritime Press. Cambridge, Md. Column 1.

HAMBIDGE, GOVE. 1938. Soils and Men. U.S. Dept. of Agr. Yearbook of Agriculture.

HARRIS, R. S., and VON LOESECKE, H. W. 1960. Nutritional Evaluation of Food Processing. John Wiley and Sons, Inc., New York. Column 7.

HOPKINS, A. A. 1953. The Standard American Encyclopedia of Formulas. Grosset and Dunlap, New York. Columns 14 and 15.

JACOB, H. E. 1935. The Saga of Coffee. George Allen and Unwin Ltd., London. Column 14.

JARRATT, VERNON. 1956. Parmesan. Wine and Food *90,* 87–92. Column 4.

JORDAN, D. S. 1923. A classification of fishes, including families and genera as far as known. Stanford Univ. Publ. Univ. Ser. Biol. Sci. 3, *2,* 79–243. Column 1.

JORDAN, D. S., and EVERMANN, B. W. 1937. American Food and Game Fishes. Doubleday, Page and Co., New York. Column 1.

JUSTIN, M. M., RUST, L. O., and VAIL, G. E. 1948. (Blood, A. F., Editor.) Foods. Houghton Mifflin Co., Boston.

KAKUZO, OKAKURA. 1926. The Book of Tea. Dodd, Mead and Co., New York. Column 14.

KASMIRE, R. F., BRENDLER, R. A., and GILLOU, RENE. 1960. Field heat removed rapidly by forced-air cooling of vine-ripe tomatoes. California Agriculture, *14,* No. 9, 10. Univ. of Calif. Div. of Agr. Sci. Berkeley, Calif. Column 10.

KIRKLAND, JOHN. 1927. The Bakers' A B C. The Gresham Publishing Co., Ltd. London. Column 5.

KLEINFELD, V. A., and DUNN, C. W. 1949. Federal Food, Drug and Cosmetic Act. 1938–1949. Food Law Institute Series. Commerce Clearing House, New York.

LIPPERT, L. F. 1960. Seedless Watermelons in Southern California. Calif. Agriculture. Vol. *14,* No. 9, 14. Column 10

LOCKHART, E. E. 1957. Chemistry of Coffee. The Coffee Brewing Institute, Inc., Publication No. 25, Sept. 1957, New York. Column 14.

LOCKHART, E. E. 1957. The Soluble Solids in Beverage Coffee as an Index to Cup Quality. Publication No. 27, Nov. 1957. The Coffee Brewing Institute, Inc., New York. Column 14.

LOCKHART, E. E. 1958. The Analysis of Coffee Grinds. Publication No. 32, April 1958. The Coffee Brewing Institute, Inc., New York. Column 14.

LOCKHART, E. E., TUCKER, C. L., and MERRITT, M. C. 1956. The effect of water impurities on the flavor of brewed coffee. Reprinted from Food Research *20,* 6, 598–605, 1955. Column 14.

VON LOESECKE, H. W. 1943. Drying and Dehydration of Foods. Reinhold Publ. Corp., New York. Column 22.

VON LOESECKE, H. W. 1949. Outlines of Food Technology. Reinhold Publ. Corp., New York.

LOEWENFELD, C. 1956. Britain's Wild Larder: Fungi. Faber and Faber, London. Columns 16, 17, and 18.

LOWE, BELLE. 1955. Experimental Cookery. John Wiley and Sons, Inc., New York.

MARKETING SERVICE, U. S. DEPT. OF AGR. 1956. U. S. Standards for Grades of Frozen Fried Fish Sticks. Washington, D. C. Column 1.

MARSDEN, S. J. 1953. Turkey Raising. U. S. Dept. of Agr. Farmers Bull. *1409.* Column 3.

MILLER, F. J. 1960. The Solubility of Carbon Dioxide in Wine. Wines and Vines, 26.

MORGAN, A. F., and HALL, I. S. 1938. Experimental Food Study. Farrar and Rinehart, Inc., New York. General.

Niven, W. W., Jr., and Shaw, B. C. 1957. Critical conditions for quantity brewing. The Coffee Brewing Inst., Inc., *19*, Apr. 1957. Reprinted from Coffee and Tea Ind., *80*, 4, 44, 75, 76, 78, Apr. 1957, Tea and Coffee Trade J. *112*, 4, 28, 30, 32, 34–35. Column 14.

Repplier, Agnes. 1933. To Think of Tea! Jonathan Cape, London and Toronto. Column 14.

Ricketts, E. F., and Calvin, J. 1952. Between Pacific Tides. Third Ed. Stanford University Press. Palo Alto, Calif. Column 1.

Roedel, P. M., 1953. Common Ocean Fishes of the California Coast. Calif. Dept. of Fish and Game. Fish Bull. *91*. Column 1.

Sanders, G. P. 1953. Cheese Varieties and Descriptions. U. S. Dept. Agr. Handbook *54*. Column 4.

Schrock, E. M. 1950. Quality Control and Statistical Methods. Reinhold Publ. Corp., New York.

Simon, A. L. 1949. A Dictionary of Gastronomy. Farrar, Strauss and Co., New York. Columns 1, 14.

Simon, A. L. 1956. Cheeses of the World. Faber and Faber, London. Column 4.

Simon, A. L. 1956. Guide to Good Food and Wines. Collins, London.

Smock, R. M., and Neubert, A. M. 1950. Apples and Apple Products. Interscience Publ., Inc., New York. Column 10.

Squire, John. 1937. Cheddar Gorge. Collins, London. Column 4.

Stefferud, A. (Editor). 1950–1951. Crops in Peace and War. U. S. Dept. of Agr. Yearbook of Agriculture.

Stefferud, A. (Editor). 1959. Food. U. S. Dept. of Agr. Yearbook of Agriculture.

Sutherland, E. P., and Nelson, P. M. 1953. Food Preparation, Principles and Procedures. Wm. C. Brown Co., Dubuque, Iowa.

Thurber, F. B. 1886. Coffee: From Plantation to Cup. American Grocer Publ. Assoc., New York. Column 14.

Tibbles, W. 1912. Foods, Their Origin, Composition and Manufacture. Brailliere, Tindall and Cox, London.

Tiedjens, V. A. 1943. The Vegetable Encyclopedia and Gardener's Guide. The New Home Library, New York. Column 5.

Tressler, D. K., and Joslyn, M. A. 1954. Chemistry and Technology of Fruit and Vegetable Juice Production. Avi Publ. Co., Inc., Westport, Conn. Column 14.

Tressler, D. K., and Evers, C. F. 1957. The Freezing Preservation of Foods. The Avi Publ. Co., Inc., Westport, Conn.

Tressler, D. K., and Lemon, J. McW. 1951. Marine Products of Commerce. Reinhold Publ. Corp., New York. Column 1.

Verrill, A. H., and Barrett, O. W. 1950. Foods America Gave the World. L. C. Page and Co., Boston. Column 10.

von Loesecke (*see Loesecke*)

Walker, W. 1957. All the Plants of the Bible. Harper and Brothers, New York. Columns 16, 17, and 18.

Walter, E. 1933. Manual for the Essence Industry. John Wiley and Sons, New York. Column 19.

Ward Artemas. 1941. The Encyclopedia of Food. Peter Smith, New York.

WATT, B. K., and MERRILL, A. L. 1950. Composition of Foods—Raw, Processed, Prepared. U. S. Dept. of Agr. Handbook *8*. Column 4.

WEATHERWAX, P. 1942. Plant Biology. W. B. Saunders Co., Philadelphia.

WEBBER, H. J., and BATCHELOR, L. D. 1943–48. The Citrus Industry. University of California Press, Berkeley, Calif. Column 10.

WESTERN CONDENSING Co. 1956. Lactose, U.S.P., and its use in the pharmaceutical industry. Bull. *L-2*. Western Condensing Co., Appleton, Wis.

WHITE, F. 1930. Flowers as Food. Jonathan Cape, London, Eng. Columns 16, 17, and 18.

WICKSON, E. J. 1923. The California Vegetables in Garden and Field. Pacific Rural Press, San Francisco. Column 6.

WILLIAMS, L. O. 1960. Drug and Condiment Plants. U. S. Dept. Agr. Handbook *172*. Column 5.

YOUNGKEN, H. W. 1951. Pharmacognosy. J. B. Lippincott Co., Philadelphia, Pa. Columns 16, 17, and 18.

ZIM, H. S., and INGLE, L. 1955. Seashores: A Guide to Animals and Plants along the Beaches. Golden Press, Inc., New York. Column 1.

ZIM, H. S., and SHOEMAKER, H. H. 1956. Fishes: A Guide to Fresh- and Salt-Water Species. Golden Press, Inc., New York. Column 1.

Appendices

Aquatic Foods

The different fresh and sea water foods are listed according to their technical orders and flavor rated according to their arbitrarily appraised flavor intensity on a logarithmic scale. Figure 33 is intended as a subdivision of Column 1 (of the Gustametric Chart) to show a few more of the many different kinds of other aquatic foods.

The Aquatic Foods Chart (Fig. 33) is provided not only to classify technically the different kinds of aquatic foods but also to show that there are many more or less common animal and vegetable foods that are truly aquatic and not terrestrial. Many of the listed animal and vegetable foods are unknown to most of us but are more or less common foods for many other peoples: they are listed here primarily for purposes of classification; secondarily to emphasize that they are aquatic rather than terrestrial.

While many aquatic foods unknown to most Americans would be acceptable when fairly well prepared, some of them, particularly waterfowl and aquatic vegetable matter, have an intrinsic flavor which may not be agreeable, and require getting used to.

Some kinds and forms of preserved fish definitely require taste education in their direction if, and it is a big *if,* such a process is desired.

Dry Botanicals for Beverages

This chart supplements Columns 14 and 15 of the Gustametric Chart. The different flavor substances are listed (a) according to their nature; (b) rated in the order of their flavor intensity on a logarithmic scale; and (c) by botanical names or vernacular terms of the beverage industry.

The chart (Fig. 34) Dry Botanicals for Beverages, is provided (a) to show and flavor rate some of the many botanicals used by the beverage industry; and (b) to suggest botanical substances, usually thought of only as components of beverages, as flavor components applicable to cookery. It is in flavored wines such as vermouth and aperitifs, liqueurs and cordials that most of the listed botanicals are used by the beverage industry. In the non-alcoholic beverages of folklore such as root beer and sarsaparilla, not only the listed botanicals are used but many others according to local availability and preferences. Here it is pointed out that the listed botanicals are those that are commercially marketed and are more or less dehydrated and sometimes in industrially processed condition. It must be obvious that there are many other botanicals used in beverages that are in a natural condition with more than 25 per cent moisture, most of which would flavor rate higher according to the chemical condition of their oils and aromatic components. For instance, fresh citrus peels and flowers will flavor rate higher and more nearly true to the nature of their aromatics than they would when dried.

Another qualification applicable to the Dry Botanicals Chart is that it does not list flavoring substances commonly known as medicinals. Nor does the Chart list botanical flavoring substances that are usually used only in cookery: most of those botanicals are listed in Columns 16, 17 and 18 of the Gustametric Chart.

In cookery many of the listed botanicals are in more or less common usage by different peoples in different parts of the world, particularly in sauces and stocks. They provide the elusive flavors encountered by tourists and by frequenters of foreign cookery restaurants which sometimes provide specialties with *secret* ingredients: examples are galangal (sometimes called wild ginger, which it isn't) in place of ginger; asafoetida for garlic or onions and canella instead of cinnamon. Many of the wild herbs, flowers and berries are frequently used for flavoring cakes and pastries.

Relative Sourness of Foods

In chemistry sourness is termed "acidity" and is proportionately expressed relative to the pH scale, which denotes both acidity and alkalinity.

Arrhenius has defined an acid as any substance which yields hydrogen ions in aqueous solution. A base (or alkali) is a material which yields hydroxyl ions. These are classical definitions and more sophisticated concepts have been developed, but for our purposes the classic definition will suffice.

Since acids yield hydrogen ions in solution, we may define acid strength (or concentration) in terms of hydrogen ion concentration. The numerical values of hydrogen ion concentration may vary tremendously. A strong acid solution may be very nearly 1, while a weak acid solution may be as low as 1×10^{-6}, a difference of 1,000,000. Because of the inconvenience of working with numbers that differ by such large amounts, Sørensen devised a method of stating hydrogen ion concentration in terms

TABLE 11
THE pH SCALE

pH		Hydrogen ion concentration in gram-ions/liter	
0		1	
1		10^{-1}	
2		10^{-2}	
3	acidity ↓	10^{-3}	
4	decrease ↓	10^{-4}	
5	↓	10^{-5}	
6		10^{-6}	
7		10^{-7}	
			pure water (neutral)
8		10^{-8}	
9		10^{-9}	
10	alkalinity ↓	10^{-10}	
11	increase ↓	10^{-11}	
12	↓	10^{-12}	
13		10^{-13}	
14		10^{-14}	

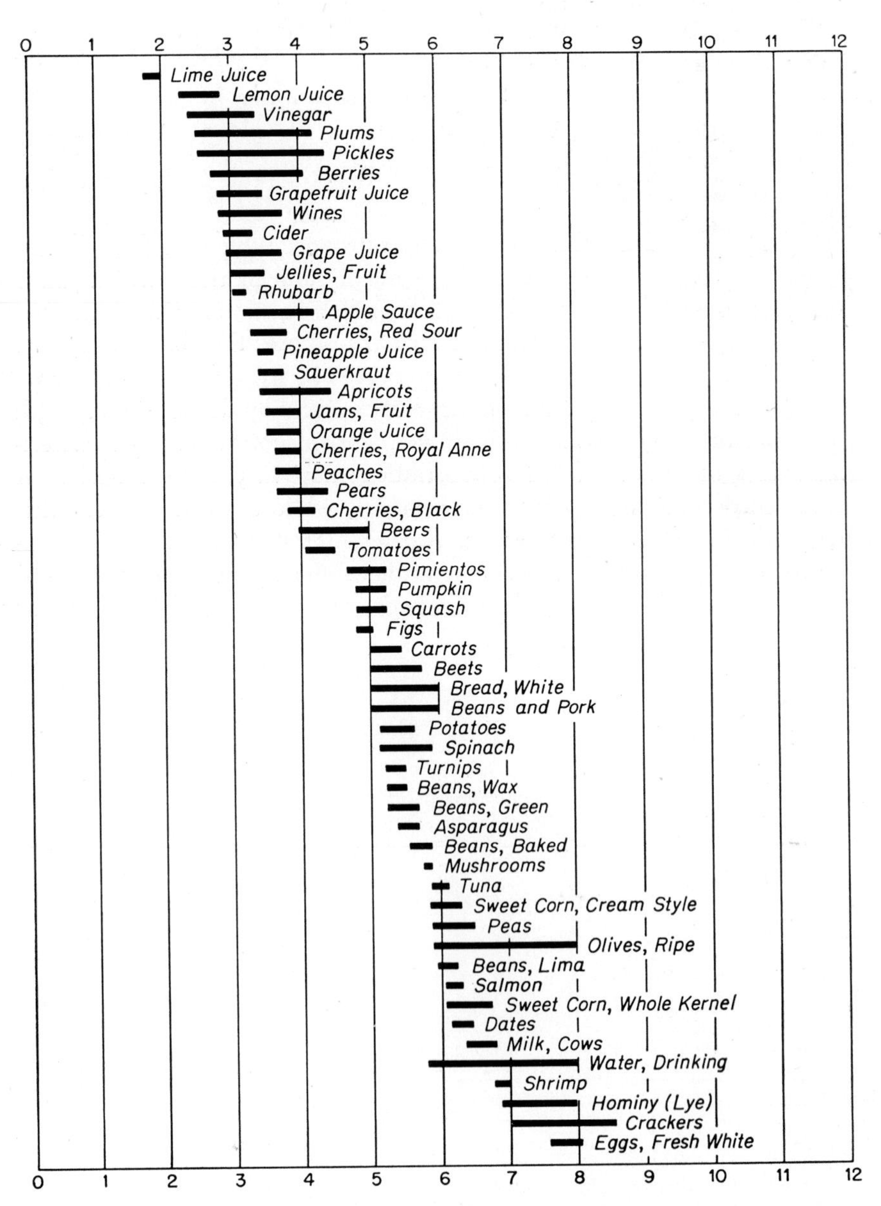

FIG. 35. RELATIVE SOURNESS OF FOODS

of the logarithm of its reciprocal. This term he called pH. Mathematically: $pH = \log 1/[H^+]$. Since the log of 1 is zero we may write: $pH = -\log[H^+]$. The relation between pH and hydrogen ion concentration can be see from Table 11.

It can be seen that as the pH increases the solution becomes less acid. Once a solution has surpassed a pH of 7 it is considered to be alkaline. It should also be noted that a decrease in pH of one unit, say from 4 to 3, represents a tenfold increase in hydrogen ion concentration. Hence, while a change of one pH unit may not seem to be very significant, it should be remembered that this represents a logarithmic change, meaning that the acid strength (or hydrogen ion concentration) is increasing exponentially.

The pH scale is usually limited to 0 through 14. Values of more than 14 or less than 0 (negative numbers) do not exist because solutions sufficiently concentrated to be in those areas would have greatly reduced ionic activity. The relative acidity of some common (mostly processed) foods is shown in Fig. 35 according to their pH ranges. Examples: the range of pH of dry wines is between 2.7 and 3.8; beers between 4.0 and 5.0.

Relative Sweetness of Wines

The normal range of the actual sugar content of different wine types and wine varieties is shown in Fig. 36. The actual sugar content of the wine is determined by chemical analysis and is reported as grams of dextrose per 100 cc. of wine. The sugar content of wines indicates the approximate relative sweetness of different wines but cannot be compared directly with the sweetness produced by the same amount of sugar in other types of foods, as sweetness is the result of the balance of the sweetness of different sugars with the other *flavor* components of a particular food.

The sweetness of a wine as determined by tasting is the effect of the sugars in relation to the other flavor variables in the wine such as acids, alcohols, esters, etc. The ratio of sugar to acid is the most significant relationship. The *sugar-acid ratio* of wine is often used as an index of the degree of balance of the flavor of the wine.

The true dry wines are made as sugar free as possible by the almost complete fermentation of the sugars present in the grape must. In the wines having an appreciable sugar content considerable variation is found within each type. Variations result from the need to balance the flavor of the particular wine as well as the interpretation of traditional type characteristics by different vintners.

In Fig. 36, the range of sweetness of typical wines is expressed as grams of dextrose per 100 cc. of wine. Particularly note the wide range of sweetness of some "dry" wines.

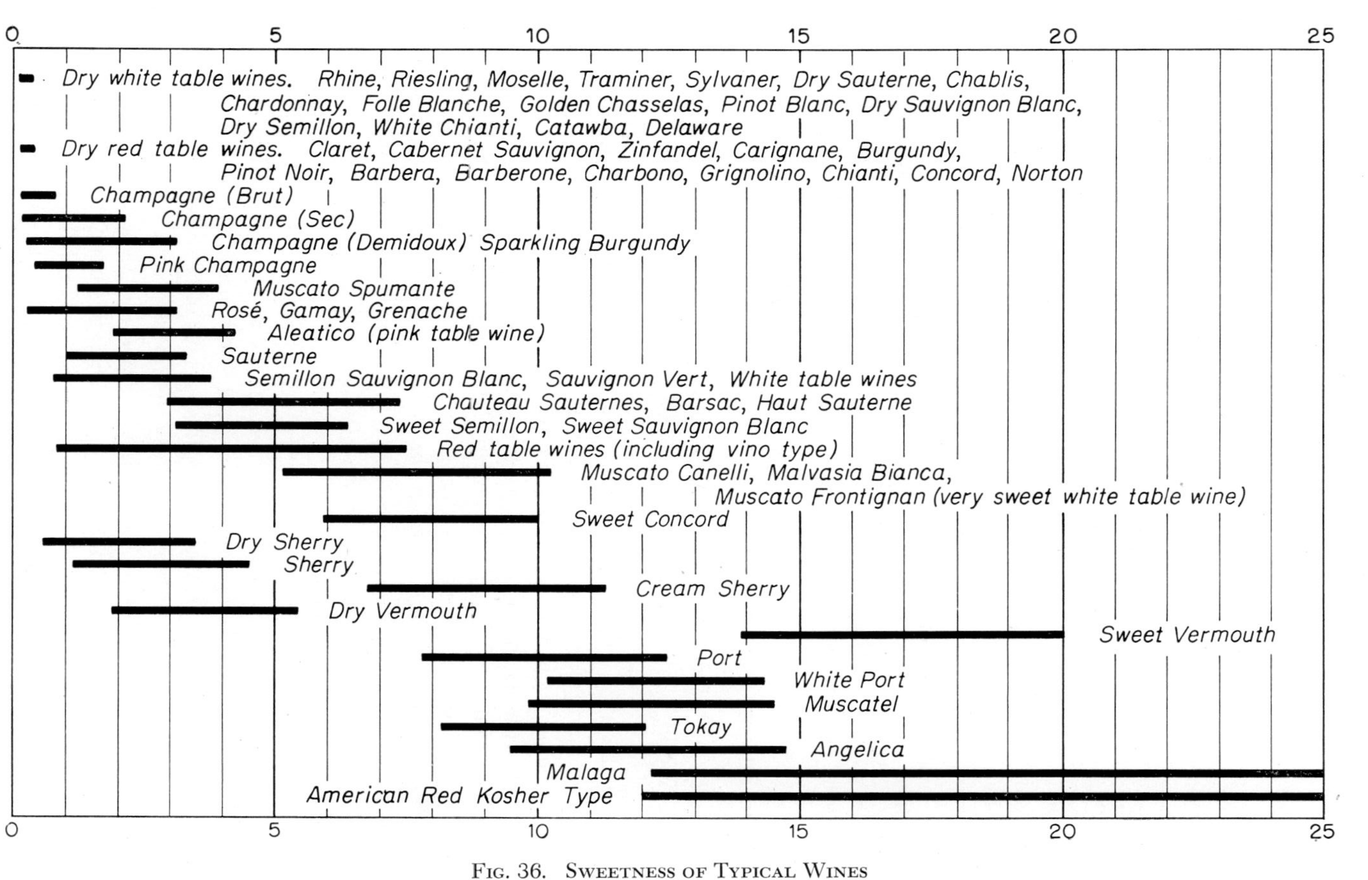

FIG. 36. SWEETNESS OF TYPICAL WINES

Sugar expressed as grams of dextrose per 100 cc. of wine.

Flavor Appraisal

RECOMMENDED PROCEDURES FOR PACKAGING FOODS TO BE COOKED FOR INTRINSIC FLAVOR APPRAISAL

To flavor-appraise raw foods is relatively easy, because most of them require little or no pre-preparation. Their intrinsic flavors are "as is," in the round, or according to their natural conditions. The flavor of cooked foods will vary with how they are cooked. Their flavors are usually diluted or dispersed in wet cookery, and not only concentrated but substantially altered in dry cookery. To process a food by either wet or dry cookery without substantially diluting or altering its flavor requires knowledge of essential techniques and careful, painstaking following of procedural steps. Sequence of initial manipulation of packaging material is required, and careful observation of subsequent operations must be followed.

First Operation: Manipulation.

With practice, manipulation of wrapping and packaging material becomes easy, but it will never be rapid, and it must never be carelessly performed. The wrapping and packaging of a food to be cooked is an extension of the ideal (which cannot be attained) of spray- or dip-coating a food in an inert plastic which would permit the food to be heat-processed without free air inclusion; but even the ideal—the plastic coated food—is subject to the defect that if in cookery the internal gas pressure rises above the tensile strength of the plastic coating, the package will explode. An example of what can happen is dropping a chestnut in hot oil: if it is left in the oil long enough to raise the temperature of the intercellular air and moisture to the point where the developed steam pressure will rupture the shell, the result can be disastrous—most of the hot oil will be blown right out of its container.

The procedures here illustrated and explained present several methods of pre-preparing foods for cookery whereby (with many qualifications) the intrinsic food and flavor values of a given food substance are retained by methods which while relatively simple and easy offer some advantages, even improvement, over ordinary cookery methods.

The envelope and packing steps may be considered a phase of bag cookery. The dry pan procedures may properly be thought of as reflection cookery, where heat exchange is effected by reflection from (a) the pan surface, (b) the wall of the hot ring or band and (c) the hot cap.

All types of bag, envelope or package cookery may be thought of as

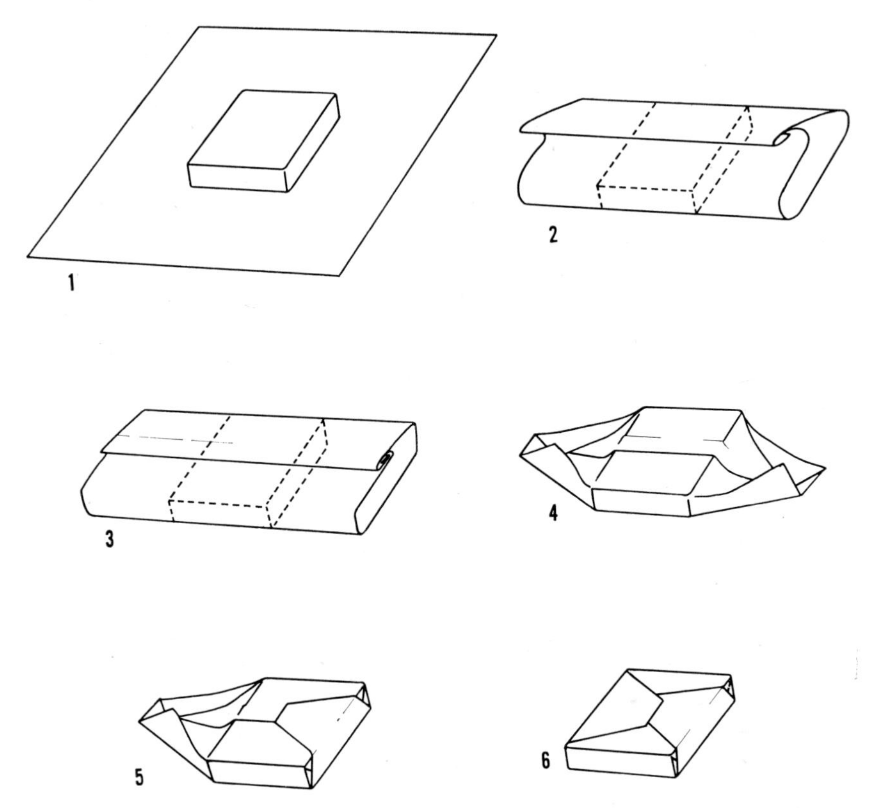

FIG. 37. THE SIX STEPS OF A "DRUG STORE" WRAP

1. Object centered in sheet.
2. First wrapping step with upper ends infolded.
3. Third step with double upper infold.
4. Fourth step with upper infold flattened downward and the ends inwardly mitred.
5. Fifth step, one end folded inward and the other ready to turn over.
6. Finished package.

steam cookery, if it is granted that the constitutional moisture of a food has its temperature raised by heat exchange to the point where internal steam is generated.

All of the illustrated procedures presuppose preparation of different foods without any additive —no water or any other fluid carrier, and no seasoning. However, it must be obvious that the same procedures applicable to simple food preparation apply to elaboration with both fluid carriers and seasoning.

In essence, many of the suggested procedures can be thought of as heating and serving a food without soiling a utensil, because the container (the envelope or package) is discarded. Further, some of the procedures

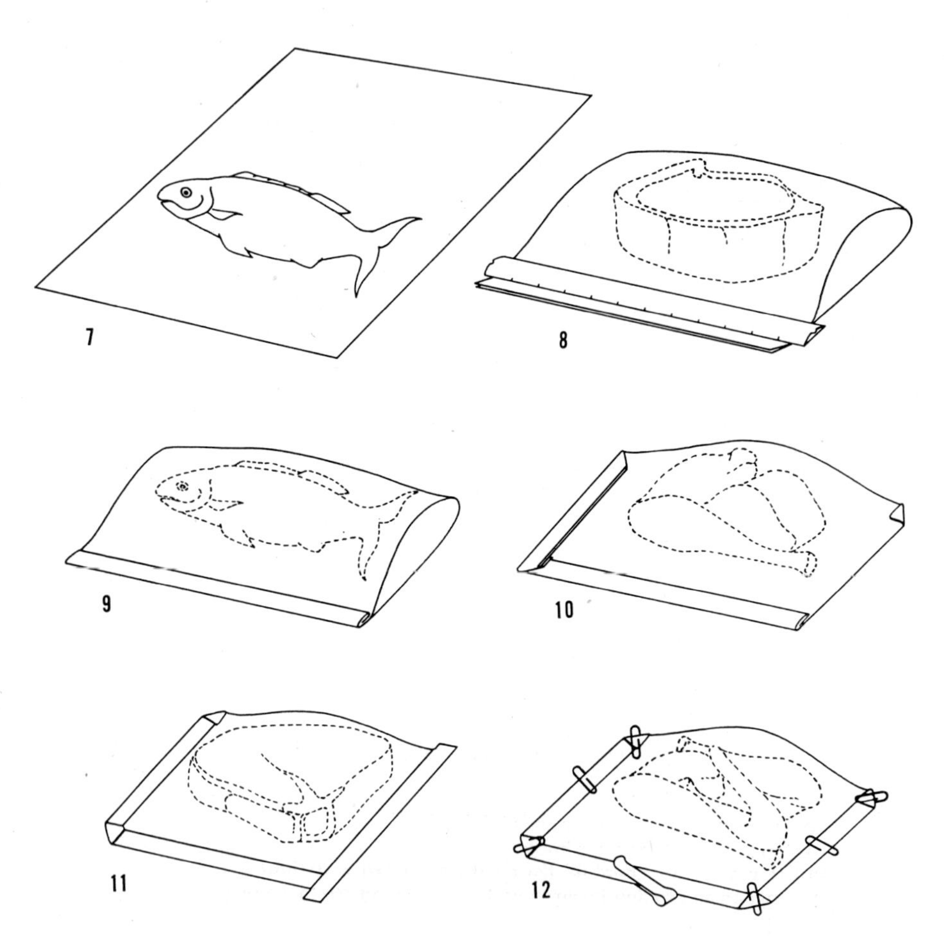

Fig. 38. Enveloping a Food for Dry Cookery

7. A whole fish positioned on a sheet to be so wrapped that sharp bones will not puncture it. Great care must be taken in wrapping foods, part of which may puncture a package.
8. A hard straightedge is so placed that it makes possible a fairly tight infold and subsequent closure.
9. A double infold is pressed flat.
10. The infolds of two envelope edges are pressed flat. The third open edge is closed at one end preparatory to infolding that end.
11. The third edge corners cover the infold.
12. The folds of the package are secured with ordinary paper clips.

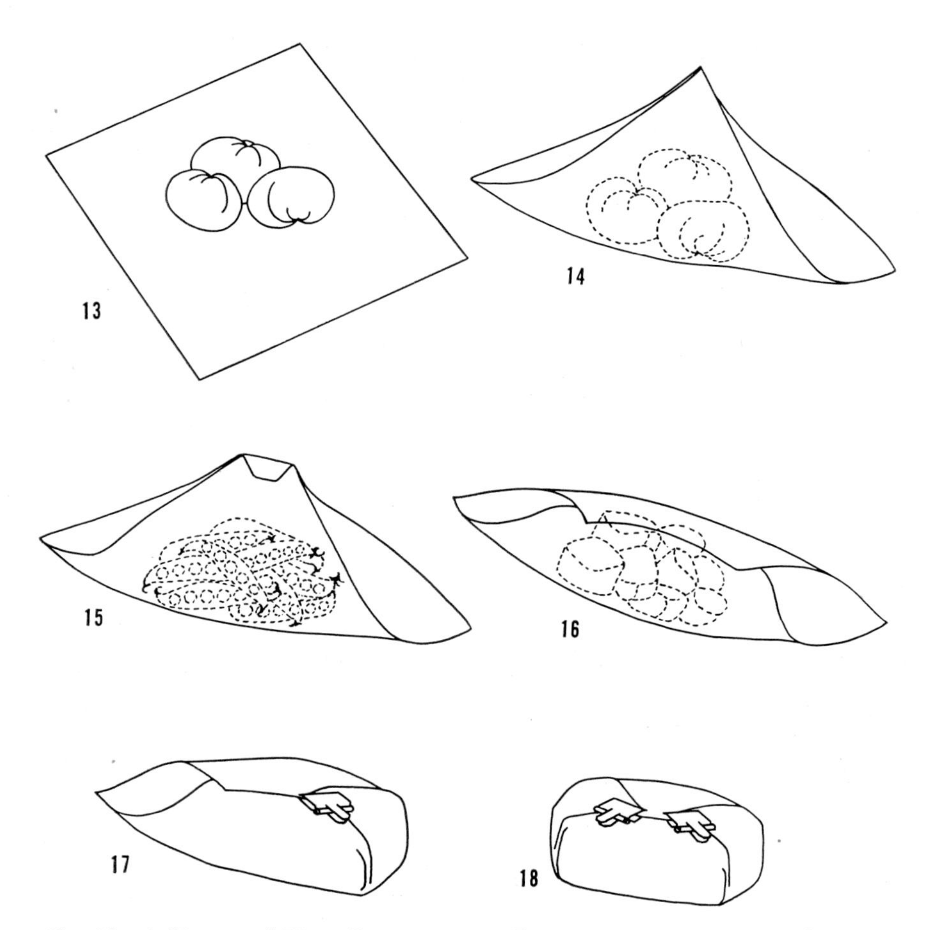

FIG. 39. A "BUTCHER" WRAP PROCEDURE FOR ENVELOPING FOOD FOR DRY COOKERY

13. Tomatoes centered in a more or less square sheet.
14. Two ends are centered and drawn upward.
15. The two upper points are bent inward, preparatory for the first and succeeding folds. Peas in the pod.
16. The upper infold pressed downward and the two ends ready to be folded in and over. Stew meat.
17. One of the two ends folded inward and clamped for closure.
18. The final package with both ends clamped to the upper infold.

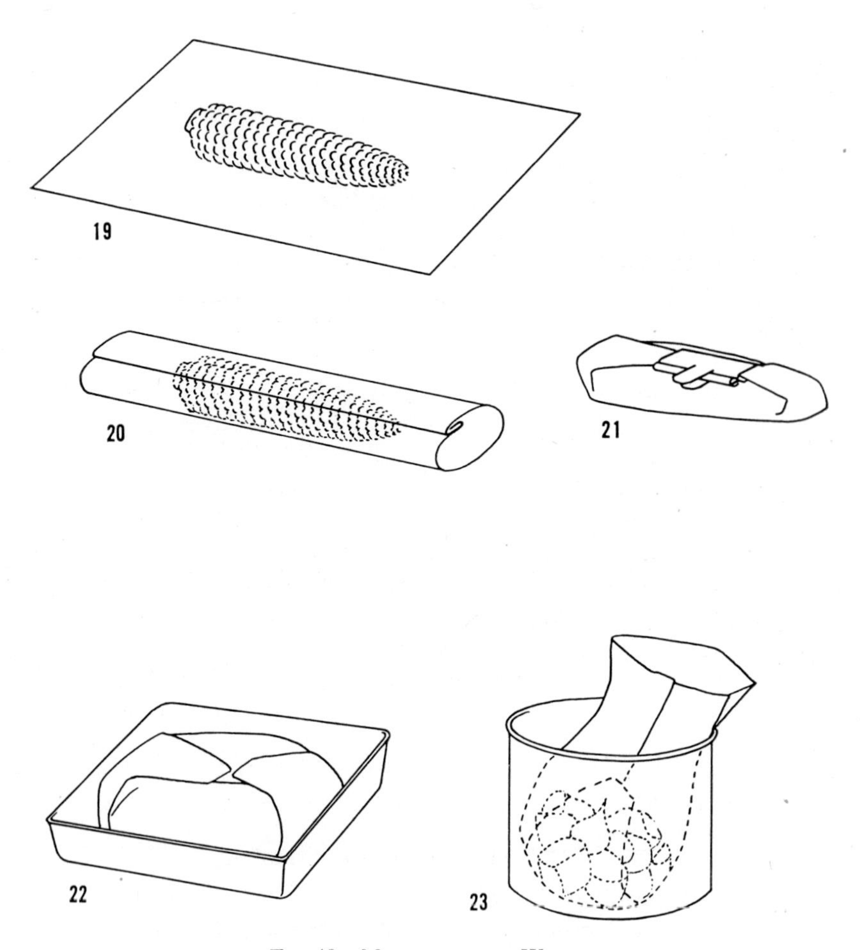

FIG. 40. MISCELLANEOUS WRAPS

19. An ear of corn to be individually wrapped (on a rectangular sheet).
20. An ear of corn partially enveloped with the two upper sheet edges double-infolded and pressed down.
21. An ear of corn with the upper wrapper edges infolded, pressed down and the two ends cornered, folded inward, and the three closures clamp-closed.
22. A food butcher-wrapped, sheet edges closed and the ends folded inward, which ends are subsequently to be held down by a hot cap.
23. Foods in a bag, which can be made from an 18 inch square foil sheet along the lines of a modified butcher wrap and finally closed by tightly twisting the upper ends. If plastic sheet is used, it must be clamp-closed.

make possible some kinds of cookery at the lowest cost of fuel and in the shortest time.

Wrapper Materials

The wrapping materials may be paper (preferably parchment), plastic or metal foil. If paper is used, it should be of high wet-strength if the final package is to be wet-cooked and fairly heavy if intended for dry cookery. Any paper to be used in cookery should be free from chemical components that may migrate to the food thus conveying an off-flavor. Plastics such as Saran Wrap[1] should be of heavy gauge, like the 200 gauge (0.002 inches thick) commercial weight; the household Saran Wrap is 50 gauge (0.0005 inches thick), which ruptures too easily. Plastics are recommended by most manufacturers only for use in wet cookery, preferably for exposure to temperatures under 212° F. Above that temperature they may melt and impart off-flavors. One exception is Mylar[2] which is usable in wet or dry cookery and is approved by the manufacturer and the government for temperatures up to 250° F. However it is questionable whether Mylar will be available for other than commercial sources in the near future. This is unfortunate, because Mylar virtually can't be manually torn, it is inert, foods don't adhere to it in dry cookery, and it withstands temperatures of at least 300° F. The production and availability of such a material and the necessary Federal approval for its use is highly desirable. One of the advantages of plastic envelopes is that they are transparent, so that the cook can see what is going on.

Aluminum foil is recommendable for both wet and dry cookery if proper closures of food packages are effected.

PROCEDURES IN PACKAGE COOKERY

While the illustrations in Appendix V and these memoranda are intended for laboratory procedures, they are applicable to everyday cookery. At least some of them have points of merit in that they provide not only the simplest but the fastest ways of cooking some plain and compound foods; assembling and packing, heating and serving. Unseasoned or seasoned, some of these procedures applied to everyday cookery will provide secondary taste and flavor results that will be surprising and gratifying to discriminating and fastidious cooks. One fact that stands out is that by restricting either a simple food or a combination of foods within a more or less tightly wrapped package and *properly* heating it, the result can be the best possible.

---

[1] Product of Dow Chemical Co.
[2] Product of du Pont.

a

b

FIG. 41. COOKERY—I

a. Aluminum foil formed to nest inside ring band (bottom pressed down flat and even, sides to conform with perimeter of ring) ground meat not quite filling foil bowl. Hot cap about to be set atop foil covered ring rim.
b. Hot cap being set atop foil covered rim to show edges of foil flaring outward;

c

d

demonstrating variant of this type of cookery where the food being cooked is not packaged, thus allowing some moisture to go to atmosphere because the crimped foil does not permit tight closure between the ring and the cap.

c. Two chicken halves enclosed within a square reflection band with the square radiation cap about to be emplaced.

d. Four trout laid out within a square reflection band, hot cap about to be emplaced.

a

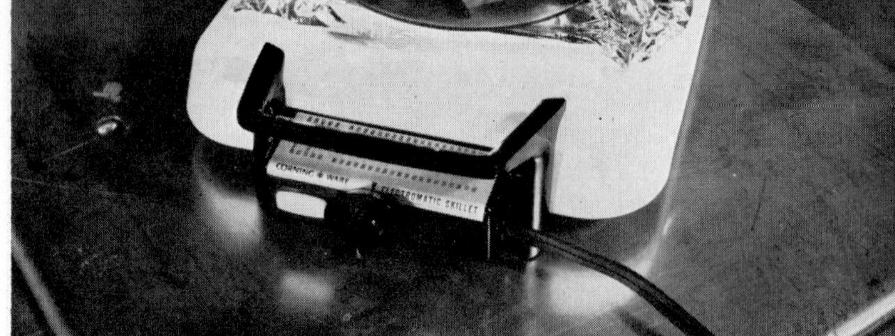

b

FIG. 42. COOKERY—II

a. Foil-enveloped steak in electric fry pan, hot cap about to be emplaced.
b. Foil-wrapped steak, hot cap being set; on a Corning electric skillet. Note the two ends of the foil wrapper are neither tightly folded nor sealed, but rolled and turned upward: intentionally to allow some vapors to escape.

c

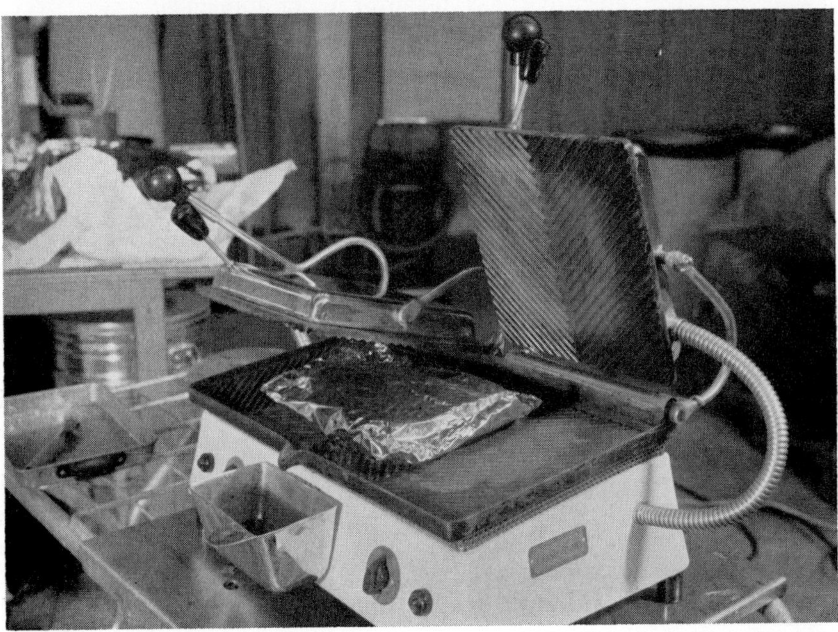

d

c. Stew meat in aluminum foil conformed inside reflection band and covered with reflection cap shows through Pyrex lid atop Corning skillet.

d. T-bone steak foil-enveloped, set on a double grill, one of the upper grill elements about to be clamped atop the foil package.

What is both exasperating and frustrating to particular cooks is to have prime food and seasoning result in a product that because of dilution or evaporation has lost much of its intrinsic delicate or subtle flavors, thus necessitating corrective seasoning. Package cookery may not wholly prevent such disappointments, but fairly practiced it can minimize them.

Package Cookery

For cookery purposes, a package may be thought of as a food container and a heat receiver somewhat like a cookpot; subject to limitations of material, closure effectiveness and heat transmission.

Consider package cookery as *sheath* cookery: as a method of exposing food to heat absorption that *shields* the enclosed food from all extraneous influences except heat; as a process that restricts intrinsic food values (including flavors) within the physical limits of a package and isolates it from extrinsic influences other than heat input.

The heat flow considerations include:

(1) The nature of the heat source—open fire (including what kind of fuel), electric or gas; major or minor appliance.

(2) Heat transmission: conduction or radiation, without or with utensils; open fire or mechanized broiler; plate or griddle, skillet or pan, pot or pressure cooker; or oven.

Then think of a package as a more or less compact food container which should be made according to:

(1) The nature and quality of the food it is to contain.

(2) Whether it is to be wet or dry processed; upon this factor rests the selection of the enveloping material—leaf, paper, plastic, foil, etc.

(3) The type of wrap, according to its inherent properties.

(4) The style of closure—bag, envelope or package, loosely closed or more or less tightly sealed.

As vapor pressure rises within a fairly closed package it will puff; at which time the heat input should be reduced to minimize evaporation, and economize on heat. Beside, high vapor pressure within packages excessively softens the surface tissues of some foods.

Caution: One should avoid production of a package that when heated will not permit internal vapor to escape short of explosive force. Water and air enclosed in a hermetically sealed cell become an explosive when sufficiently heated: the combination can burst with the border effects of an exploding shell.

Wet Cookery with the Package

The term "wet cookery" is ordinarily applied to cooking in or with water, or where water is a medium of heat exchange.

(1) The envelope or package should as nearly as possible be sealed to minimize possible intrusion of extraneous moisture.

(2) Use a pot with a loosely fitting lid, or a pressure cooker with the vent open to atmosphere. If the lid is so tight that it allows internal rise of vapor pressure, some moisture may be forced into the package.

(3) Place the package on a rack that clears the floor of the pot and add water to the rack level. The water level should be *below* the wrap closures.

(4) Raise the temperature of the water to *under boiling*, between 185° and 205° F., preferably under 200° F., to avoid internal pot steam penetrating the package.

Dry Cookery with the Package

"Dry cookery" is a term of many interpretations and subject to many qualifications: ordinarily it refers to waterless heat exchange (between heat source and food), where there is no water as a medium of heat exchange. The term is also applied to baking, broiling, roasting and shallow and deep fat "frying." Here with reference to package cookery it applies to dry pan and oven heat exchange.

(1) For ordinary dry cookery programs envelope closures should be toward looseness, never hermetically sealed.

(2) Package construction may vary from open face foil pan or bowl shapes (Fig. 41a) to partly closed forms, but never sealed.

Package Cookery in Ovens

(1) In pre-heated ovens package surfaces are equally exposed to heat (except for pan or rack contacts).

(2) Packages are unequally heated if auxiliary broilers are used.

Package Cookery with Dry Pans

Here the term "dry pan" may apply to a lipless plate or griddle, to a pan or skillet, or to a walled cooking utensil that is intermediate between a heat source and a package.

Most package cookery can be accomplished on dry pans, but the products will vary with the different techniques (and the accessories) that are applicable. A package emplaced on a hot plate is heated only from

its under side. This should be clearly realized. The other sides of a package so heated gradually rise in temperature, according to the temperature of the package contents and, of course, the base heat input. But the outer surfaces of the package remain at low temperatures for surprisingly long periods, even with high heat bases. This is especially true if frozen food is in the package. The outer surfaces of packages, while they restrict physical contents, allow much heat loss. If it is practicable to invert a package (without leakage) after a period of base heating, its heat processing will be accelerated. If a lid-covered pan is used the time in which the whole package is heated will be shortened; but even so the lid temperature will be much lower than that of the base. For example, with a base temperature of 260° F. the lid temperature of an electric skillet does not exceed 200° F. in ten minutes of average package cookery. Without a lid the air temperature one-fourth inch above the 260° F. base will not exceed 140° F.

Hot Band and Cap, and Dome

An assemblage of a hot band and cap on a hot base may be thought of as a hot box, and utilized like a miniature oven; for dry pan package cookery or for applying some baking techniques to frypan cookery.

The functions of a band are:

(1) Wall support for a cap.

(2) Intimate enclosure of a package or food, to volumetrically restrict a cooking process within a practicably minimum area.

(3) To set up a boundary heat source, the effectiveness of which depends on (a) its nature and dimensions (heat transmitting properties) and (b) its mechanical fit to hot base and cap (preheated or not, a band ordinarily is primarily and continuously heated from a base heat source and secondarily from a cap).

The functions of a cap are to provide a secondary heat source:

(1) To *contact heat* a food or package.

(2) To roof heat the area restricted by a band.

The functions of a dome are:

(1) Constriction of a cooking area, to minimize air or vapor gap between food or package and heat source base.

(2) Provision of a secondary heat source.

The services of both caps and domes vary (a) with their nature, dimensions and fit to food, package or band and (b) their hotness. Adequately heated caps and domes can sear the upper sides of (unpackaged) meats while allowing some fluid fat and moisture to escape from under their rims.

Suggestions

Temperature: Check both wet and dry processing temperatures from time to time, with both surface and immersion thermometers. Periodically check temperature performances of thermostatically equipped minor and major gas and electric appliances; their "sensing elements" are frequently aberrational. They may be inaccurate when new or operate over too wide a range, and they seem to deteriorate, become altogether unreliable, as they age with usage. This observation is particularly pertinent to electric pans and skillets because of rough handling or knocking around.

Time: Use mechanical timers or alarm clocks with audible signals as governors of the periodicity factors of cookery, especially of packaged foods. Remove foods or packages from contact with heat sources at the end of the planned cooking period, or they will to some extent keep on cooking. Allow packages to cool for a few minutes, to avoid hot vapor scalding; or punch a hole on top.

Handling: Manipulate hot packages with an offset spatula; clamps or tongs may puncture or tear them (and burnt fingers hurt!).

Index

D

E

F

N

O

P

Q